FIRST PAST THE POST® SER

Mathematics Dictionary Plus

Illustrated maths dictionary
with examples, questions and answers

Published by University of Buckingham Press.

ISBN: 9781908684493

Contents Page

This maths dictionary comprises more than 450 entry words with fully illustrated mathematical definitions and examples in addition to over 1500 questions and answers.

How to use this maths dictionary

Maths Dictionary Plus is perfect for understanding some of the jargon you may come across in your studies of 11 plus maths and beyond. All the words in this book are arranged in alphabetical order with their definition accompanied by an example, 'Test yourself' questions and 'Challenge yourself' questions to test your understanding.

Alphabet
Each section is introduced with a **bold** letter of the alphabet.

Entry word
- The word or name being defined is written in **bold** text.
- Unusual forms and/or abbreviations of the word are given in brackets next to the entry word.

Questions
- Questions are provided with every word.
- 'Test yourself' sections are comprised of introductory questions that can be answered using the information given in the definition.
- 'Challenge yourself' sections are comprised of difficult exam-style questions that may require additional knowledge.
- Some questions may require the use of diagrams or tables from the examples.

D

datum (plural: data)
A piece of information represented by numbers (quantitative) or words (qualitative).
Note: Data cannot be both quantitative and qualitative.
e.g. Quantitative data: length, weight, age... etc.
Qualitative data: colour, shape, texture... etc.

Test yourself
1. Which of the measurements are quantitative?
mass height taste scent

2. Which of the measurements are qualitative?
speed temperature mood humidity

Challenge yourself
Answer the following questions using the table below.

Person	Gender	Shoe size	No. of siblings
A	Male	8	3
B	Female	5	2

1. Which data categories are qualitative?

2. Which data categories are quantitative?

maximum point
The highest point on a curve, i.e. the peak.
e.g.

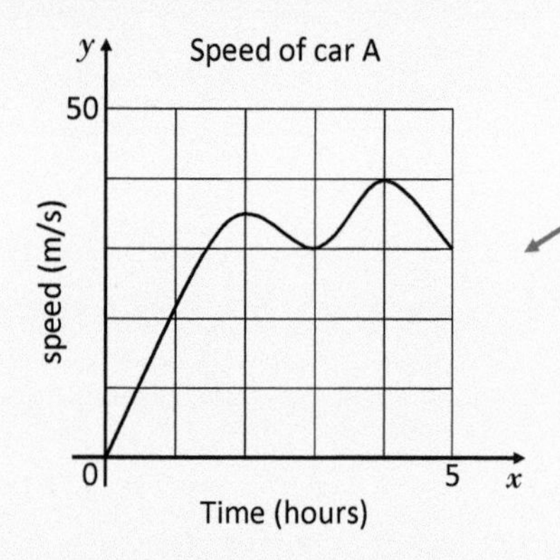

The greatest speed achieved by car A is 40 m/s.

Test yourself
1. On the graph in the example above, draw a cross at the maximum point.

Challenge yourself
Answer the following questions using the graph in the example above.
1. If car A travels for 3.5 hours at the greatest speed it has achieved, how far does it travel?

2. What was the maximum speed of car A during the first 3 hours of its journey?

Example
- This section provides an example related to the entry word.
- These examples may give additional information about the word being defined and are often illustrated with diagrams.

acute triangle (acute-angled triangle)
A *triangle* in which all three *angles* inside (*interior angles)* are less than 90°. See also *acute angle*.
e.g.

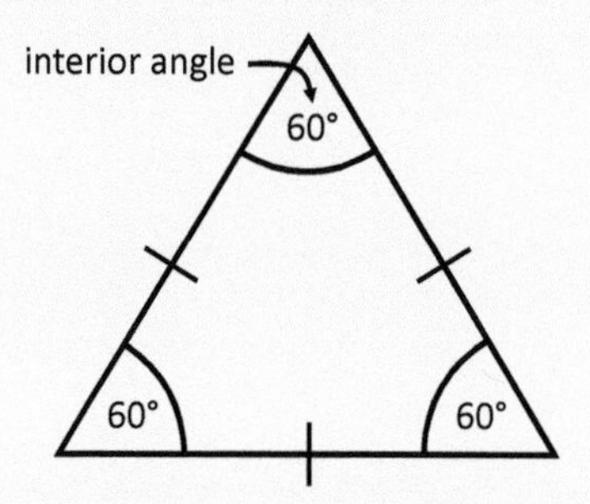

All the interior angles of the equilateral triangle above are 60°. These are less than 90° (right angle). Therefore, it is an acute triangle.

Definition

- This provides the meaning (and symbol) of the entry word.
- *Italics* within the definition indicate the words are defined elsewhere in this dictionary.
- Some definitions will include a 'Note' and/or 'Rule' with useful facts and principles to remember.
- When the defined word has a related equation, it is given in a dotted box.
- Roman numerals are used for words with multiple meanings with each definition having its own example.
- 'See also ...' indicates words that are related or relevant to the entry word and they too can be found in this dictionary.
- Three asterisks (i.e. ***) below an entry word indicates that the entry is already aptly defined elsewhere in this dictionary. Hence, no definitions, examples or questions accompany this entry. The reader should refer to the alternate entry indicated in *italics*.

arithmetic average

See *average*.

***

arithmetic sequence (linear sequence)

A number sequence in which the *difference* between consecutive *terms* is *constant*, i.e. it has a *common difference*. See also *consecutive numbers*.

e.g. 1, 3, 5, 7, 9 has a common difference of +2.

apothem

A *line segment* from the centre of a regular *polygon* to the *midpoint* of one of its *sides*.

Note: An apothem is used to calculate the *area* of a *regular* polygon by using the equation:

$$\text{area of a regular polygon} = {}^{(\text{apothem} \times \text{perimeter})}/_{2}$$

e.g.

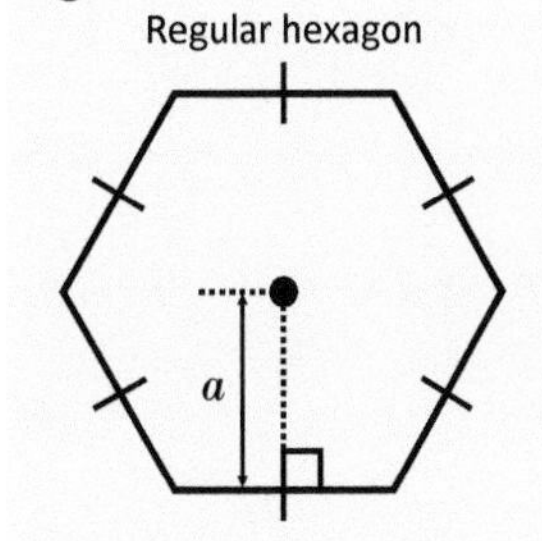

a is the apothem of the regular hexagon on the left.

base

i. In *geometry*, the base is the bottom line of a *two-dimensional* shape or the bottom *face* of a *three-dimensional* shape.

e.g.

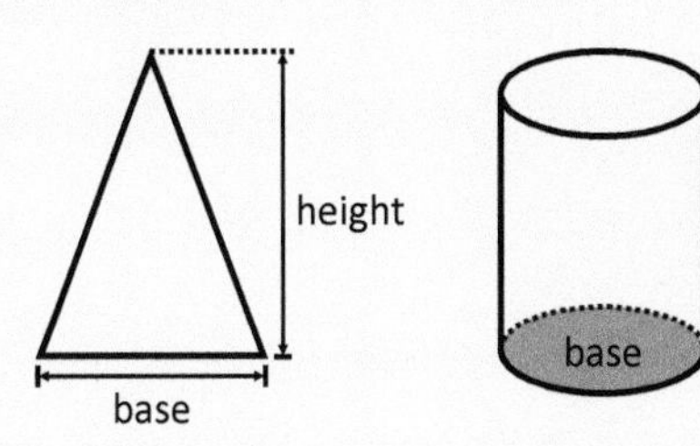

ii. In the numeral system, the base is the counting system being used. See also *denary*.

e.g. The base 10 number system (denary) uses 0, 1, 2, 3, 4, 5, 6, 7, 8 and 9.

iii. The base is the number b in an exponential *expression* of the form b^n. See also *power*.

e.g. In the exponential expression 9^3, 9 is the base and 3 is the exponent. Therefore, b = 9 and n = 3.

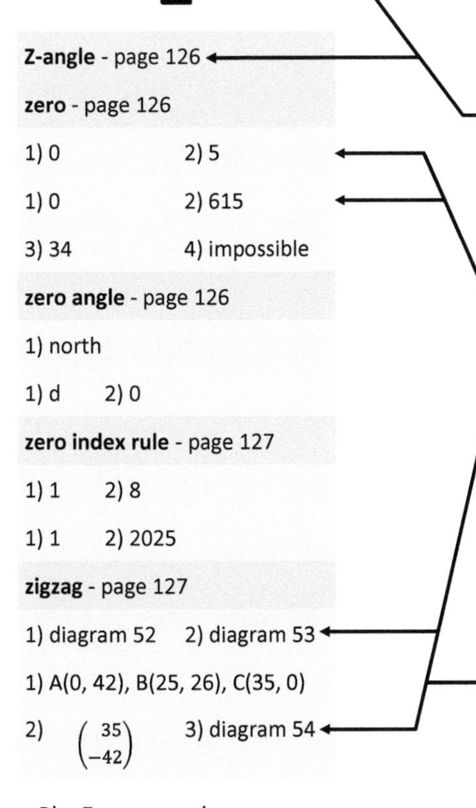

Z

Z-angle - page 126

zero - page 126

1) 0 2) 5

1) 0 2) 615

3) 34 4) impossible

zero angle - page 126

1) north

1) d 2) 0

zero index rule - page 127

1) 1 2) 8

1) 1 2) 2025

zigzag - page 127

1) diagram 52 2) diagram 53

1) A(0, 42), B(25, 26), C(35, 0)

2) $\begin{pmatrix} 35 \\ -42 \end{pmatrix}$ 3) diagram 54

Answers

- Answers to all of the questions can be found in the 'Index & Answers' section at the back of this dictionary, where all the entry words are listed alphabetically along with the page number.
- Answers to the 'Test yourself' questions are highlighted in blue, and answers to the 'Challenge yourself' questions are highlighted in yellow.
- Some answers require diagrams and they can be found in the 'Diagram Answers' section.

diagram 53

y; 90, 75, 60, 45, 30, 15; 0; 25 45 65 85 105 x; A, B, C

diagram 54

y; 50, 10; 0; 25, 45 x; A, B, C, D, E

acute angle

An *angle* between 0° and 90°.

e.g.

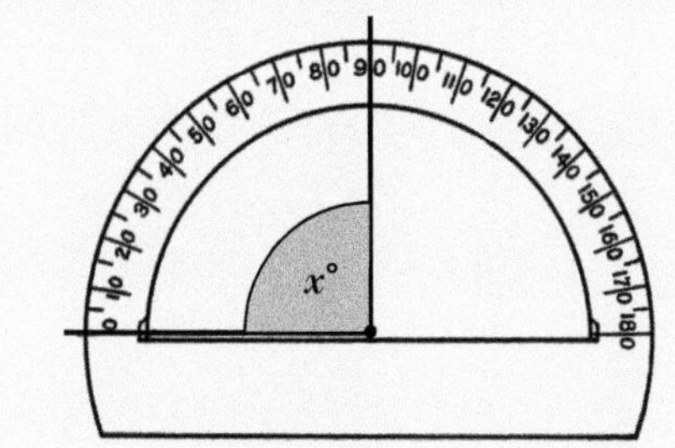

Angles within the shaded region, $x°$, are acute angles.

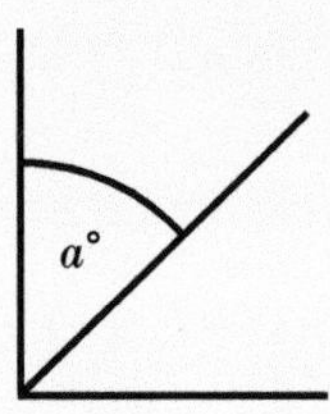

Angle $a°$ on the left is less than 90° but greater than 0°. Therefore, it is an acute angle.

<u>Test yourself</u>

1. Is the angle below an acute angle?

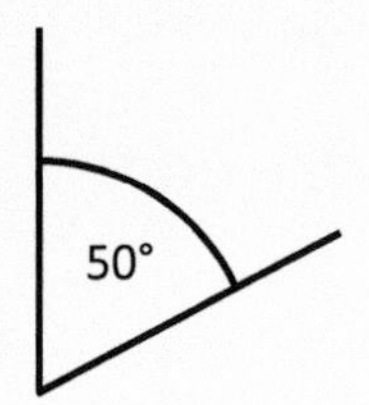

2. Which of the angles below are not acute angles?

8° 19° 90° 87° 0°

<u>Challenge yourself</u>

1. Is the sum of 55° + 45° an acute angle?

2. Which of the angles shown below can be classified as an acute angle?

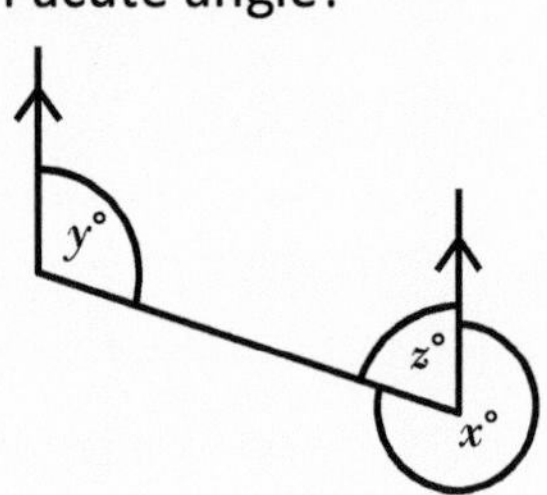

acute triangle (acute-angled triangle)

A *triangle* in which all three *angles* inside (*interior angles)* are less than 90°. See also *acute angle*.

e.g.

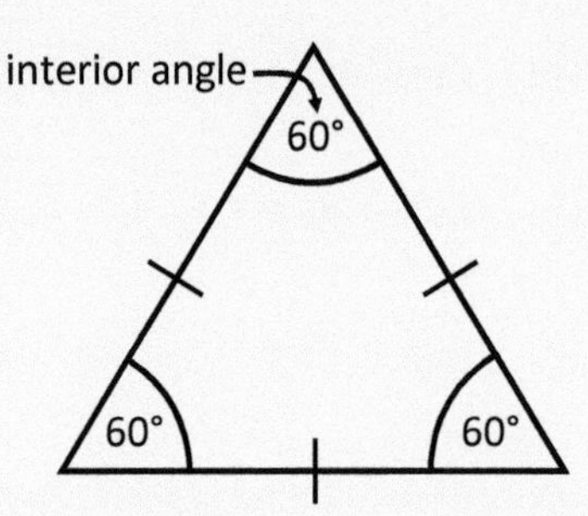

All the interior angles of the equilateral triangle above are 60°. These are less than 90° (right angle). Therefore, it is an acute triangle.

<u>Test yourself</u>

1. Which one of the shapes below is an acute triangle?

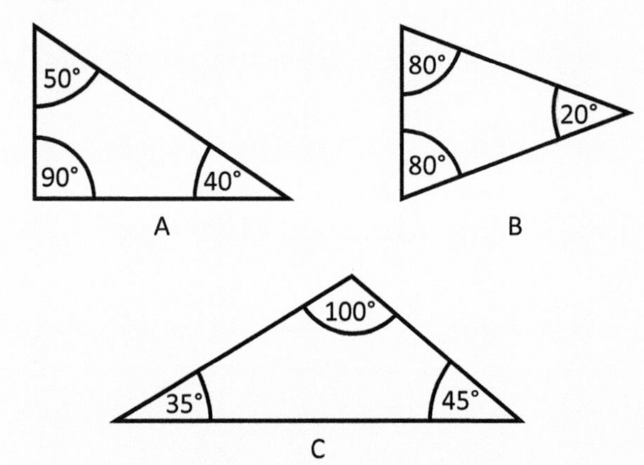

<u>Challenge yourself</u>

1. Which of the triangles shown below are not acute triangles?

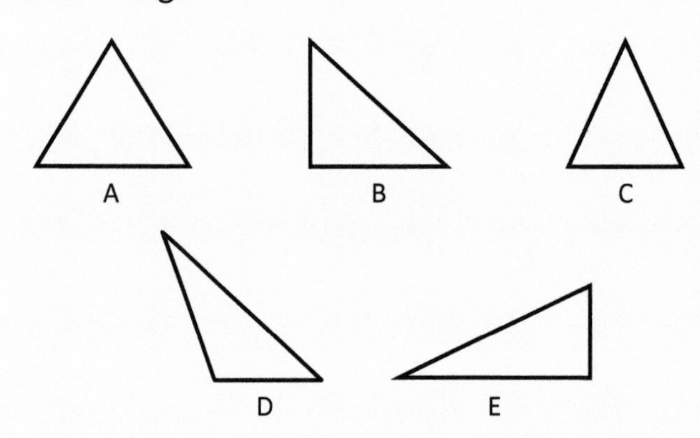

2. Calculate the size of angle $a°$ and state whether the triangle below is an acute triangle.

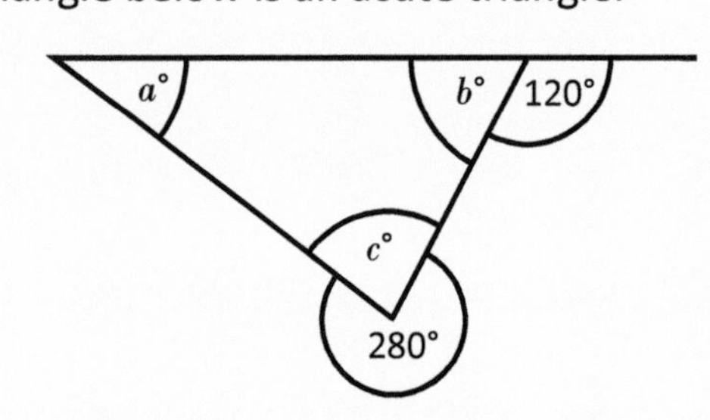

addition

The *arithmetic operation* that calculates the *sum* of two or more numbers. It has the symbol '+'.

e.g.

$$6 \quad + \quad 3 \quad = \quad 9$$

(+ ↑ operation; 9 ↑ sum)

Test yourself

1. Calculate 8 + 7.

2. What is 17 + 37?

3. Work out 320 + 200.

Challenge yourself

1. What is the sum of 0.57 and 1.2?

2. What is (-25) + (-16)?

3. Calculate £8.04 + £2.87.

adjacent angles

Angles with a common point (*vertex*) and common line.

e.g.

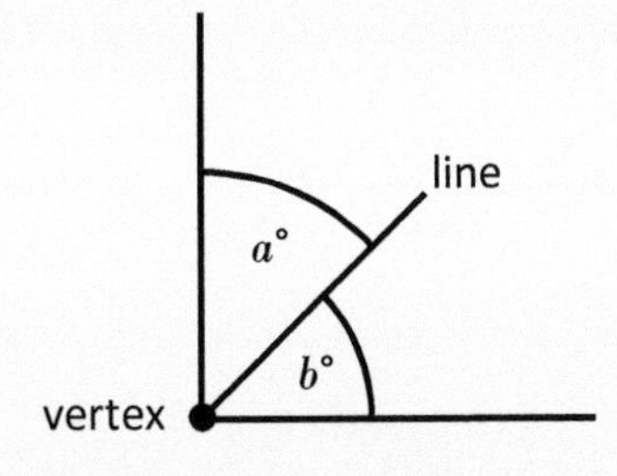

Angle $a°$ and angle $b°$ are adjacent angles because they have a common vertex and line.

Test yourself

Look at the diagram below and answer the following questions.

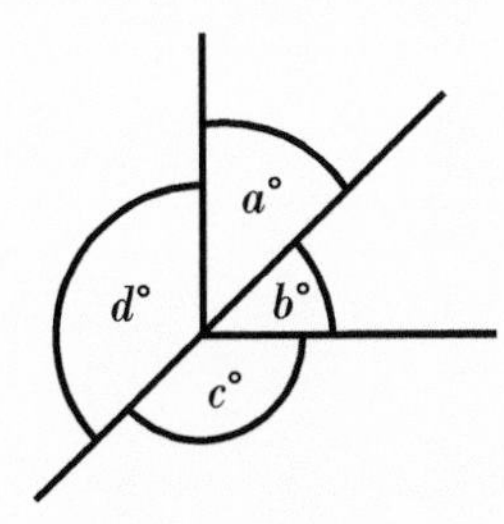

1. Are $c°$ and $d°$ adjacent angles?

2. Which other angle is adjacent to angle $d°$?

3. Which two angles are adjacent to $b°$?

Challenge yourself

Look at the diagram below and answer the following questions.

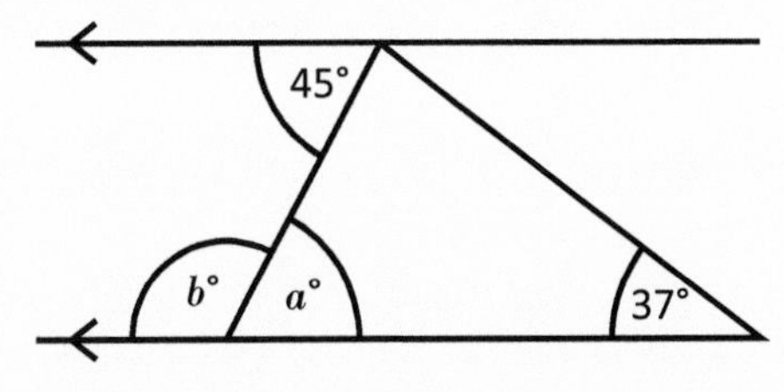

1. Calculate the size of angle $a°$.

2. Given that angles $a°$ and $b°$ are adjacent, work out the size of angle $b°$.

algebra

The branch of mathematics that uses letters (such as x or y) or other symbols in place of unknown *values*. See also *equation*.

e.g.

$$x + 5 = 8$$
$$x = 3$$

Subtracting 5 from both sides.

(x ↑ unknown)

Test yourself

1. What is the value of x?

$$x + 1 = 7$$

2. What is the value of y?

$$y + y = 10$$

3. What is the value of z?

$$z + 2z + 2 = 11$$

Challenge yourself

1. A rectangle has a width of $2x$ and a length of $3x$. Write down an expression for the perimeter in terms of x.

2. An isosceles triangle has a base of length $3x$ and a perpendicular height of $2x$. Write down an expression for the area in terms of x.

algebraic equation

See *equation*.

***

A
B
C
D
E
F
G
H
I
J
K
L
M
N
O
P
Q
R
S
T
U
V
W
X
Y
Z

alternate angles (Z-angles)

The *angles* on opposite sides of a straight line that intersects two *parallel* lines.

Note: Alternate angles are always *equal* in size.

e.g.

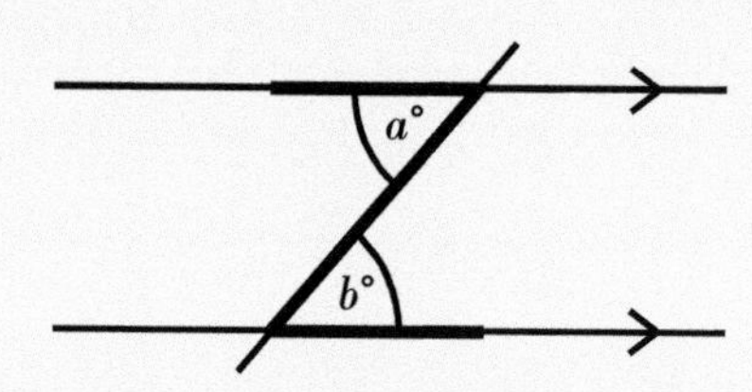

Angles $a°$ and $b°$ are alternate angles. Therefore, they are equal in size, i.e. $a° = b°$.

Test yourself

1. What is the size of angle $y°$ shown in the diagram below?

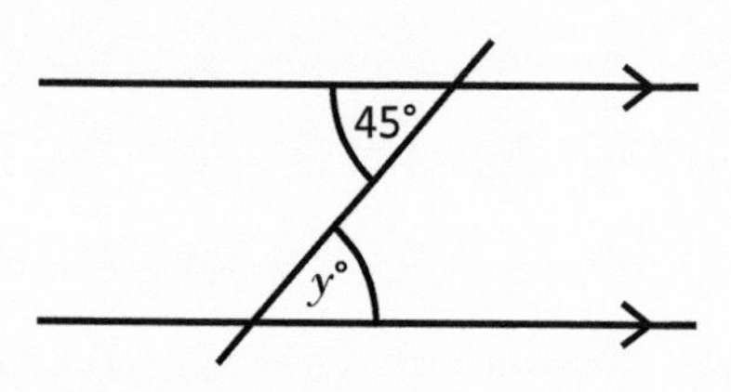

2. If the sum of two alternate angles is 142°, what is the size of one of the angles?

Challenge yourself

1. Calculate the angles $x°$ and $y°$.

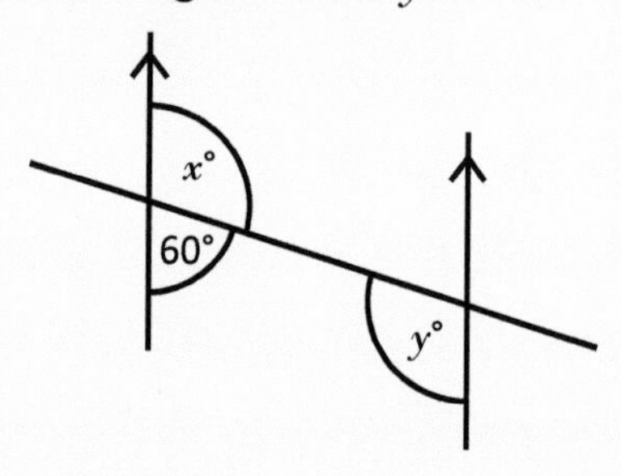

AM (a.m.)

The abbreviation of 'ante meridiem', meaning 'before *midday*' and referring to the period from *midnight* to *noon*.

Note: AM and PM are only used in the *12-hour clock* format. See also *PM*.

e.g. 10:15 is expressed as 10.15am in 12-hour clock format.

Test yourself

1. Express 07:30 in 12-hour clock format.

2. Express 11:46 in 12-hour clock format.

Challenge yourself

1. Express 00:00 in 12-hour clock format.

2. How many minutes are there between 5.42am and 9.50pm on the same day?

angle (°)

The amount of turn about a point of *intersection* of two lines. It is measured in *degrees* (°) and can be done so using a protractor.

e.g.

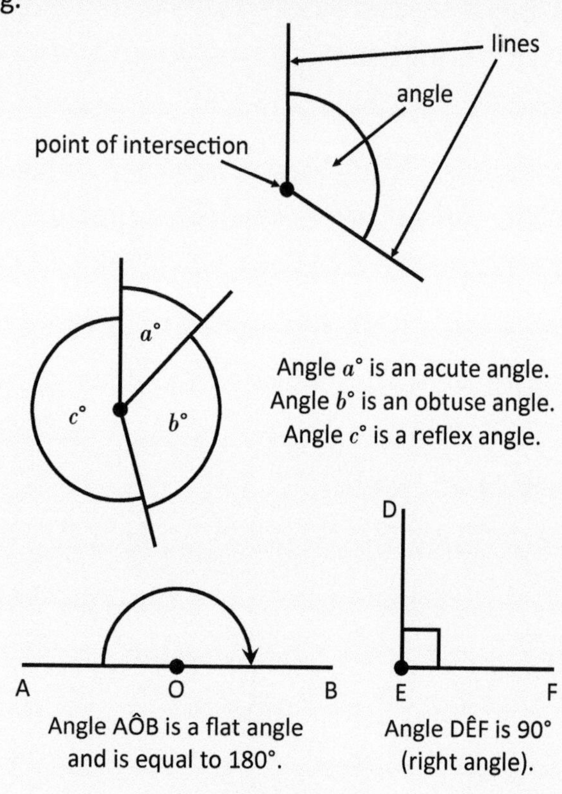

Angle $a°$ is an acute angle.
Angle $b°$ is an obtuse angle.
Angle $c°$ is a reflex angle.

Angle AÔB is a flat angle and is equal to 180°.

Angle DÊF is 90° (right angle).

Test yourself

1. Using the protractor, measure the angle $x°$.

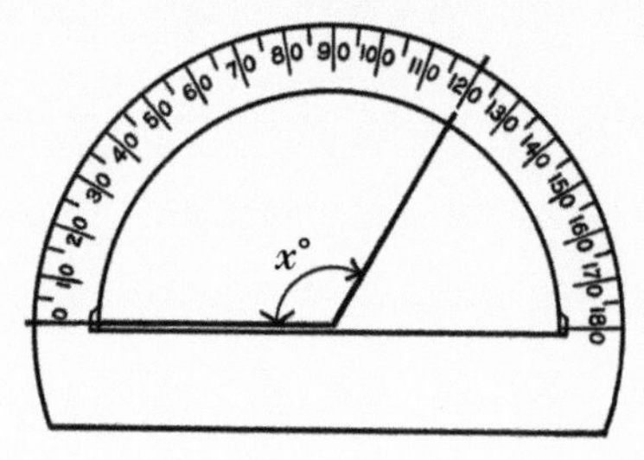

2. What is 5° × 5?

Challenge yourself

1. Calculate 5° × 4 ÷ 2 + 24°.

2. What is the size of the interior angle of a 15-sided regular polygon?

annual

Something that happens once every *year*, i.e. yearly.

e.g. Christmas occurs once every year. Therefore, it is an annual festival.

Test yourself

1. Which of the following events do not occur annually?

a. Bank holiday
b. Good Friday
c. Leap year

2. A charity sells 100 sweets annually. How many sweets do they sell in 3 years?

Challenge yourself

1. A factory produced 595,000 toys over 5 years. How many toys did the factory produce in a year assuming a constant annual production?

2. A company buys 350 pens annually. If each pen costs £0.99, how much does the company spend on pens over a four-year period?

anticlockwise (counter-clockwise)

The opposite *direction* to the *rotation* of the hands of a clock. See antonym *clockwise*.

e.g.

Test yourself

1. Which one of the arrows below is rotating anticlockwise?

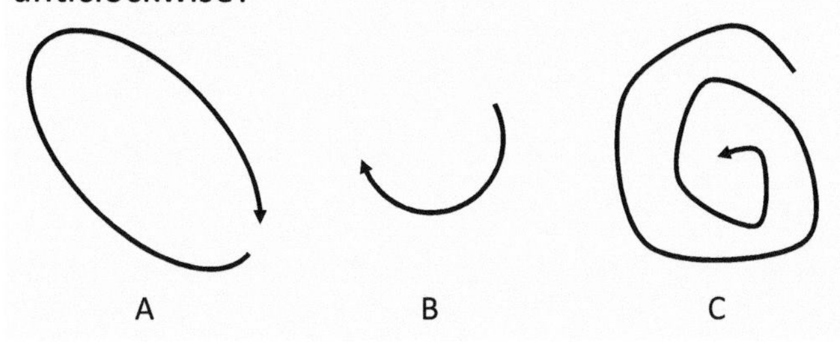

2. In which direction do the hands of a clock turn?

Challenge yourself

1. Songyo, Guwon and Yedam are all facing north. Guwon is standing directly to the left of Yedam and directly to the right of Songyo. In which direction and by how much does Guwon have to turn to face Songyo in the quickest manner?

2. Shape ABCD is rotated 90° about the origin in an anticlockwise direction to give shape A'B'C'D'. Label the vertices of the rotated shape A'B'C'D'.

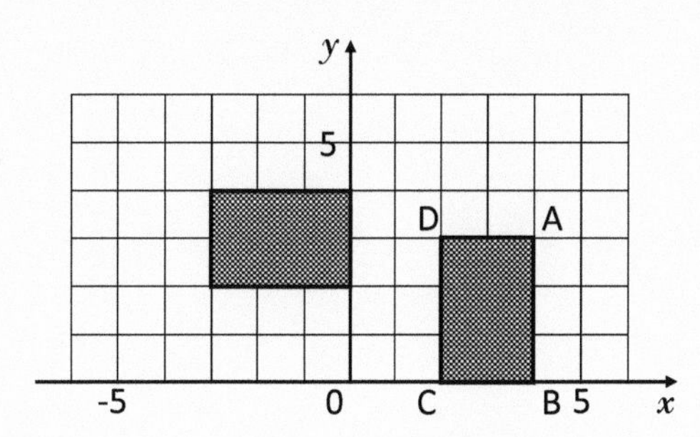

apex

The *vertex* opposite the *base* of an object, i.e. the vertex furthest from the base of an object. See also *edge, face*.

e.g.

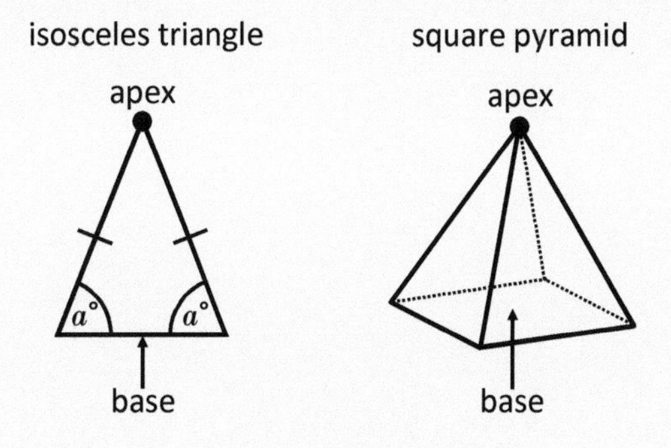

Test yourself

1. Identify the apex of the shape below.

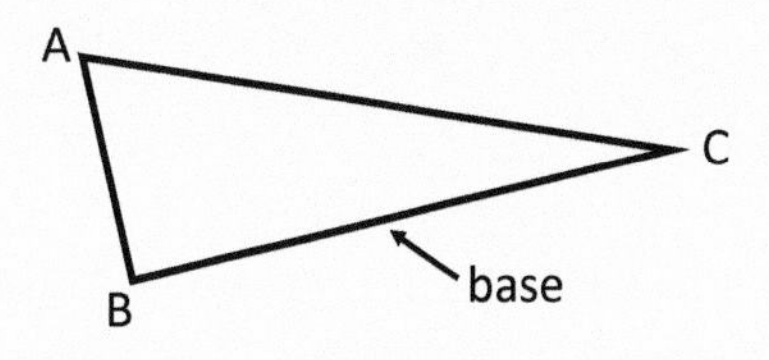

2. Does a circle have an apex?

Challenge yourself

1. An isosceles triangle has an area of $130cm^2$ and its base is 10cm wide. What is the perpendicular distance from the base to the apex? Give your answer in cm.

A
B
C
D
E
F
G
H
I
J
K
L
M
N
O
P
Q
R
S
T
U
V
W
X
Y
Z

apothem

A *line segment* from the centre of a regular *polygon* to the *midpoint* of one of its *sides*.
Note: An apothem is used to calculate the *area* of a *regular* polygon by using the *equation*:

area of a regular polygon = $^{(\text{apothem} \times \text{perimeter})}/_2$

e.g.

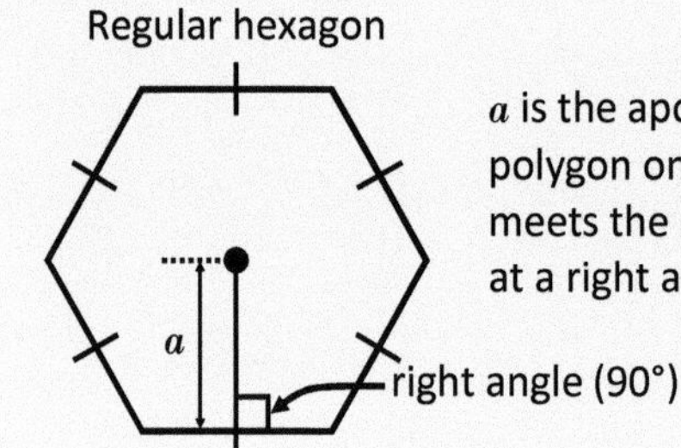

a is the apothem of the regular polygon on the left and it always meets the midpoint of the edge at a right angle.

Test yourself

1. Draw an apothem for each of the shapes below.

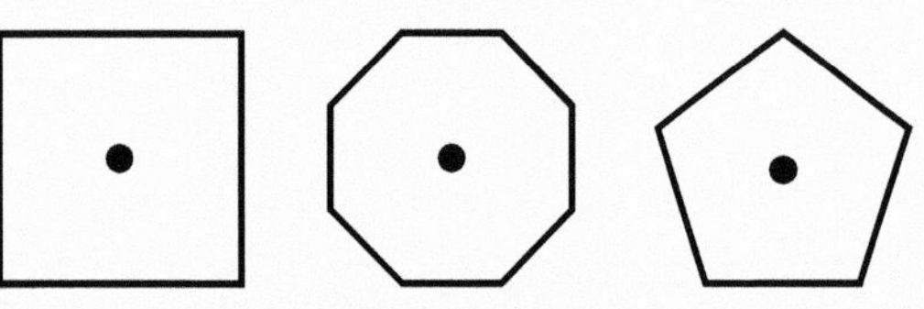

Challenge yourself

1. If each side of a regular pentagon is 64cm and its apothem measures 44cm, what is its area? Give your answer in cm^2.

2. If the area of a regular hexagon is $600mm^2$ and the apothem is 10mm, what is the length of one side? Give your answer in cm.

approximation

A rough *estimate* of an answer indicated by the symbol '≈'.
Note: This can be achieved by *rounding*.
e.g. If a pen costs £0.99, the cost of 100 pens is approximately £100, i.e. £0.99 × 100 ≈ £100.

Test yourself

1. If a book costs £2.99, approximate the total cost of 11 books.

2. A cup of tea costs £0.99. How much would 13 cups of tea cost to the nearest pound?

Challenge yourself

1. Give an approximation for the product of 5.86 and 20.3 to the nearest hundred.

2. Round the sum of 1500cm + 2.57m to the nearest ten metres.

arc

A portion of a curve. See also *major arc, minor arc*.
e.g.

A portion of the circumference of a circle is an example of an arc, and it can be drawn using a pair of compasses.

Test yourself

1. Draw an arc to complete the circle below.

Challenge yourself

1. A full circle with a circumference of 108cm is cut in a ratio of 4:5. What is the length of the smaller arc? Give your answer in cm.

area

A measure of the *two-dimensional surface* enclosed within a boundary.
Note: Area is measured in *square units* such as cm^2 or m^2.
e.g.

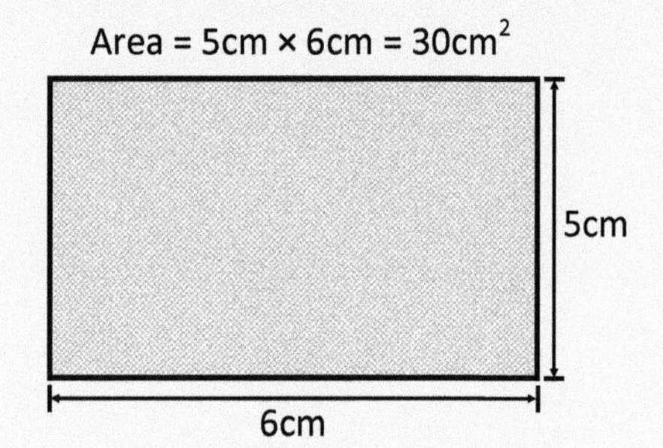

Test yourself

1. Shade the parts which represent the areas of shapes below.

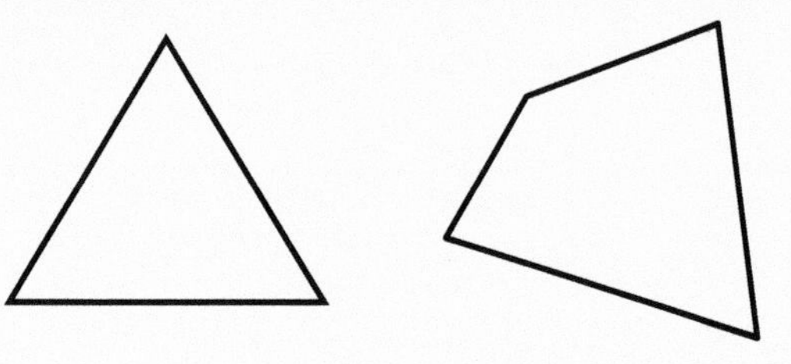

2. What is the area of a square with sides of 5cm? Give your answer in cm^2.

Challenge yourself

1. What is the area of the parallelogram below?

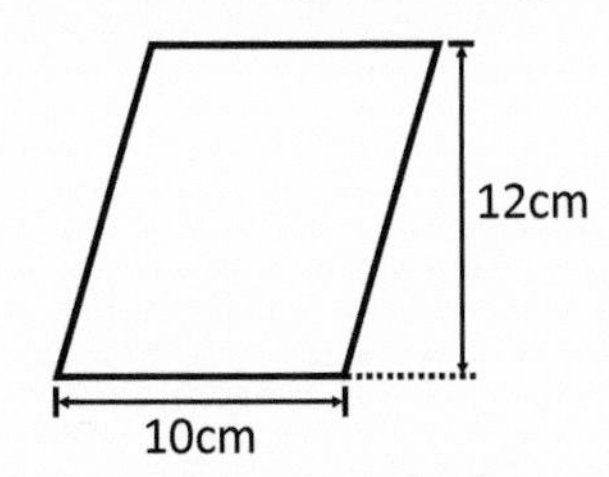

arithmetic

The branch of mathematics dealing with numbers under the four *operations*: *addition*, *subtraction*, *multiplication* and *division*. See also *BIDMAS*.

e.g.

Addition: 10 + 5 = 15
Subtraction: 10 - 5 = 5
Multiplication: 10 × 5 = 50
Division: 10 ÷ 5 = 2

Test yourself

1. What is 20 + 7?

2. Calculate 14 - 8.

3. What is 8 × 5?

4. Calculate 15 ÷ 3.

Challenge yourself

1. What is (81 ÷ 9) × (3 × 2)?

2. Calculate 6 ÷ 2 + 3 × (-2) - 3.

3. What is (144 ÷ 4) ÷ (3 × 2)?

arithmetic average

See *average*.

***

arithmetic sequence (linear sequence)

A number *sequence* in which the *difference* between consecutive *terms* is *constant*, i.e. it has a *common difference*. See also *consecutive numbers*.

e.g. 1, 3, 5, 7, 9 has a common difference of +2.

Test yourself

1. Complete the arithmetic sequence below so that the pattern stays the same.

0	5	10		20		

2. Complete the arithmetic sequence below so that the pattern stays the same.

2	4			10	12	

Challenge yourself

1. Complete the arithmetic sequence below so that the pattern stays the same.

11	15	19	23	27		

2. Complete the arithmetic sequence below so that the pattern stays the same.

25		45	55		75	

ascending order (increasing order)

Numbers are in ascending order when they are arranged from smallest to largest. See antonym *descending order*.

e.g. 1, 2, 3, 4, 5

Test yourself

1. List the values below in ascending order.
4, 5, 7, 6, 3, 1

2. List the values below in ascending order.
0, 4, 6, 2, 2, 10

Challenge yourself

1. List the values below in ascending order.
14, 15, 2, 4, -10, 5

2. List the values below in ascending order.
100, 2, 0, -55, 32, 46

3. List the fractions below in ascending order.
$^5/_8$, $^7/_9$, $^1/_2$, $^5/_2$, $-^1/_5$

average

A number that is used to represent a set of *data*. The three types of average are *mean*, *median* and *mode*.

A B C D E F G H I J K L M N O P Q R S T U V W X Y Z

A
B
C
D
E
F
G
H
I
J
K
L
M
N
O
P
Q
R
S
T
U
V
W
X
Y
Z

Note: Sometimes the mean of a *dataset* is referred to as the (*arithmetic*) average. This is calculated by dividing the *sum* of data by the number of items in the *dataset*.

arithmetic average = $^{\text{sum of values}}/_{\text{number of values}}$

e.g. The (arithmetic) average of 2, 4, 6, 8 and 10 is (2 + 4 + 6 + 8 + 10) ÷ 5 = 6.

Test yourself

1. What is the mean of the numbers 5 and 7?

2. What is the median of the numbers 4, 5 and 6?

3. What is the mode of the numbers 1, 2 and 1?

Challenge yourself

1. What is the mean of the numbers -5, 0 and 38?

2. What is the sum of the median and the mode of the following set of numbers?
10, 4, 5, 3, 7, 9, 10, 3, 7, 3

3. What is the mean of the following distances? Give your answer in metres.
14m, 11km, 170m, 14km, 20m

average speed

The average speed is calculated by dividing the total *distance* travelled by the total time taken.

average speed = $^{\text{total distance travelled}}/_{\text{total time taken}}$

e.g. If a taxi covered a distance of 40 kilometres in 2 hours, the average speed was 20km/h.

Test yourself

1. What distance does a car have to cover in an hour for it to have an average speed of 20km/h?

Challenge yourself

1. Nikhil travelled 20 miles in 30 minutes while driving his car. What was his average speed in mph?

2. An aeroplane was travelling at an average speed of 550mph. What was the distance covered by the aeroplane in 3.5 hours in miles?

3. Which is the fastest of the following speeds?
30m/s, 43km/h, 300km/day

axis (plural: axes)

A reference line drawn on a *graph*.
Note: The *horizontal* axis is called the x-*axis* and the *vertical* axis is called the y-*axis*. They are at *right angles* (90°) to each other.
e.g.

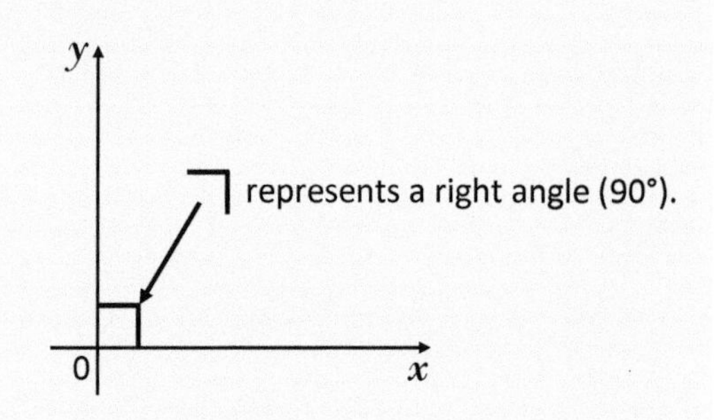

Test yourself

1. Draw two axes that are at right angles to each other and go through the fixed point below.

•

Challenge yourself

Answer the following questions using the graph below.

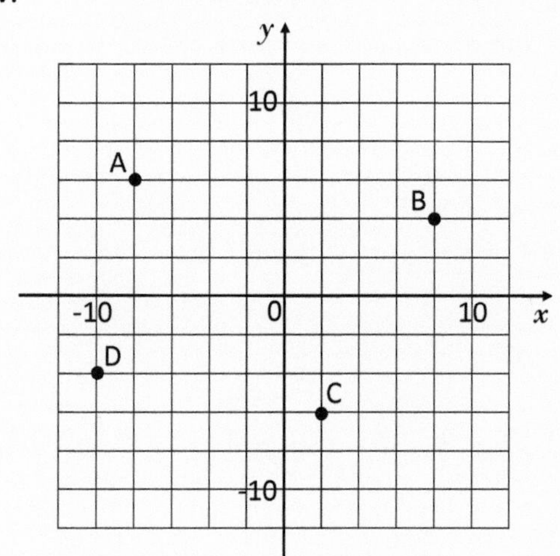

1. What is the name given to the point where the axes intersect?

2. What are the coordinates of points C and D?

axis of symmetry

See *line of symmetry*.

***

B

balance

i. Applying *equal weight* to both sides of a *scale*.
e.g. Three apples weigh half a kilogram and a hollow pumpkin also weighs half a kilogram. Therefore, they balance the scale.

ii. Making both sides of an *equation equivalent*.
e.g. In $2x = 4$, the value of x must be 2 in order to balance the equation.

Test yourself

1. Given the scale below is balanced and each apple weighs 100 grams. How much does half a small watermelon weigh in grams?

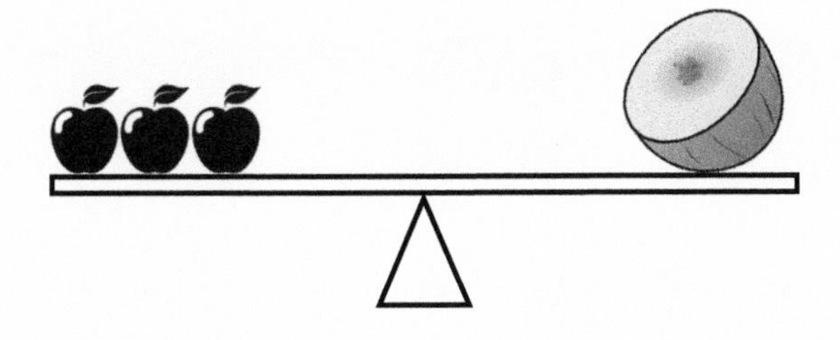

2. Which value of x balances the following equation?

$$5x = 15$$

Challenge yourself

1. Given that 6 apples weigh the same as 3 large oranges, how many extra oranges are needed to balance the scale below?

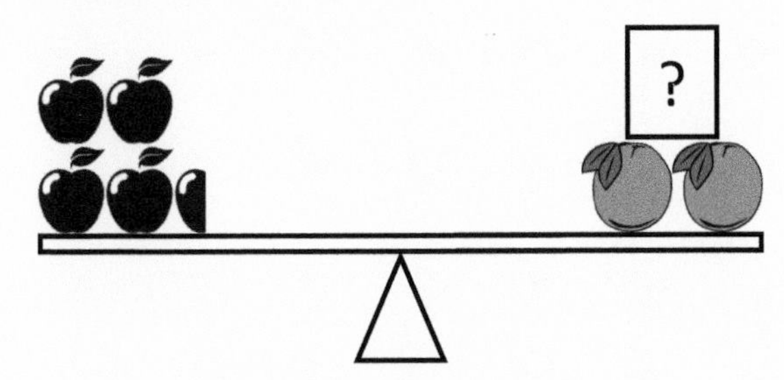

2. If $y = 1$, what value must x take in order to balance the following equation?
$3x + 6 = 19 + 2y$

bar chart/graph (column graph)

A pictorial representation of *data* in the form of bars, which can be either *horizontal* or *vertical*.
e.g.

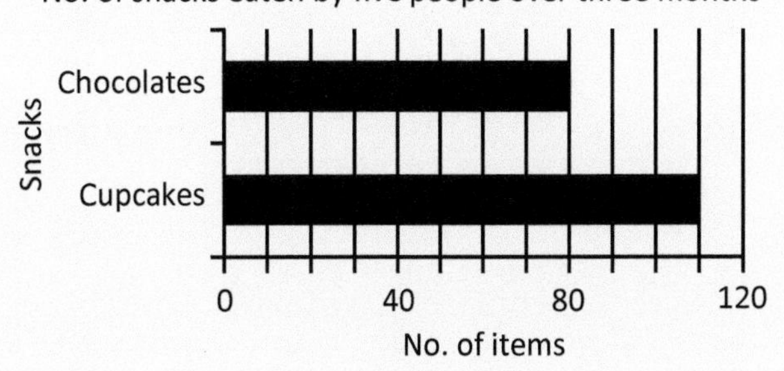

Test yourself

Answer the following questions using the horizontal bar graph in the example above.

1. How many cupcakes are eaten in total?

2. How many chocolates are eaten in total?

Challenge yourself

Answer the following questions using the horizontal bar graph in the example above.

1. How many more cupcakes were eaten than chocolates?

2. What is the mean number of snacks eaten by one person over three months?

base

i. In *geometry*, the base is the bottom line of a *two-dimensional* shape or the bottom *face* of a *three-dimensional* shape.
e.g.

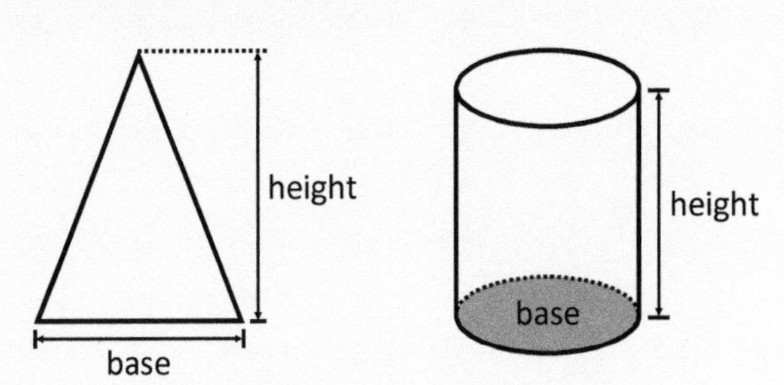

ii. In the numeral system, the base is the counting system being used. See also *denary*.
e.g. The base 10 number system (denary) uses 0, 1, 2, 3, 4, 5, 6, 7, 8 and 9.

iii. The base is the number b in an exponential *expression* of the form b^n. See also *power*.
e.g. In the exponential expression 9^3, 9 is the base and 3 is the exponent. Therefore, b = 9 and n = 3.

A B C D E F G H I J K L M N O P Q R S T U V W X Y Z

A B C D E F G H I J K L M N O P Q R S T U V W X Y Z

Test yourself

1. What is the base in the exponential 2^4?

2. In the given orientation, which letter represents the base of each shape below?

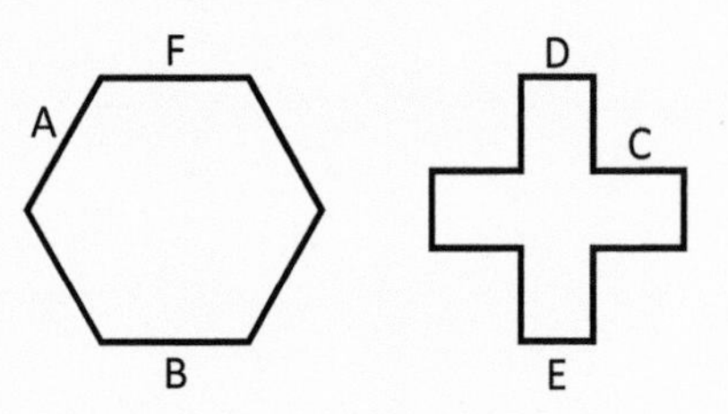

Challenge yourself

1. The volume of a cylinder is 288cm^3 and its height is 12cm. What is the area of its base?

2. Using the denary number system, write 'five hundred and fourteen thousand, six hundred and forty five' as a number.

3. In the exponential expression $b^3 = 343$, what is the value of the base?

bearing

An *angle*, given in three *figures*, that is measured *clockwise* from the *north* direction. It indicates the *direction* in which an object lies or moves relative to another object.

e.g.

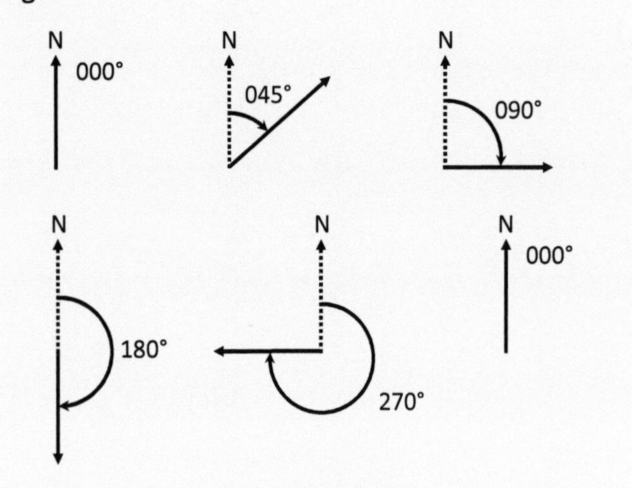

Test yourself

1. In the diagram below, what is the bearing of A from B?

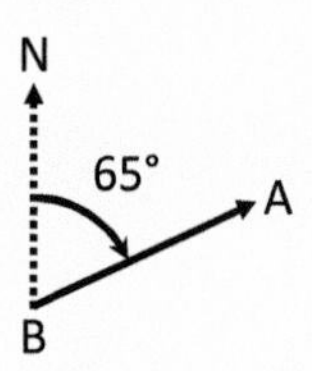

2. In the diagram below, what is the bearing of C from B?

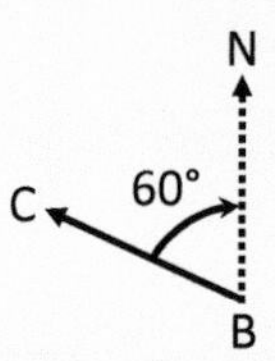

Challenge yourself

1. Rey's school lies directly north of his house. What is the bearing of his house from his school?

2. Shape ABC is an equilateral triangle. What is the bearing of C from B?

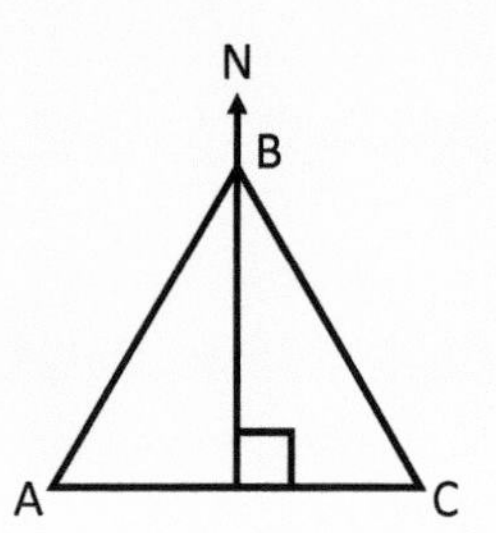

bias

See *unfair*.

***

BIDMAS (BODMAS)

An acronym for brackets, *indices* (or *order*), *division* and *multiplication*, and *addition* and *subtraction*. It is the agreed order of *operations* used to clarify which should be performed first in a given *expression*.

Note: For addition and subtraction, or for division and multiplication, do the calculation as it occurs from left to right.

e.g.

$(7 - 2) \times 3 + 3$
$= (5) \times 3 + 3$ — First, solve the sum in the brackets.
$= 15 + 3$ — Second, multiply 5 and 3.
$= 18$ — Finally, add 15 and 3.

Test yourself

1. Calculate $1 + 2 \times 2$.

2. What is $(3 + 1) \div 4$?

Challenge yourself

1. What is $6 \times 3 - 7 + 4 \times 7 \div 2$?

2. What is $(8 - 7)^2 \times (2 \times 6) - 12 \times 2^2$?

bimodal

When a collection of *data* has two *modes*.
e.g. If the dataset is {1, 1, 1, 2, 4, 5, 5, 5}, the two modes are 1 and 5.

<u>Test yourself</u>

1. What are the modes of the following sets of numbers?

a. 1, 0, 1, 3, 0
b. 2, 3, 4, 2, 5, 3

<u>Challenge yourself</u>

1. What are the modes of the following dataset?
5, 6, 2, 5, 9, 8, 6, 0, 8, 6, 5

2. Ignoring the sales of books and chocolates, which items have the modal number of sales?

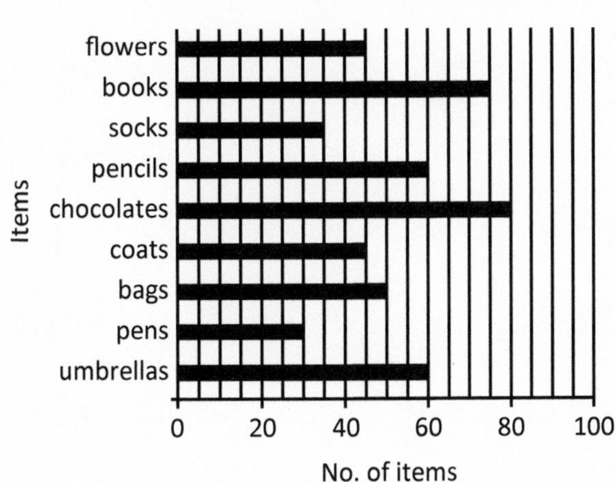

binomial

A mathematical *expression* that has two separate *variables*, such as x and y, each with a *coefficient*.
e.g.

$5x + 2y \quad y + 2x \quad x + 2y \quad x^2 - y^3$

<u>Test yourself</u>

1. Which of the following expressions are binomial?

A	B	C	D
$x^2 - 2y$	$5x^3 + x$	$3k + k$	$a + b$

<u>Challenge yourself</u>

1. Simplify the expression below into a binomial.
$51x + 14y - 21x + 5x + 2y$

2. Simplify the expression below into a binomial.
$7x + 3y^2 + 7x - 2y$

bisect

To cut or divide into two *equal* parts.
e.g.

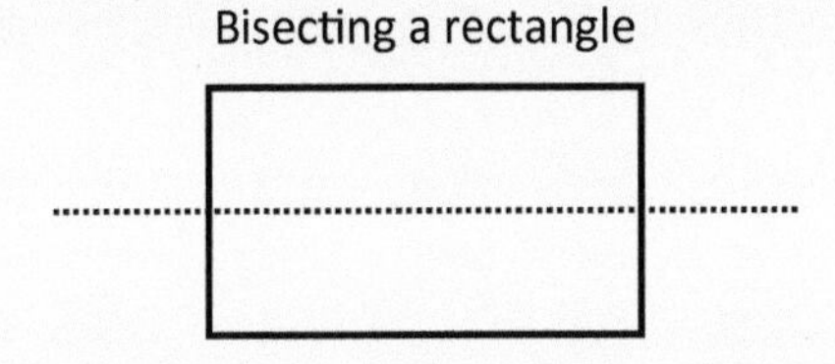

<u>Test yourself</u>

1. Can you bisect a square?

2. How many ways can you bisect an equilateral triangle?

<u>Challenge yourself</u>

1. What is the name given to the two shapes produced when a circle is bisected?

2. What is the name given to the two shapes produced when an equilateral triangle is bisected?

bisector

A line which divides an *angle* or a line exactly into two *equal* halves.
e.g.

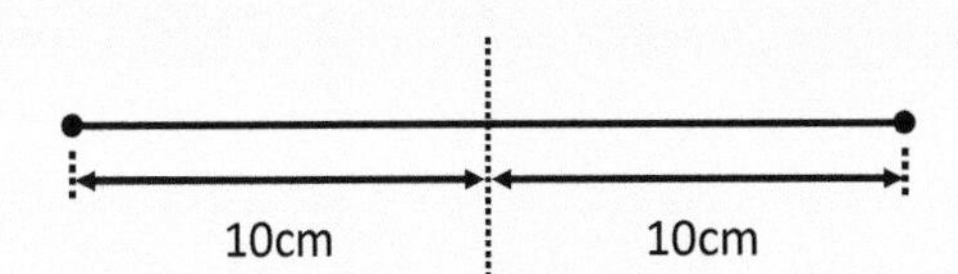

This is an example of a perpendicular bisector.

<u>Test yourself</u>

1. Draw the bisector for the following angle using a protractor.

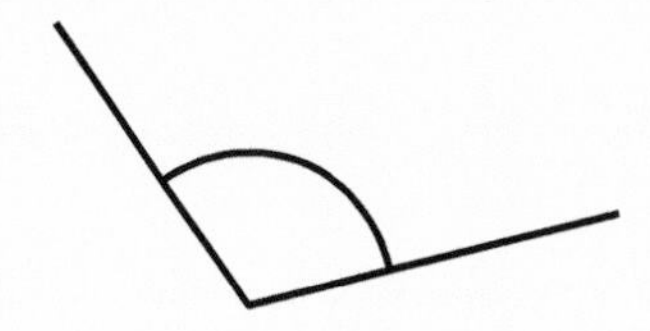

<u>Challenge yourself</u>

1. A reflex angle is divided by a bisector. If the size of the reflex angle was originally 278°, what is the size of one of the new angles?

BODMAS

See *BIDMAS*.

***

A
B
C
D
E
F
G
H
I
J
K
L
M
N
O
P
Q
R
S
T
U
V
W
X
Y
Z

C

cancel (cancellation)

To *simplify* a *fraction* by dividing both the *numerator* and the *denominator* by a *common factor*, so that it is in its *lowest form*.

e.g.

numerator → $\frac{\not{5}^{1}}{\not{10}_{2}} = \frac{1}{2}$ ← denominator

The highest common factor of 5 and 10 is 5. Therefore, the given fraction can be simplified by dividing both the numerator (5) and the denominator (10) by 5.

$$\frac{\not{6}^{3}}{10} \times \frac{1}{\not{2}_{1}} = \frac{3}{10}$$

In fraction multiplication, cross cancelling can be used to simplify the fractions. To cross cancel, divide the diagonals by a common factor. For example, the highest common factor of 6 and 2 is 2. Therefore, the fractions can be simplified as shown above.

<u>Test yourself</u>

1. Simplify $^{2}/_{20}$.
2. Simplify $^{8}/_{24}$.
3. Simplify and work out the following multiplication $^{1}/_{4} \times {}^{2}/_{5}$.

<u>Challenge yourself</u>

1. Simplify $^{125}/_{500}$.
2. Simplify and work out the following multiplication $^{11}/_{14} \times {}^{7}/_{132}$.
3. Simplify and work out the following division $^{3}/_{16} \div {}^{27}/_{8}$.

capacity

See *volume*.

***

Cartesian coordinate

See *coordinates*.

***

Celsius

See *temperature*.

***

centigram (cg)

A *metric unit* of *mass equivalent* to one *hundredth* of a *gram*.

e.g. 100 centigrams is equivalent to 1 gram.

<u>Test yourself</u>

1. Convert 200cg to grams.
2. Convert 3 grams to centigrams.

<u>Challenge yourself</u>

1. Convert 23.5 centigrams to grams.
2. Convert 0.7 grams to centigrams.

centilitre (cl)

A *metric unit* of *volume equivalent* to one *hundredth* of a *litre*.

e.g. 100 centilitres is equivalent to 1 litre.

<u>Test yourself</u>

1. Convert 300cl to litres.
2. How many centilitres are there in 4 litres?

<u>Challenge yourself</u>

1. Convert 9.50cl to litres.
2. Convert 27 litres to centilitres.

centimetre (cm)

A *metric unit* of *length equivalent* to one *hundredth* of a *metre*.

e.g. 100 centimetres is equivalent to 1 metre.

<u>Test yourself</u>

1. Convert 500cm to metres.
2. How many centimetres are there in 9 metres?

<u>Challenge yourself</u>

1. Convert 48,500cm to kilometres.
2. Convert 0.57 metres to centimetres.

centre of rotation

A fixed point about which a *plane* (flat) *figure* is rotated. See also *rotation*.

e.g.

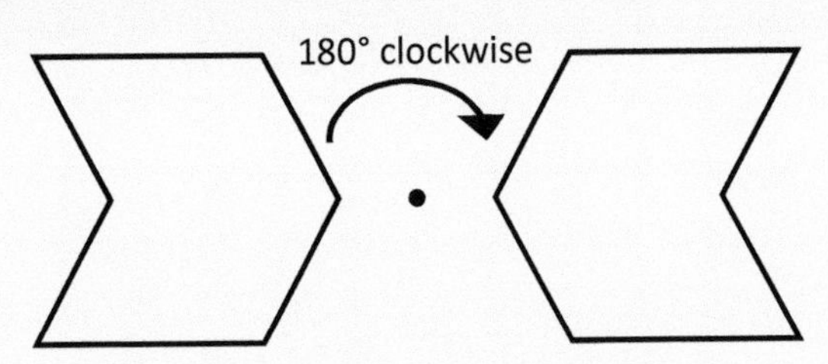

The dot marks the centre of rotation.

Test yourself

1. Shape A is rotated by 180° to give shape B. On the diagram below, draw the centre of rotation.

Shape A

Shape B

Challenge yourself

Answer the following questions using the graph below.

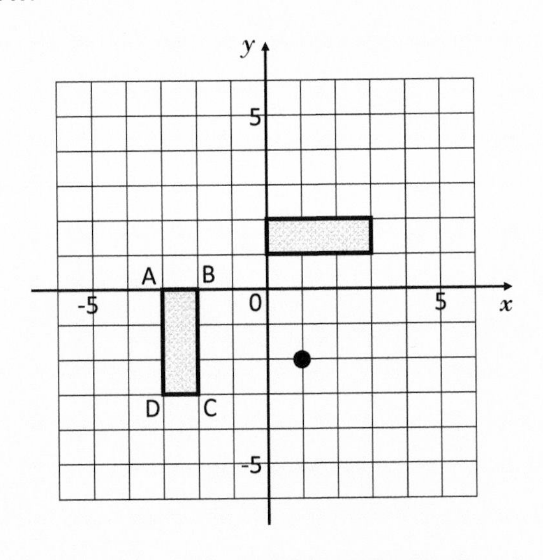

1. Shape ABCD is rotated 90° clockwise about the point (1, -2) to give shape A'B'C'D'. Label the vertices of the rotated shape A'B'C'D'.

2. What are the coordinates of A' and D'?

3. If shape A'B'C'D' is rotated clockwise about the point (1, -2) to give shape ABCD, by how many degrees has it been rotated?

4. What are the coordinates of A and D?

centre of rotational symmetry

A point around which a *figure* can be rotated to fit exactly onto itself. See also *rotational symmetry*.

e.g.

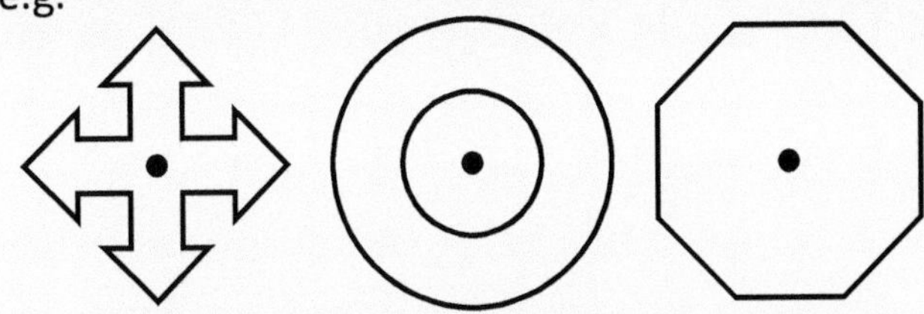

Each dot marks the centre of rotational symmetry of the shape.

Test yourself

1. On each figure below, mark the centre of rotational symmetry with a dot.

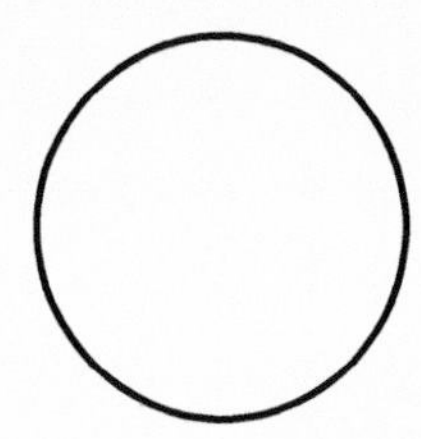

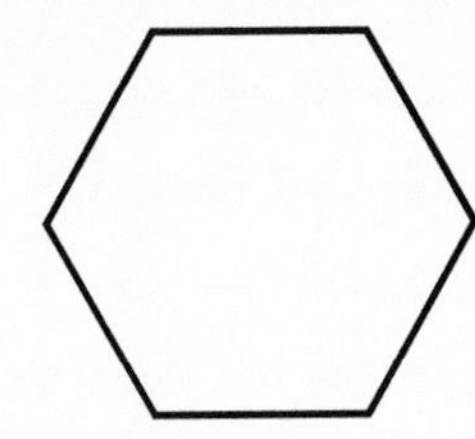

Challenge yourself

1. On each figure below, mark the centre of rotational symmetry with a dot and state the order of rotational symmetry.

chance

See *probability*.

***

chord

A line *segment* that *joins* two points on the *circumference* of a *circle*.

e.g.

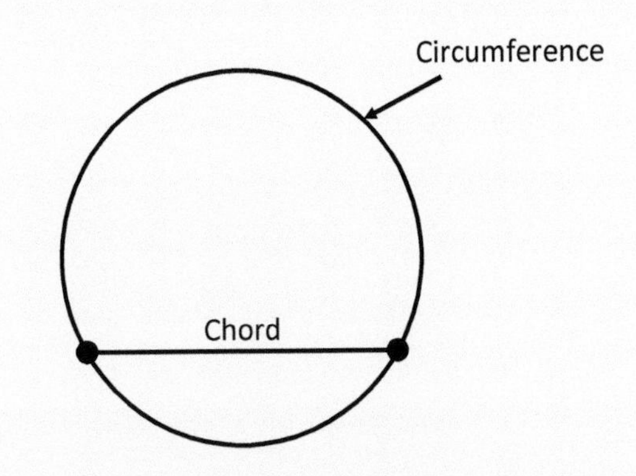

A B C D E F G H I J K L M N O P Q R S T U V W X Y Z

A B C D E F G H I J K L M N O P Q R S T U V W X Y Z

Test yourself

1. On the diagram below, draw a chord that joins points A and B.

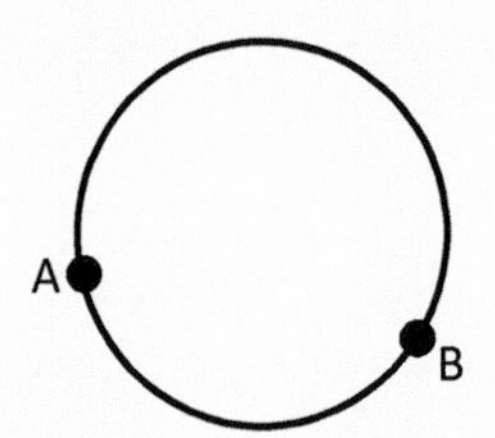

Challenge yourself

1. What is the special name given to a chord that passes through the centre of the circle?

2. A chord divides a full circle with a circumference of 112mm in a ratio of 3:11. What is the length of the smaller arc in mm?

circle

A closed plane curve on which every point is the same *distance* from a fixed point (the centre). See also *plane figure*.

e.g.

Circle:
It has 1 curved edge.
It has an infinite order of rotational symmetry.
It has infinite reflective symmetry.
It turns through 360°.

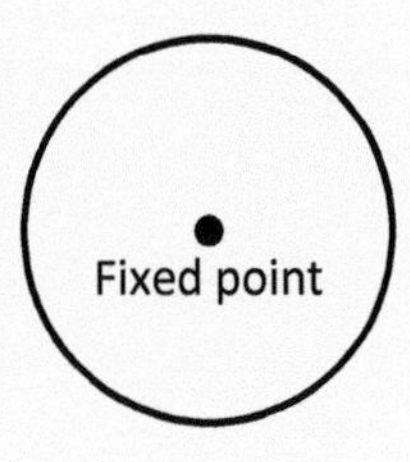

Test yourself

1. How many curved edges does a circle have?

Challenge yourself

1. Assuming π is equal to 3, calculate the area of a circle with a radius 7cm.

circumference

The *distance* around the *edge* of a *circle*. It is also known as the *perimeter* of a *circle*. See also *pi*.

circumference = 2 × pi × radius = 2πr

e.g.

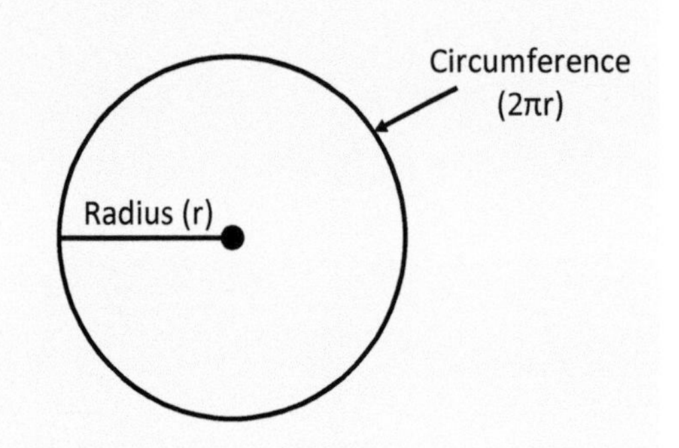

Test yourself

1. Draw the circumference of a circle with radius of 2cm.

Challenge yourself

1. What is the circumference of a circle that has a radius of 5cm? Use π = 3.14 (2 d.p.)

2. What is the area of a circle that has a circumference of 10π cm? Use π = 3.14 (2 d.p.)

clock: 12-hour clock

A method of measuring the time using the hours 1 to 12 with *AM* or *PM*.

e.g. 13:00 in 12-hour clock format is 1.00pm.

Test yourself

1. What is 11:00 in 12-hour clock format?

2. Express 18:30 in 12-hour clock format.

3. Write 07:59 in 12-hour clock format.

Challenge yourself

1. It is currently 17:15. What was the time 45 minutes ago in 12-hour clock format?

2. If Damian leaves for work at 8.30am and it takes him 2 hours 23 minutes to get there, at what time does he arrive at work? Give your answer in 12-hour clock format.

clock: 24-hour clock

A method of measuring the time using the hours 00 to 23 in HH:MM format, without using *AM* or *PM*. See also *midday*, *midnight*.

e.g. 2.30pm in 24-hour clock format is 14:30.

Test yourself

1. What is 5.12pm in 24-hour clock format?

2. Express 12.01am in 24-hour clock format.

3. Write 12.30pm in 24-hour clock format.

Challenge yourself

1. If Tanvi leaves for work at 11:30 and it takes her 3 hours 43 minutes to get there, at what time does she arrive? Answer in 24-hour clock format.

clockwise

The *direction* in which the hands of a *clock* rotate. See also *anticlockwise*.

e.g.

Test yourself

1. Draw an arrow on the arc below to indicate a clockwise rotation.

2. Which of the arrows below are rotating clockwise?

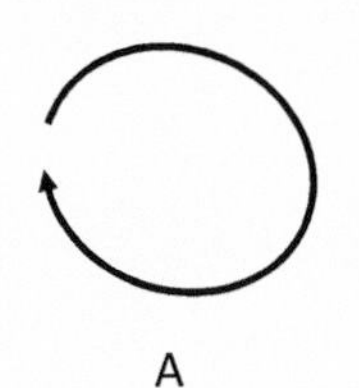

A

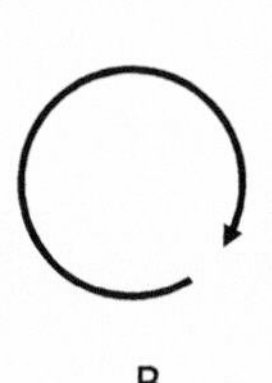

B

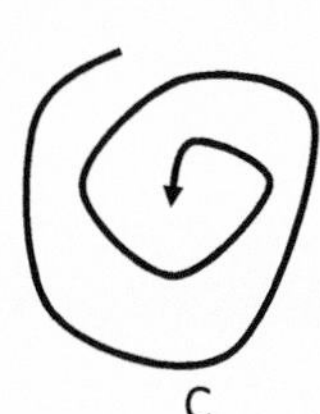

C

Challenge yourself

1. I am facing south east and I turn 225° clockwise. In which direction am I now facing?

2. The final position of the shape ABCD after a clockwise rotation of 90° about the origin is shown on the graph below. What were the coordinates of vertex A when the shape was in its original position?

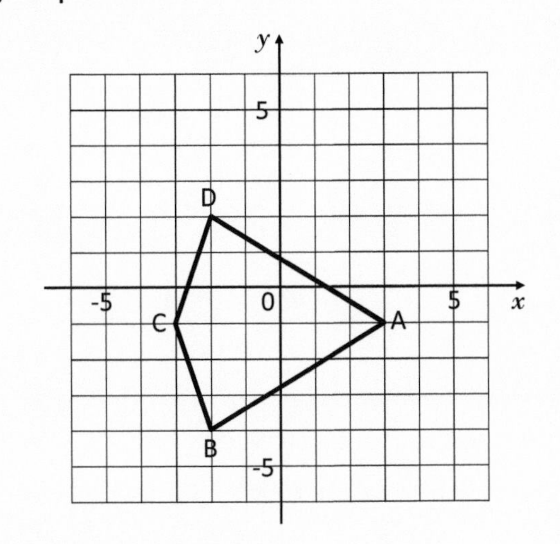

coefficient

A number that is placed before a *term* such as x or y in an *expression* used in *algebra*.

e.g. In the term $4x$, the coefficient is +4.

Test yourself

1. What is the coefficient of the term $5x$?

2. What is the coefficient of the term $-7y$?

Challenge yourself

1. Simplify the algebraic expression below and state the coefficient of the variable x.

$7x + 4x^2 + 2x + 11x$

2. In the algebraic expression $14x^2 + 4x + 3x^3 + x^2$, what is the coefficient of x^2?

column graph/chart

See *bar chart*.

***

column vector (column matrix)

A *matrix* consisting of a single column, written in the form $\binom{x}{y}$. A column vector is used to describe a position or a *translation* of a point. See also *coordinates*, *vector*.

Rule: A positive x and y represent a *translation* to the right and up. A negative x and y represent a translation to the left and down.

e.g. A translation of a point 2 units right and 3 units down is expressed as $\binom{2}{-3}$.

Test yourself

1. Write a column vector which represents a translation 3 units right and 5 units up.

Challenge yourself

1. What is the vector for the translation of shape A to shape B below?

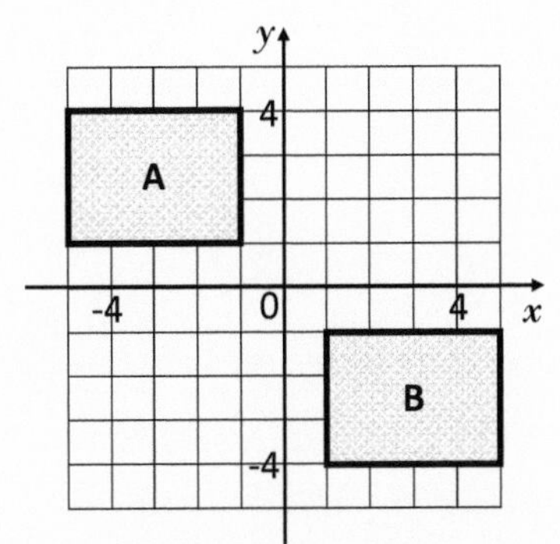

A B C D E F G H I J K L M N O P Q R S T U V W X Y Z

A B C D E F G H I J K L M N O P Q R S T U V W X Y Z

common difference

The *difference* between two *consecutive terms* in an *arithmetic sequence*.

e.g. In the arithmetic sequence 4, 9, 14, 19, 24,…, the common difference is +5.

Test yourself

1. Calculate the sum of the common differences for the arithmetic sequences below:

a. 1, 2, 3, 4, 5,…

b. 2, 5, 8, 11, 14,…

Challenge yourself

1. A sequence has a common difference of -3. If the initial value is 27, what is the value of the fifth term?

2. The sixth term of a sequence with a common difference of -4 is 54. What is the value of the second term?

common factor

A number that divides exactly into two or more numbers to give a positive *integer*. See also *highest common factor, positive number*.

e.g. Common factors of 12 and 8 are 1, 2 and 4.

Test yourself

1. List the common factors of 8 and 16.

Challenge yourself

1. What is the highest common factor of 36 and 12?

2. Jenar has 36 chocolates and 8 sandwiches, and he wants to pack the greatest number of identical packed lunches. How many chocolates will there be in each lunch box?

common multiple

A number that is a *multiple* of two or more other numbers. See also *lowest common multiple*.

e.g. The multiples of 5 are: 5, 10, 15, 20, 25, 30,… and multiples of 15 are: 15, 30,…

Therefore, the first two common multiples of 5 and 15 are 15 and 30. Another common multiple can always be calculated by multiplying the two given numbers: 5 × 15 = 75.

Test yourself

1. What is the first common multiple of 9 and 15?

2. What are the first two common multiples of 5 and 6?

3. Using the fact that a common multiple can be calculated by multiplying two given numbers together, what is the common multiple of 11 and 15?

Challenge yourself

1. If there are 20 students in a maths class and 16 students in a physics class, what is the lowest common multiple of the numbers of students in the two classes?

2. Simon goes jogging every 4 days and goes weightlifting every 15 days. If he did both activities today, in how many days will he next do both activities on the same day?

common ratio

The *ratio* between two *consecutive terms* in a *geometric sequence*.

e.g. In the geometric sequence 2, 4, 8, 16, 32,…, the common ratio is +2, i.e. each term is multiplied by +2 to get the next term.

Test yourself

1. Calculate the common ratio of the following geometric sequence: 2, 6, 18, 54, 162.

2. Calculate the common ratio of the following geometric sequence: 1, 3, 9, 27, 81.

Challenge yourself

1. Calculate the sum of the common ratios for the geometric sequences below:

a. 200, 100, 50, 25, 12.5

b. 100000, 10000, 1000, 100

2. The fourth term of a geometric sequence with a common ratio of $+^1/_2$ is 8. What is the value of the initial term?

3. The third term of a geometric sequence with a common ratio of -2 is 220. What is the value of the initial term?

complementary angles

Two *angles* that add up to 90°.

e.g.

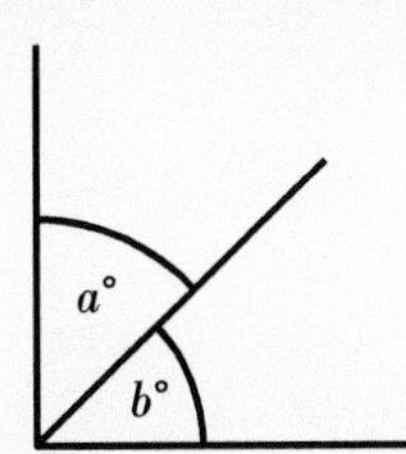

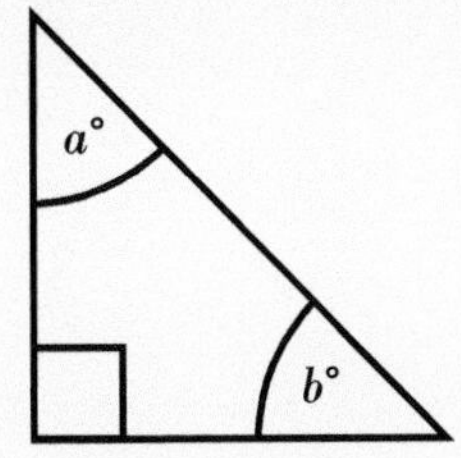

Since $a°$ + $b°$ = 90°, angles $a°$ and $b°$ are complementary, i.e. angle $a°$ is the complement of angle $b°$, and vice versa.

Test yourself

1. If angles $x°$ and $y°$ add up to 90°, are they complementary angles?

Challenge yourself

1. What is the complementary angle of 57°?

2. What is the sum of 8 pairs of complementary angles?

composite number

Any number *greater than* one that is not a *prime number*.

e.g. 4, 6, 8, 9 etc.

Test yourself

1. Ten is an even number and thirteen is an odd number. Which one of them is a composite number?

Challenge yourself

1. How many of the numbers in the set below are composite numbers?

19, 15, 13, 5, 8, 6, 10, 17, 23, 21

concave polygon

A *polygon* that has one or more *angles* inside (*interior angles*) that are *greater than* 180° (*reflex angle*).

e.g.

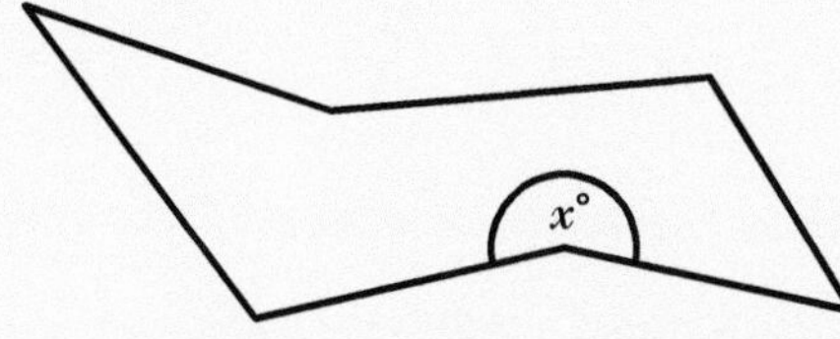

Angle $x°$ shown above is an interior angle and it is greater than 180°. Therefore, the polygon is a concave polygon.

Test yourself

1. Is the shape below a concave polygon?

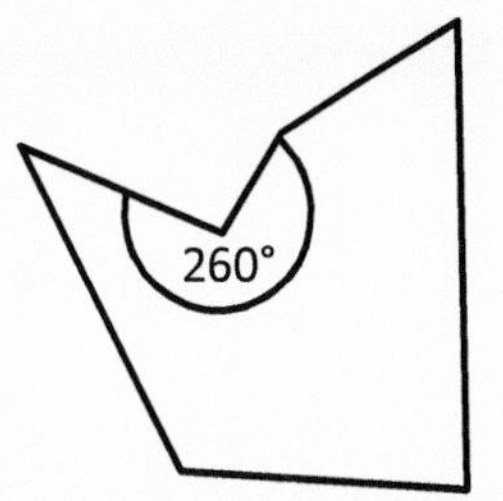

Challenge yourself

1. The interior angle of a concave hexagon at one of the vertices is 103° as shown below. What is the size of the angle $x°$?

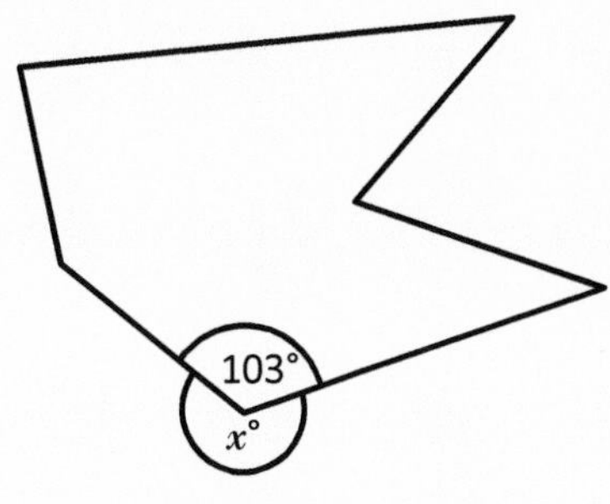

concentric shapes

Two or more shapes with a common centre.

e.g.

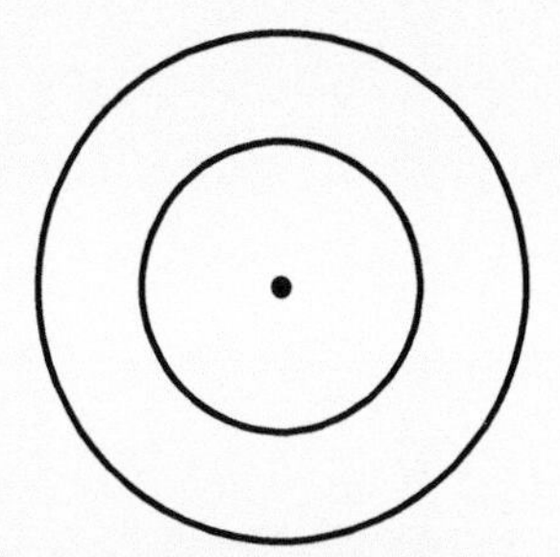

The two circles are concentric to one another, i.e. they share the same centre point.

Test yourself

1. Can the following shapes be described as concentric?

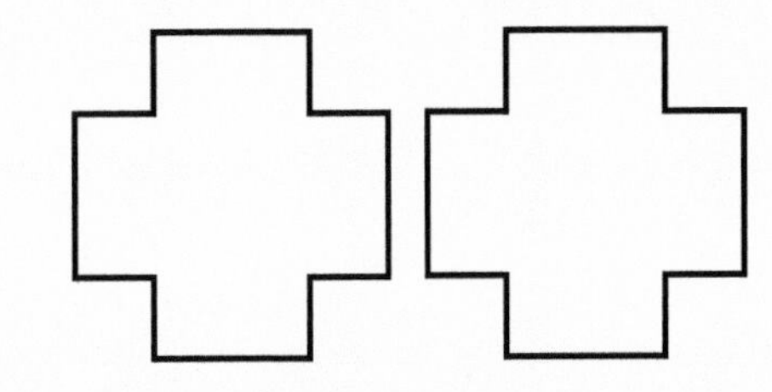

Challenge yourself

1. A shape is made of a circle and a regular hexagon that are concentric to one another. How many lines of symmetry does the shape have?

A B C D E F G H I J K L M N O P Q R S T U V W X Y Z

cone

A circular-based *pyramid* that becomes gradually smaller towards the *apex* (*vertex*).

e.g.

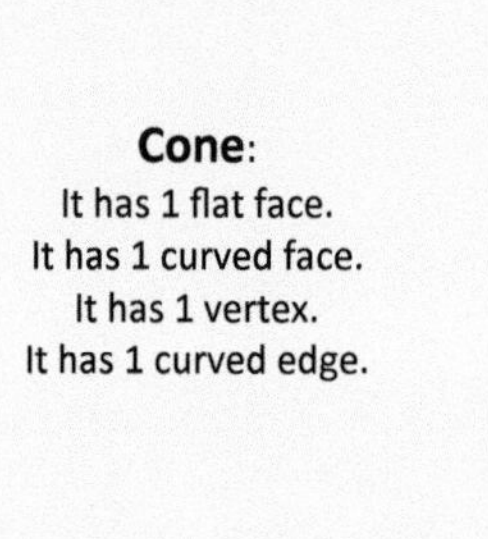

apex

base

Test yourself

1. How many circular faces does a cone have?

2. How many straight edges does a cone have?

Challenge yourself

1. The total surface area of a cone is $525m^2$. If the diameter of the base is 20m, what is the area of the curved face? Use $\pi = 3.14$ (2 d.p.)

congruent

Shapes that are *identical*.

Note: Congruent *figures* can be produced using *transformations* such as *reflection*, *translation* and *rotation*.

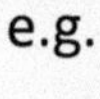

e.g.

All the figures above are congruent and can be rotated to fit on top of each other.

Test yourself

1. Are the shapes below congruent?

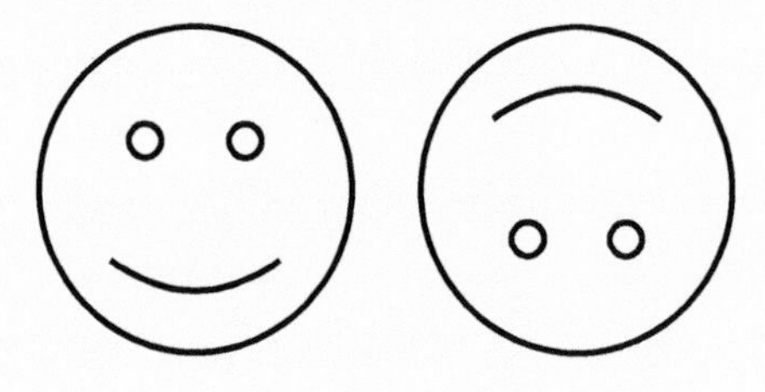

2. Are the shapes below congruent?

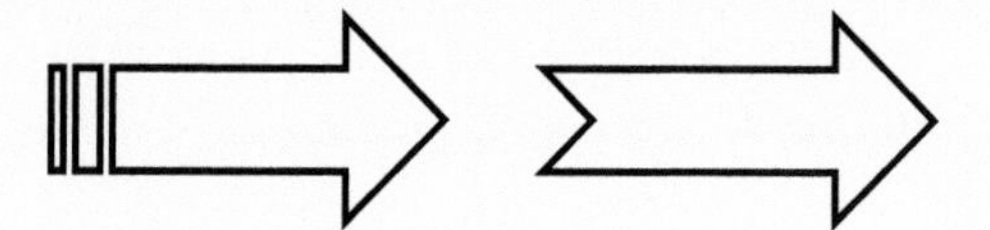

Challenge yourself

1. Which two of the three shapes below are congruent?

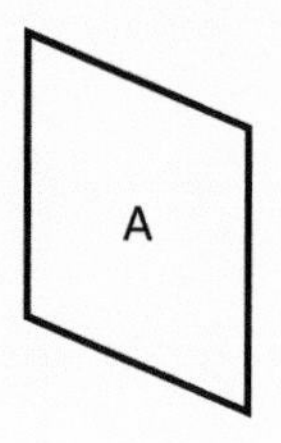

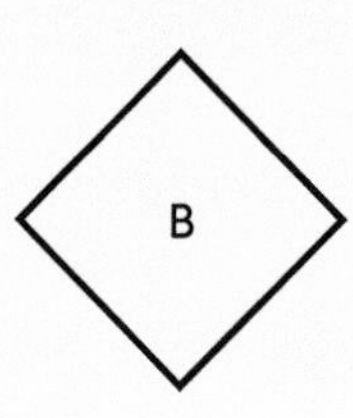

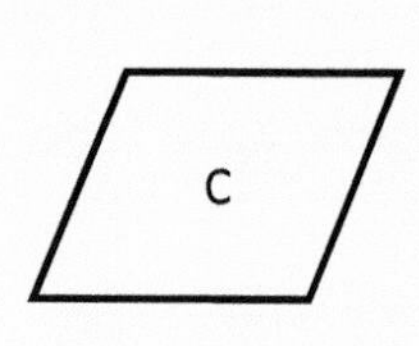

2. Which two of the three shapes below are congruent?

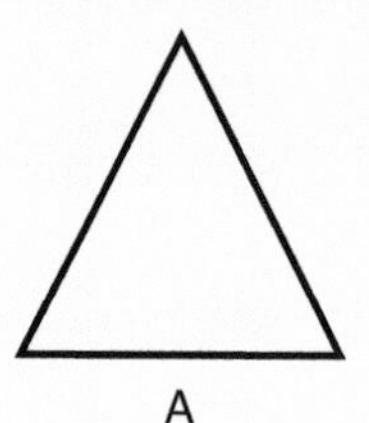

A

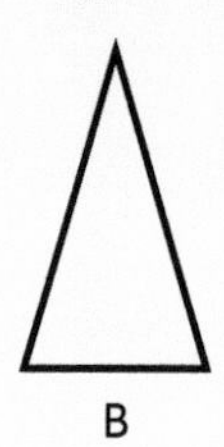

B

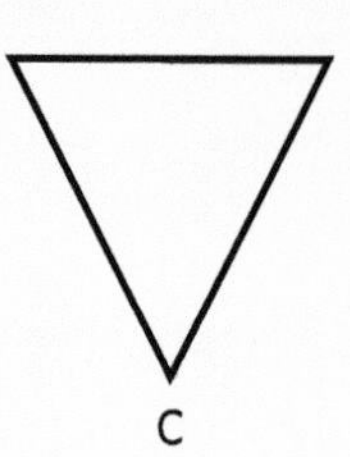

C

consecutive numbers/terms

Numbers that follow each other in a *sequence*.

e.g. 1, 2, 3 and 4 are consecutive numbers.
2, 4, 6 and 8 are consecutive even numbers.

Test yourself

1. Write the next three consecutive numbers in the following sequence.

5, 6, 7, 8, 9, 10

Challenge yourself

1. Write the first four consecutive odd numbers starting from 3.

2. Which three consecutive cube numbers have a sum of 216?

constant

A quantity that does not vary.

e.g. In the equation $y = 2x + 6$, +6 is a constant because its *value* does not change even if the values of y and x change.

Test yourself

1. What is the constant in the following equation?

$$y = x + 1$$

2. What is the constant in the following equation?

$$y = 2x - 9$$

Challenge yourself

1. In the equation $y = 4x + c$, if $x = 4$ and $y = 7$, what is the value of the constant, c?

2. In the equation $y = 4x + c$, if $x = -8$ and $y = -41$, what is the value of the constant, c?

conversion graph

A straight *line graph* which shows the relationship between one *unit* of measurement and another.

e.g.

The conversion graph for temperature
Temperature (Kelvin) = Temperature (°C) + 273

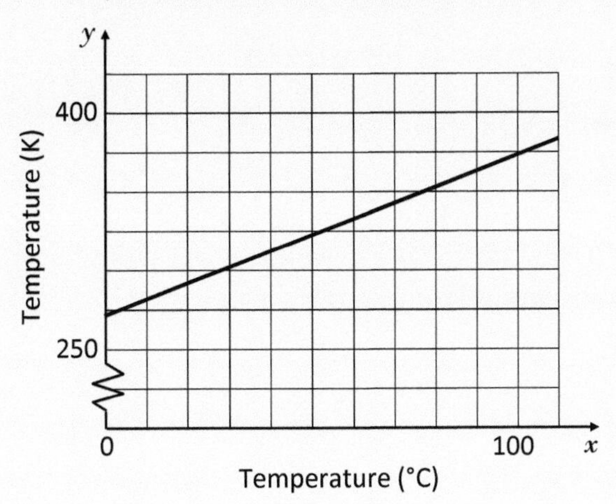

Test yourself

Answer the following questions using the graph below.

1. Is the graph a conversion graph?

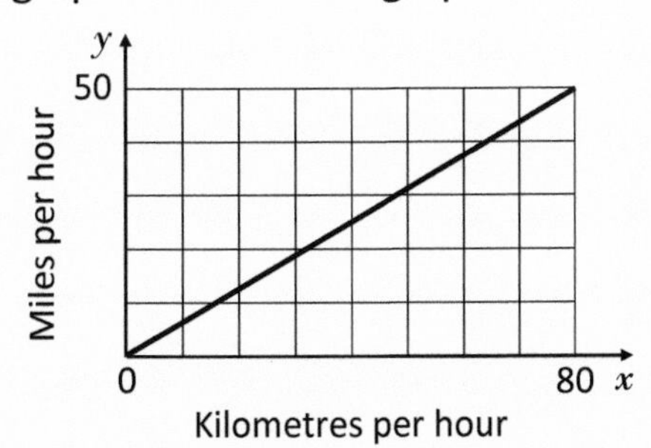

2. Convert 50 miles per hour into kilometres per hour.

Challenge yourself

1. Using the conversion graph for temperature in the example, convert 375K to degrees Celsius. Give your answer to the nearest whole number.

coordinates (Cartesian coordinates)

Coordinates are a set of *values* that define the position of a point. It is written in the form (x, y).

e.g.

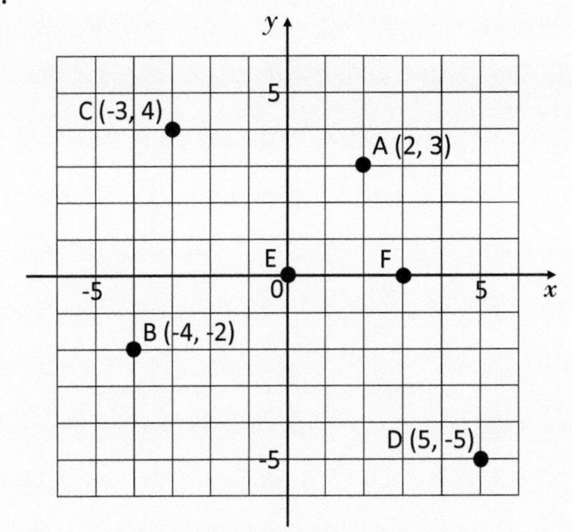

Test yourself

1. What are the coordinates of point E?

2. What are the coordinates of point F?

Challenge yourself

1. What are the new coordinates of points A (2, 3) and B (-4, -2) after a reflection in the x-axis?

2. What are the new coordinates of point D after a clockwise rotation of 90° about the origin?

corresponding angles (F-angles)

The *angles* that are located at the same position at each *intersection* when a straight line crosses two *parallel* lines.

Note: Corresponding angles are always *equal* in size.

e.g.

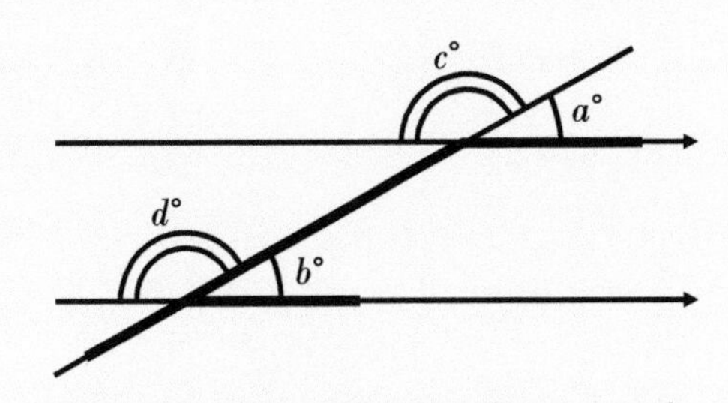

Corresponding angles are always equal, i.e. $a° = b°$ and $c° = d°$.

Test yourself

1. $x°$ and $y°$ are corresponding angles. If $x° = 57°$, what is the size of angle $y°$?

2. $w°$ and $z°$ are corresponding angles. If $w° = 12°$, what is the sum of angles $w°$ and $z°$?

A B C D E F G H I J K L M N O P Q R S T U V W X Y Z

A
B
C
D
E
F
G
H
I
J
K
L
M
N
O
P
Q
R
S
T
U
V
W
X
Y
Z

Challenge yourself

1. Suppose A° and B° are supplementary angles. If angle A° equals 123°, and another angle C° is a corresponding angle to B°, what is the size of angle C°?

2. Work out the sizes of angles $y°$ and $z°$ shown below.

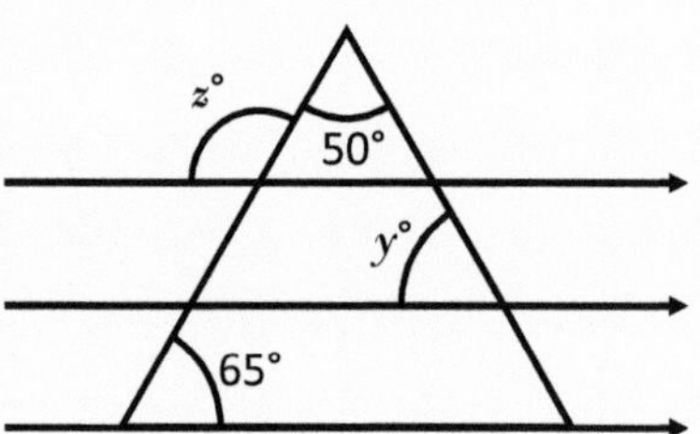

counter-clockwise

See *anticlockwise*.

***

cross cancel

See *cancel*.

***

cross-section

A flat *two-dimensional surface* formed by 'cutting a slice' through a *three-dimensional* shape *parallel* to its *base*.

Note: The *volume* of a *prism* can be calculated by multiplying the cross-sectional *area* by its *length*.

e.g.

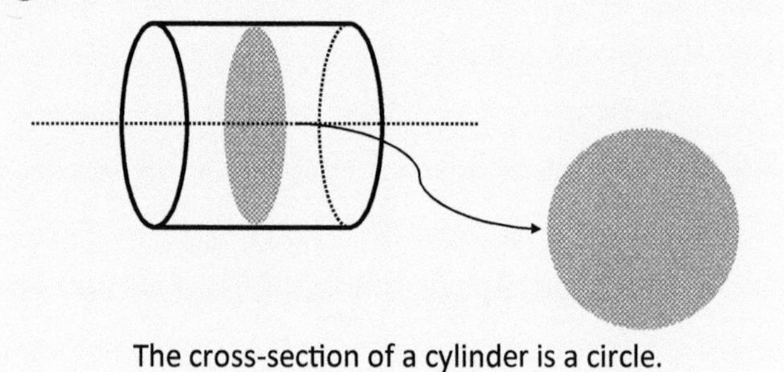

The cross-section of a cylinder is a circle.

Test yourself

1. Draw the cross-sections of the shapes below.

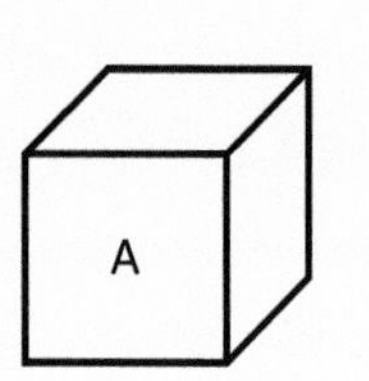

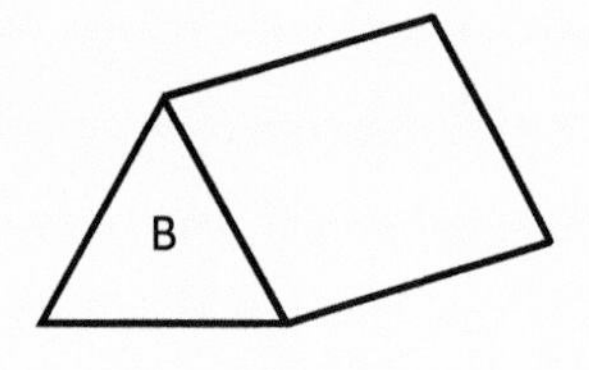

Challenge yourself

1. If the cross-sectional area of a hexagonal prism is 9cm^2 and its length is 12cm, what is its volume?

cube (square prism)

A *three-dimensional* shape with 6 *faces*, 8 *vertices* and 12 *edges*, where all the faces are *squares*.

e.g.

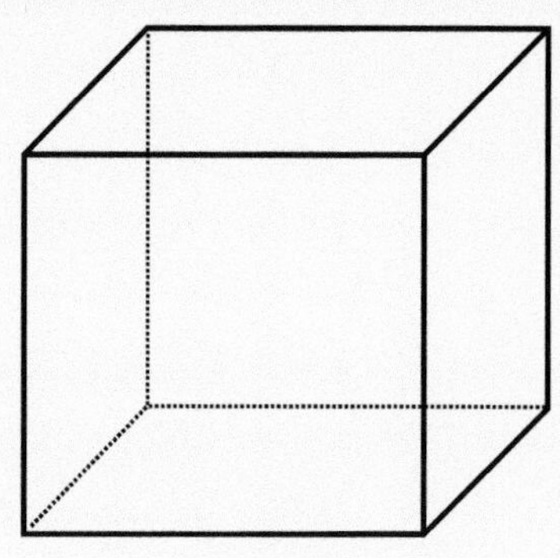

Test yourself

1. The width of a cube measures 8cm. What is its height in cm?

Challenge yourself

1. What is the sum of the number of faces, vertices and edges of a cube?

2. If the volume of a cube is 4800mm^3, what is the maximum number of smaller cubes with a volume of 3cm^3 that would fit inside the larger cube?

cube number

A number which is calculated by using a given number three times in a *multiplication*. The *cube* number of a is $a \times a \times a = a^3$. See also *cube root*.

e.g. 4 × 4 × 4 = 64.

Test yourself

1. What is 2 × 2 × 2?

Challenge yourself

1. What is the sixth cube number?

2. What cube number is more than 500 but less than 700?

cube root

A *value* that, when used three times in a *multiplication*, gives the number stated. It has the symbol '$\sqrt[3]{}$.' See also *cube number*.

e.g. The cube root of 64 is 4 since 4 × 4 × 4 = 64.

Test yourself

1. If 3 × 3 × 3 is 27, what is the cube root of 27?

Challenge yourself

1. What is the cube root of 125?

2. Given that the answer lies between 5 and 15, calculate the cube root of 1728.

3. What is the length of the edge of a cube that has a volume of $1331cm^3$?

cubic centimetre (cm^3)

A *metric unit* of *volume equivalent* to a *cube* with an *edge* that is 1cm in *length*, i.e. $1cm^3$.
e.g. $1cm^3$ is equivalent to 1 millilitre.

Test yourself

1. What is $2cm^3$ in millilitres?

2. What is 3ml in cubic centimetres?

Challenge yourself

1. Convert $1.54cm^3$ to millilitres.

2. Convert $3.74cm^3$ to cubic millimetres.

cubic metre (m^3)

A *metric unit* of *volume equivalent* to a *cube* with an *edge* that is 1m in *length*, i.e. $1m^3$.
e.g. $1m^3$ is equivalent to 1000 litres.

Test yourself

1. What is $4m^3$ in litres?

2. What is 6000 litres in cubic metres?

Challenge yourself

1. Convert $0.245m^3$ to litres.

2. Convert $0.053m^3$ to cubic centimetres.

cubic millimetre (mm^3)

A *metric unit* of *volume equivalent* to a *cube* with an *edge* that is 1mm in *length*, i.e. $1mm^3$.
e.g. $1mm^3$ is equivalent to 0.001 millilitres.

Test yourself

1. What is $7mm^3$ in millilitres?

2. What is 0.005 millilitres in cubic millimetres?

Challenge yourself

1. Convert $547mm^3$ to millilitres.

2. Convert $48,000mm^3$ to cubic centimetres.

cuboid (rectangular prism)

A *three-dimensional* rectangular *prism* with 6 *faces*, 8 *vertices* and 12 *edges*, where opposite faces are *equal* in *length* and *width*.
e.g.

Cuboid:
It has 6 flat faces.
It has 8 vertices.
It has 12 edges.

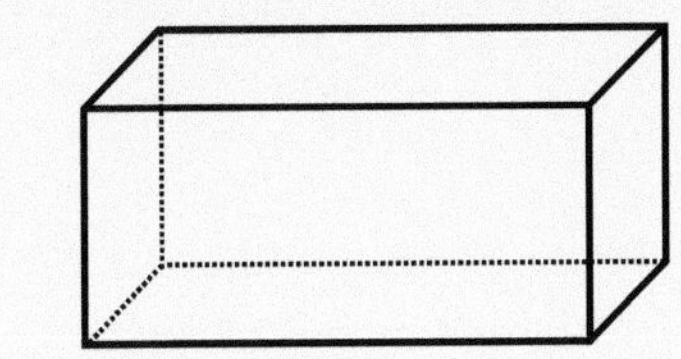

Test yourself

1. Is the shape below an example of a cuboid?

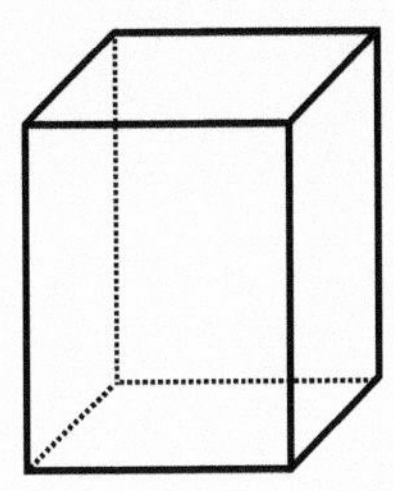

2. How many faces does a cuboid have?

Challenge yourself

1. What is the volume of a cuboid with a height of 9cm, a length of 4cm and a width of 15mm? Give your answer in cm^3.

2. What is the volume of a cuboid that is made up of twelve smaller cubes, each of volume $27mm^3$?

cyclic quadrilateral

A four-sided shape with all of its corners (*vertices*) touching the *circumference* of a *circle*, i.e. it fits exactly into a circle.
e.g.

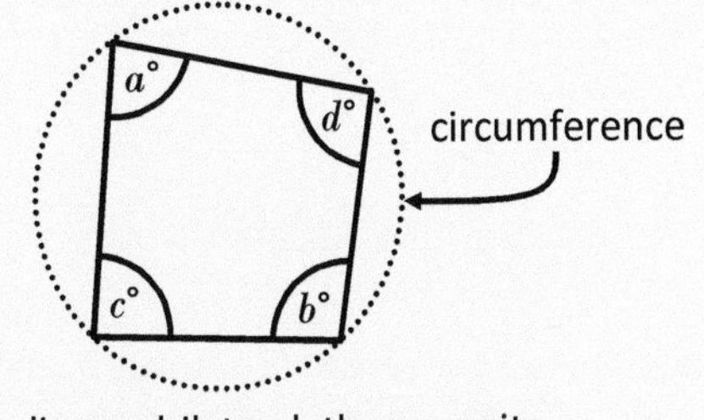

In a cyclic quadrilateral, the opposite angles always add up to 180°, i.e. $a° + b° = 180°$ and $c° + d° = 180°$.

A B C D E F G H I J K L M N O P Q R S T U V W X Y Z

A B C D E F G H I J K L M N O P Q R S T U V W X Y Z

Test yourself

Answer the following questions using the diagram in the example.

1. In a cyclic quadrilateral, $a°$ and $b°$ are opposite angles. If $a°$ = 20°, what is the size of angle $b°$?

2. What is the sum of angles $c°$ and $d°$?

Challenge yourself

Answer the following questions using the diagram in the example.

1. What is the sum of all the interior angles in a cyclic quadrilateral?

2. Given that the interior angle is an integer, what is the maximum size of angle $a°$?

3. Draw a cyclic quadrilateral with all interior angles that are 90°. What is the name given to this shape?

cylinder

A cylinder is a *three-dimensional* shape consisting of two circular *faces* connected by a curved *surface*.

e.g.

It has 2 flat faces.
It has 1 curved face.
It has 2 curved edges.
It has no vertices.

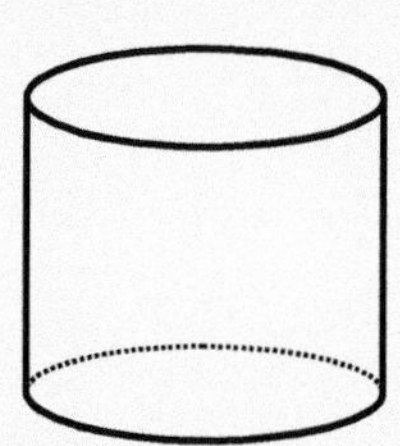

Test yourself

1. How many straight edges does a cylinder have?

2. How many faces does a cylinder have?

3. How many vertices does a cylinder have?

Challenge yourself

1. What is the name given to the cross-section of a cylinder?

2. If the cross-sectional area of a cylinder is $150cm^2$ and it has a length of 2cm, what is its volume?

3. What is the volume of a cylinder if its cross-sectional area is $50cm^2$ and its length is 7cm?

D

datum (plural: data)

A piece of information represented by numbers (quantitative) or words (qualitative).

Note: Data cannot be both quantitative and qualitative.

e.g. Quantitative data: length, weight, age... etc.
Qualitative data: colour, shape, texture... etc.

Test yourself

1. Which of the measurements are quantitative?

mass height taste scent

2. Which of the measurements are qualitative?

speed temperature mood humidity

Challenge yourself

Answer the following questions using the table below.

Person	Gender	Shoe size	No. of siblings
A	Male	8	3
B	Female	5	2

1. Which data categories are qualitative?

2. Which data categories are quantitative?

dataset

A collection of numbers or information (*data*).

e.g. The exam scores of 5 students out of 15 were: 20%, 50%, 60%, 65% and 80%.

Test yourself

Answer the following questions using the dataset below.

Student	Gender	Age	Test 1 (%)	Test 2 (%)
1	Male	10	50	48
2	Female	12	80	83
3	Female	11	77	71
4	Female	9	63	78

1. Which student had the highest score on Test 1?

2. What was the minimum score on Test 2?

<u>Challenge yourself</u>

Answer the following questions using the dataset below.

Student	Gender	Age	Test 1 (%)	Test 2 (%)
A	Female	16	80	61
B	Female	18	55	82
C	Male	17	66	65
D	Female	19	47	32

1. What is the median age of the students?

2. What is the mean score on Test 1? Give your answer as a decimal.

3. What is the sum of the ranges of scores on Tests 1 and 2?

4. If student C retook Test 2 and the mean score increased by 2%, what percentage did student C achieve in the retake?

day

The time taken for Earth to make one complete *revolution* on its *axis*; that is 24 *hours*.
<u>Note:</u> There are 7 days in a *week*, and the number of days in a *month* varies.
e.g. A day is approximately equal to $^1/_{365}$ of a year.

<u>Test yourself</u>

1. How many days are there in 50 weeks?

2. How many days are there in 2 years and 3 weeks?

3. How many hours are there in 6 days?

4. How many minutes are there in one day?

<u>Challenge yourself</u>

1. How many seconds are in one day?

2. How many hours are there in a standard year?

3. If today is Tuesday, what day would it be after 8 weeks and 18 days?

4. If today is Friday, what day would it be after 46 days?

decagon

A 10-sided *polygon*.
e.g.

Regular decagon:
All 10 sides are equal.
Each interior angle is 144°.
Each exterior angle is 36°.

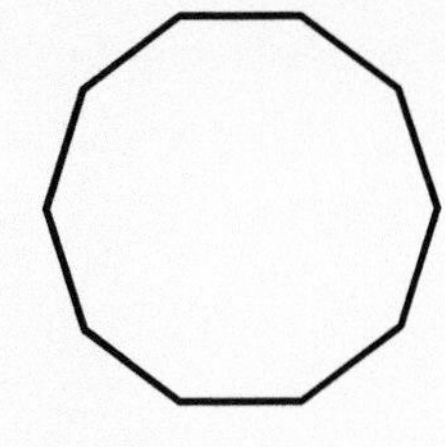

<u>Test yourself</u>

1. How many edges are needed to complete the decagon below?

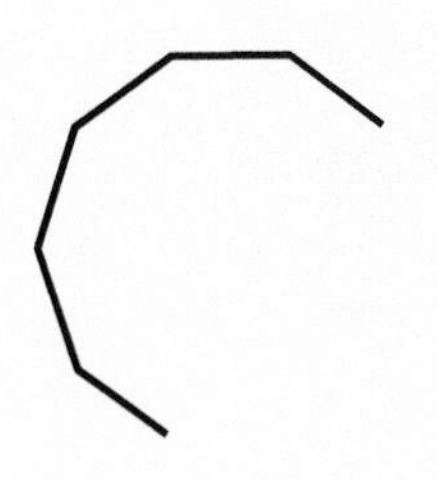

<u>Challenge yourself</u>

1. How many lines of symmetry does a regular decagon have?

2. What is the ratio of the size of the interior angle to the size of the exterior angle of a regular decagon?

decimal number (decimal)

A number that contains a *decimal point*.
e.g. 0.15, 1.25 and 21.2 are decimal numbers because each one contains a decimal point.

<u>Test yourself</u>

1. What is 0.3 + 0.75?

2. Calculate 0.4 × 0.8.

3. What is 0.98 - 0.7?

4. Calculate 0.88 ÷ 2.

<u>Challenge yourself</u>

Answer the following questions using BIDMAS.

1. What is 0.7 - 0.6 + 0.1 - 0.05?

2. Work out 0.9 × 0.5 - 0.7 + 11.

3. Calculate (5.8 × 10) + 0.8 - 0.09.

4. Solve (0.2 × 0.1) × 0.02 + 0.4.

A
B
C
D
E
F
G
H
I
J
K
L
M
N
O
P
Q
R
S
T
U
V
W
X
Y
Z

decimal place (d.p.)
The position of a *digit* counted to the right of the *decimal point*.
Note: A number can be rounded to a particular decimal place. See also *rounding*.
e.g. In the figure 1.234, the digit in the second decimal place is 3. Therefore, 1.234 correct to 2 decimal places is 1.23 because the number in the third decimal place, 4, is less than 5.

Test yourself
1. In the figure 3.266, which digit is in the second decimal place?

2. Write 3.266 correct to one decimal place.

Challenge yourself
1. What is 25.1 × 0.12 correct to 2 d.p.?

2. What is 0.789 as a percentage correct to 1 d.p.?

decimal point
A point that separates the *units* column and the *tenths* column.
Note: A number that contains a decimal point is known as a *decimal* or *decimal number*.
e.g. 0.15, 1.25 and 21.2 are decimal numbers because each one contains a decimal point.

Test yourself
1. What is 0.54 + 15.94?

Challenge yourself
1. Using BIDMAS, calculate (0.35 × 0.2) + 0.8 - 0.1.

decrease
To make something smaller in size or number.
Note: The synonym of decrease is *reduce*.
e.g. The price of a football decreased from £20 to £10; that is a decrease of 50%.

Test yourself
1. Decrease £20 by 5%.

2. The price of a phone decreased from £110 to £90. By how much did the price decrease?

3. A bottle of water holds 500ml. If half is poured out, how much water is left?

Challenge yourself
1. Decrease £141 by 39%.

2. In a sale, the price of a phone decreased by 15%. If the original price was £450, what is the reduced price?

decreasing order
See *descending order*.

***

degree
i. A degree (°) is the *unit* of an *angle*.
e.g. 1° is equal to $^1/_{360}$ of a full turn.

ii. See *power*.

***

Test yourself
1. In the expression $x^2 + 3$, does x have a degree of 2?

2. Is 3° equivalent to $^3/_{360}$ of a full turn?

Challenge yourself
1. Identify the degree of each variable, x, y and z, in the expression $7x^5y^{10}z^5$.

denary
The name given to the *base* 10 counting system, i.e. a system that uses the *digits*: 0, 1, 2, 3, 4, 5, 6, 7, 8 and 9.
e.g. Writing 'eighty seven' as a number using the denary system is 87.

Test yourself
Using the denary system, answer the following questions.
1. Write 'one hundred and twelve' as a number.

2. Write 'seventy six' as a number.

Challenge yourself
Using the denary system, answer the following questions.
1. Write 'five million, seventy four thousand and fifty' as a number.

2. Write 'eight thousand and seven, and one tenth' as a number.

denominator

The *divisor* of a *fraction*, i.e. the bottom number of a fraction.
e.g. The denominator of the fraction $^5/_9$ is 9.

Test yourself
1. What is the denominator of $^7/_{10}$?

2. What is the denominator of $^9/_{19}$?

Challenge yourself
1. What is the denominator of the sum $^2/_5 + ^1/_6$?

2. Simplify $^{15}/_{40}$ and state the denominator.

3. What is the lowest common denominator of $^7/_{16}$ and $^9/_{13}$?

dependent event

An *event* with an *outcome* that is affected by previous events.
e.g. If a red marble is removed from a bag and is not replaced, the probability of drawing another red marble from the same bag decreases.

Test yourself
1. If a blue marble is picked from a bag and is replaced, has the probability of picking a blue marble changed?

Challenge yourself
1. There are 5 red marbles in a bag of 12. If a red marble is removed from the bag and is not replaced, what is the probability of drawing out another red marble?

2. A card is chosen randomly from a deck of 52 playing cards and is not replaced. If the first card was a Jack, what is the probability that the second card is a King?

descending order (decreasing order)

Numbers are in descending order when they are arranged from largest to smallest.
e.g. 5, 4, 3, 2, 1 are in descending order.

Test yourself
1. Put the values below in descending order.
1, 5, 3, 9, 10

2. Put the values below in descending order.
0, 11, 20, 30, 52

Challenge yourself
1. Put the values below in descending order.
21, -5, -14, 2, 0, 1, 99

2. Put the values below in descending order.
-25, 10, 23.2, 11, 2.3

diagonal

A straight line connecting two non-adjacent corners (*vertices*) of a *plane figure,* or any two vertices of a *solid* that are not on the same *edge*.
e.g.

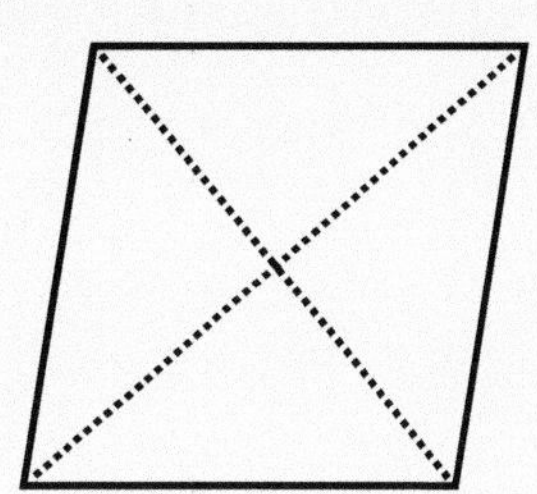

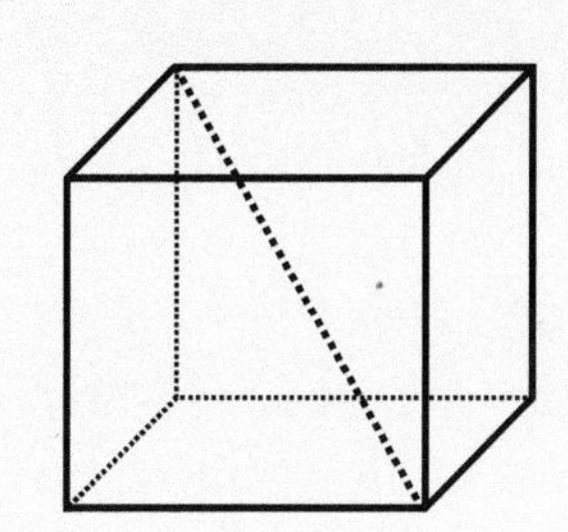

Diagonals are drawn using a dotted line.

Test yourself
1. How many diagonals can you draw on a square?

2. How many diagonals can you draw on a regular pentagon?

Challenge yourself
1. The two diagonals of a rhombus are 6cm and 8cm in length, and one of its sides is 5cm long. What is the area of the rhombus in cm^2?

diameter

The *length* of a straight line that *joins* two points on the *circumference* of a *circle*, passing through the circle's centre.
Note: The diameter of a circle is *equivalent* to twice the *radius*.
e.g.

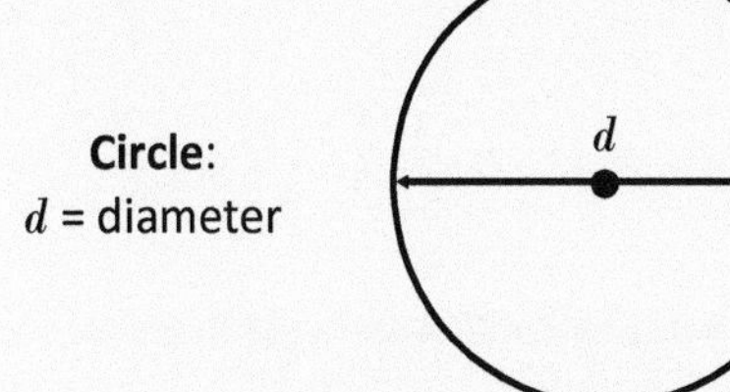

A B C D E F G H I J K L M N O P Q R S T U V W X Y Z

Test yourself

1. The radius of a circle measures 10mm. What is the diameter of the circle?

2. The diameter of a circle measures 10mm. What is the radius of the circle?

Challenge yourself

1. If the area of a circle is $196\pi cm^2$, what is the length of its diameter?

2. Given that the circumference of a circle is 56πmm, calculate the diameter.

diamond

See *rhombus*.

***

difference

The *value* that remains after the *subtraction* of one number from another, i.e. the change between two numbers.

e.g. The difference between 5 and 2 is 5 - 2 = 3.

Test yourself

1. What is 9 - 6?

2. Calculate 150 - 16.

3. Calculate the difference between 15 and 11.

Challenge yourself

1. What is the difference between 5842 and 456?

2. Calculate the difference between 251 and -47.

3. Calculate the difference between -0.255 and -0.957.

digit

Any of the *figures* between 0 and 9 used to represent a number.

e.g. 1993 has four digits: 1, 9, 9 and 3.

Test yourself

1. How many digits does the number 125 have?

2. How many digits does the number 91,851 have?

Challenge yourself

1. Which three-digit square number lies between 300 and 350?

2. Which three-digit cube number lies between 300 and 350?

dimension

A parameter needed to specify the position of a point or describe a shape. See also *three-dimensional, two-dimensional*.

e.g.

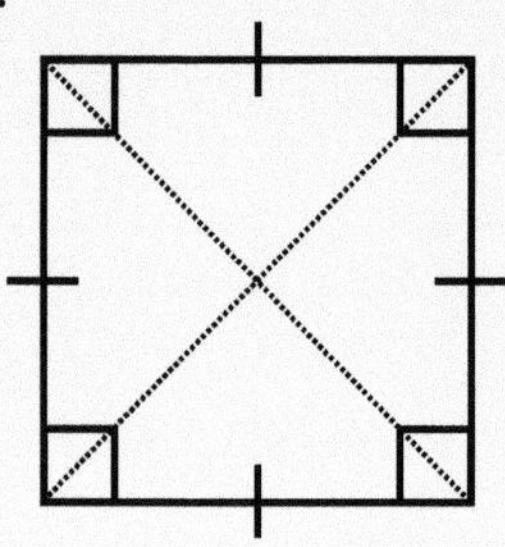

Square:
All 4 angles are equal (90°).
All 4 sides are of equal length.
It has 4 vertices.
The diagonals bisect each other at 90°.

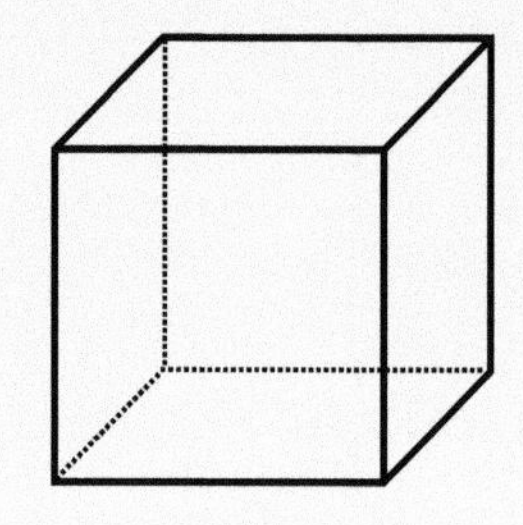

Cube:
It has 6 faces.
It has 8 vertices.
It has 12 edges.

A square has two parameters: length and width.
A cube has three parameters: length, width and height.
Therefore, a square is a two-dimensional shape and a cube is a three-dimensional shape.

Test yourself

1. Which of the following shapes are two-dimensional?

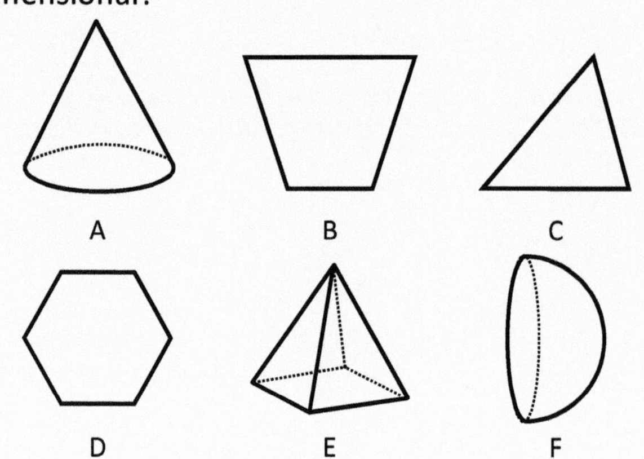

Challenge yourself

1. How many dimensions does a hexagonal prism have?

2. How many dimensions does a line have?

3. How many dimensions does an equilateral triangle have?

direction

A line along which something moves or points towards, i.e. a line leading to a particular point or place. See also *bearing*, *east*, *north*, *south*, *west*.
e.g.

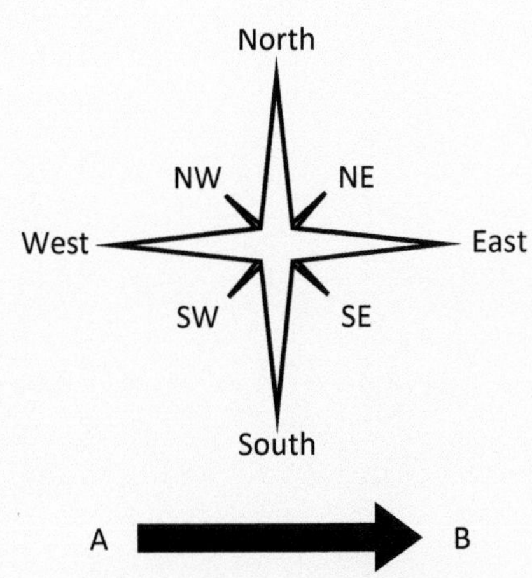

The arrow points from A to B,
i.e. it is directed towards the east.

Test yourself

1. List the eight compass directions.

Challenge yourself

1. A point at the origin is translated 8 units up, 11 units to the right and 4 units down. What are the coordinates of the new position?

2. Describe the direction of point A relative to point B using the points on a compass.

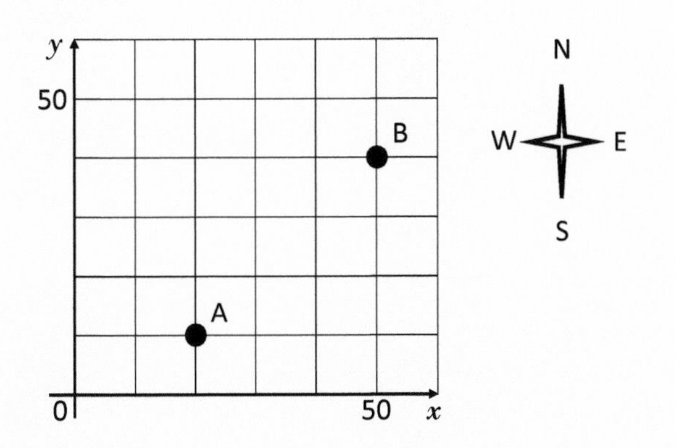

disjoint sets

Sets of numbers are said to be disjoint if they have no common *values*. See also *dataset*, *subset*.
e.g. A = {2, 4, 6, 8} and B = {3, 5, 7, 9} are disjoint sets because they have no common values.

Test yourself

1. If C = {1, 3, 5} and D = {5}, are the sets disjoint?

2. If C = {9, 8} and D = {7, 6}, are the sets disjoint?

Challenge yourself

1. Given that set A = {first 5 square numbers}, set B = {first 5 triangular numbers} and set C = {2, 6, 10, 15}, which sets are disjoint?

distance

The *length* of a gap between two points or objects. See also *equidistant*.
e.g.

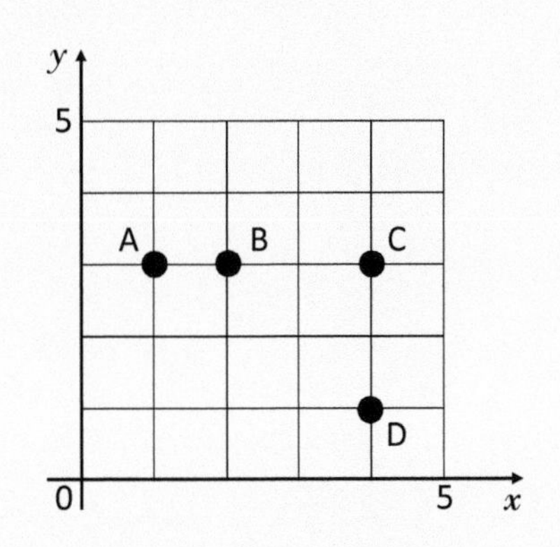

The distance between point A and B is 1 unit.

Challenge yourself

Answer the following questions using the graph in the example above.

1. What is the distance between points A and C?

2. What is the distance between points B and C?

3. Which points are positioned equidistant to point C?

distance-time graph

A *graph* relating the *distance* travelled by a body and the time taken. The *gradient* represents the *speed* of the body.
e.g.

Distance travelled by a plane over time

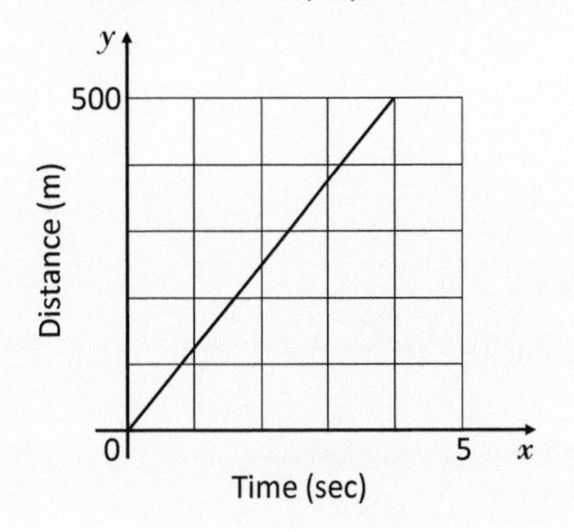

A B C D E F G H I J K L M N O P Q R S T U V W X Y Z

Challenge yourself

Answer the following questions using the graph in the example.

1. What is the speed of the plane? Give your answer in metres per second.

2. How far did the plane travel in 2 seconds? Give your answer in metres.

3. Draw a straight line on the graph that represents a speed of 200m/s.

distribution table

See *frequency distribution table*.

***

dividend

The number that is being divided by another number. See also *numerator*.

e.g. The dividend in the fraction $^{8}/_{13}$ is 8, which is also known as the numerator.

Test yourself

1. State the dividend in the equation $^{66}/_{11} = 6$.

2. State the dividend in the equation $^{24}/_{2} = 12$.

Challenge yourself

1. Simplify and state the dividend in the fraction $^{25}/_{200}$.

2. Simplify and state the dividend in the fraction $^{22}/_{78}$.

3. Solve $^{x}/_{13} = 5$.

4. Solve $^{x}/_{7} = 7 + 12$.

divisible

A given number is divisible by another number if it can be divided by the other number to give a *whole number*.

e.g. $3 \times 4 = 12$ so 12 is divisible by both 3 and 4.

Test yourself

1. Is 10 divisible by 2 and 5?

2. Is 12 divisible by 7?

3. Which numbers between 1 and 11 are divisible by 2?

4. Which numbers between 1 and 16 are divisible by 3 and 5?

Challenge yourself

1. Is 154 divisible by $(5 + 12 \times 5 \div 3)$?

2. Which number between 20 and 30 is divisible by both 2 and 12?

3. Is $(5 + 105 \div 7 + 115)$ divisible by $(\sqrt{9} \times 15)$?

4. Which number is divisible by both 4 and 6, and is less than 20?

division

The mathematical *operation* which separates a number into *equal* groups. It has the symbol '÷'.

e.g. $9 \div 3 = 3$.

Test yourself

1. What is $6 \div 3$?

2. Calculate $8 \div 2$.

3. There are 30 pencils and 6 pencil cases. If all the pencils were divided equally into the 6 pencil cases, how many pencils are there in each case?

4. There are 32 chocolates and 4 friends want to share them. How many does each one receive?

Challenge yourself

1. Calculate $630 \div 15$.

2. The volume of a cube is $228cm^3$. If each jug has a volume of $19cm^3$, how many jugs are needed to completely fill the cube with water?

3. Given that x is a negative integer, find the value of x from the equation $(x + 15) \div 14 = x + 2$.

divisor

A number by which a *dividend* is divided.

e.g. The divisor in the fraction $^{8}/_{13}$ is 13, which is also known as the denominator. See also *denominator*.

Test yourself

1. State the divisor in the equation $^{66}/_{2} = 33$.

2. State the divisor in the equation $^{88}/_{4} = 22$.

Challenge yourself

1. State the divisor in the equation $^{180}/_{4} = 45$.

2. Solve $12 = 144 \div x$.

3. A cube has a volume of 50mm^3, and 20 cubes can fit inside a container. What is the volume of the container?

4. Solve $(x + 7) \div 14 = 3$.

double

Increasing a *value* or quantity by a *factor* of two, i.e. multiplying a given value by two.
e.g. Doubling 8 gives 16, $8 \times 2 = 16$.

Test yourself

1. What value is obtained when 12 is doubled?

2. What number do you get if you double 11, and subtract 14 from the result before doubling it again?

3. Max read 12 books in the last 6 months and Jess read double that amount. How many books did Jess read?

4. Kushal scored 15 points in a basketball match and Guwon scored double those points. If Songyo scored double Guwon's points, how many points did Songyo score?

Challenge yourself

1. Calculate the input, x, of the number machine below.

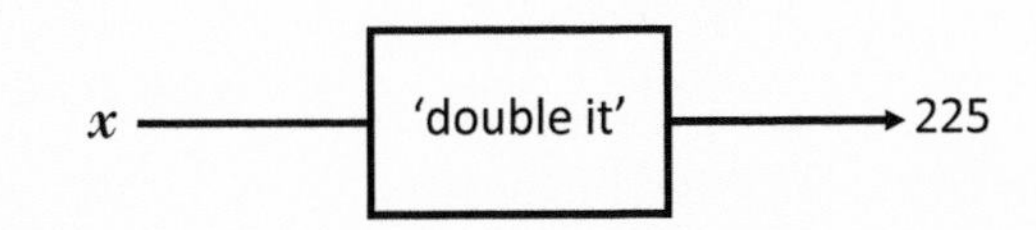

2. Calculate the input, x, of the number machine below.

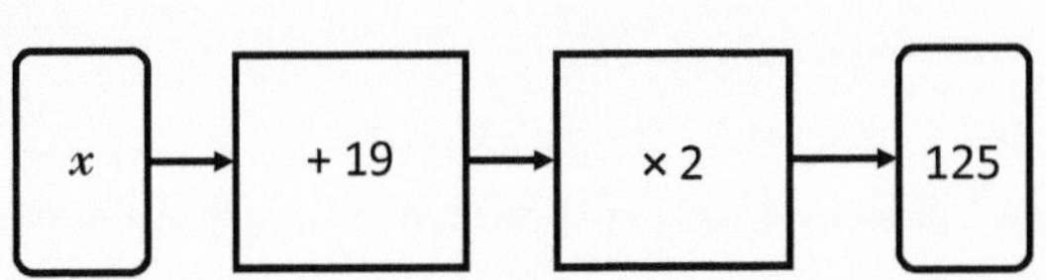

3. A number is doubled and raised to the power of 3. Then 36 is subtracted from it to give an answer of 180. Calculate the original value.

4. A number is doubled twice and then a value of 71 is added to give 119. What is the original value?

dozen

Referring to a quantity of 12 items.
e.g. Three dozen is $12 \times 3 = 36$.

Test yourself

1. How much is two dozen?

2. How much is half a dozen?

3. What is $^{3}/_{4}$ of a dozen?

4. What is $^{7}/_{12}$ of a dozen?

Challenge yourself

1. If five dozen water bottles weigh 42kg, how much does one bottle weigh?

2. Two dozen pens are bought. If the total cost of the pens is £72, how much does each pen cost?

3. A factory produces three dozen chocolates every 28 minutes. How many chocolates are produced over a period of 1 hour and 38 minutes?

4. If a baker can bake half a dozen cakes in 78 minutes, how long does it take to bake 54 cakes? Give your answer in seconds.

E

east

The *direction* corresponding to the compass point that is 90° *clockwise* and 270° *anticlockwise* of *north*, i.e. it points to the right of north.

e.g.

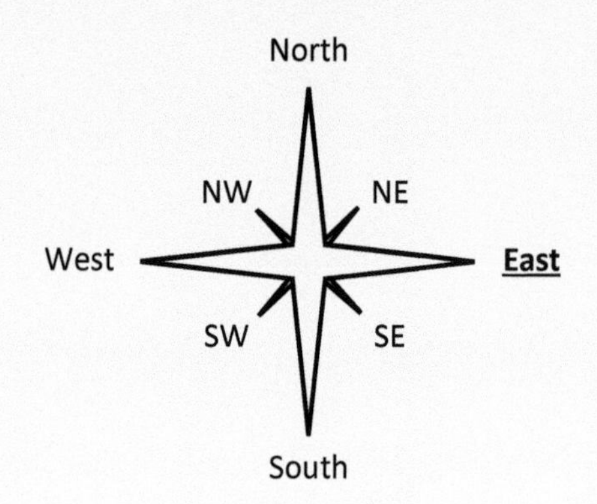

Test yourself

1. Michael is facing east and Oliver is standing to his left. If he turns to face Oliver, in which direction will he be facing?

2. Kate is facing east. If she turns 90° anticlockwise, in which direction will she be facing?

Challenge yourself

1. How many right angles are there in a clockwise turn from south to east?

2. Jenny is facing east. In which direction will she be facing after turning 540° anticlockwise?

edge

A *line segment* that *joins* two *vertices* of a *two-dimensional* shape, or a line segment at which two *faces* meet in a *three-dimensional* shape. See also *side*.

e.g.

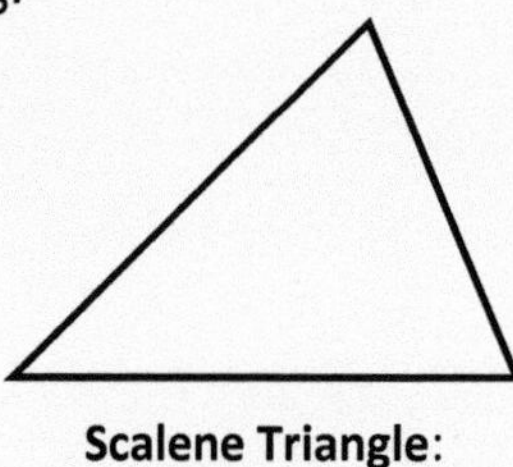

Scalene Triangle:
It has 3 edges.
No angles are equal.
No sides are of equal length.

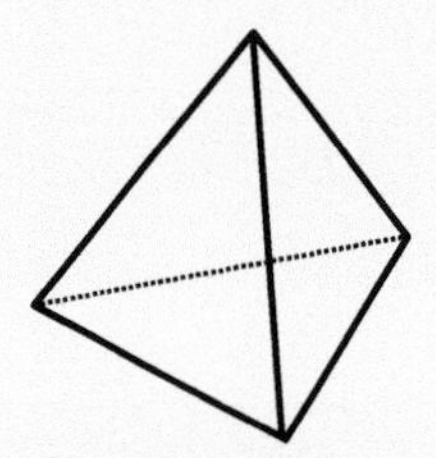

Triangular Pyramid:
It has 6 edges.
It has 4 faces.
It has 4 vertices.

Test yourself

1. How many edges does the shape below have?

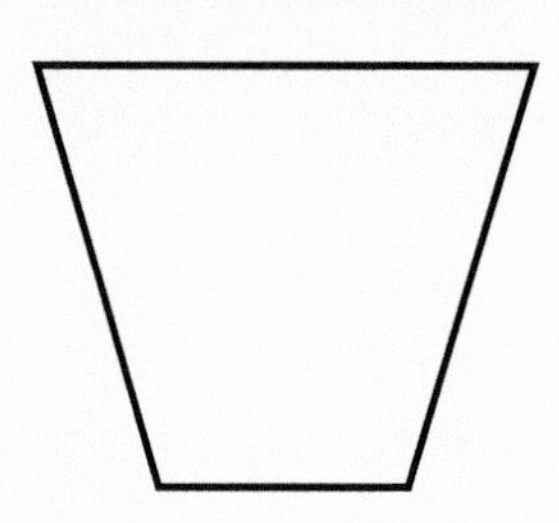

2. How many edges does a cube have?

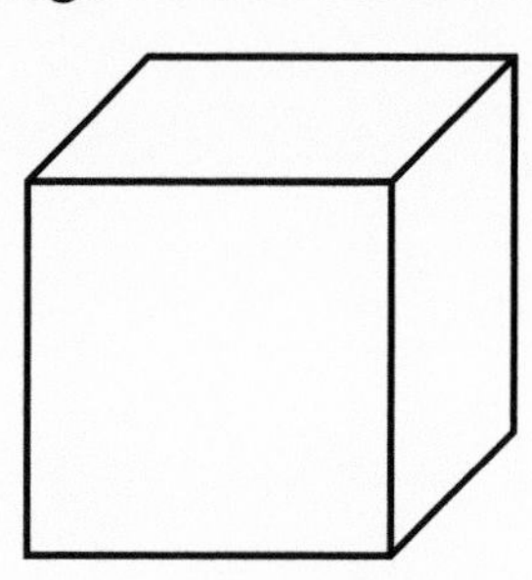

Challenge yourself

1. What is the product of the number of edges of a pentagon and a decagon?

2. What is the mean number of edges of the shapes below?

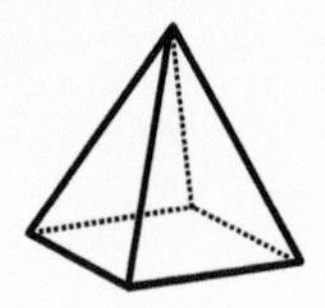

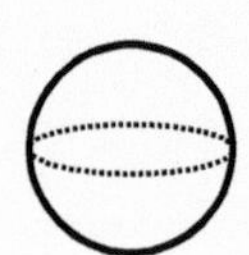

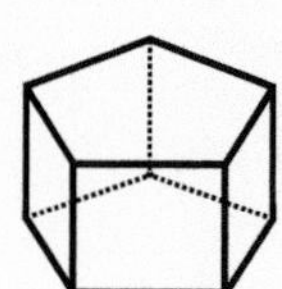

element

A member of a collection of numbers. See also *data*, *set*.

e.g. If set A = {1, 2, 3, 4, 5}, the number 3 is an element of set A, i.e. it belongs to set A.

Test yourself

1. If set B = {1, 3, 6, 8}, is 8 an element of set B?

2. If set C = {11, 2, 7, 9}, is 2 an element of set C?

Challenge yourself

1. If set D = {15, 8, 11, 2, 66}, how many elements of set D are even numbers?

2. Set E comprises the first two odd numbers and the first five triangular numbers. List all the elements of set E.

3. Set S = {5, 10, 15, 25} and set T = {10, 15, 20}. Which elements belong to set S but not to set T?

elevation

A *two-dimensional* drawing of a *three-dimensional* shape as if viewed directly from a single side.

e.g.

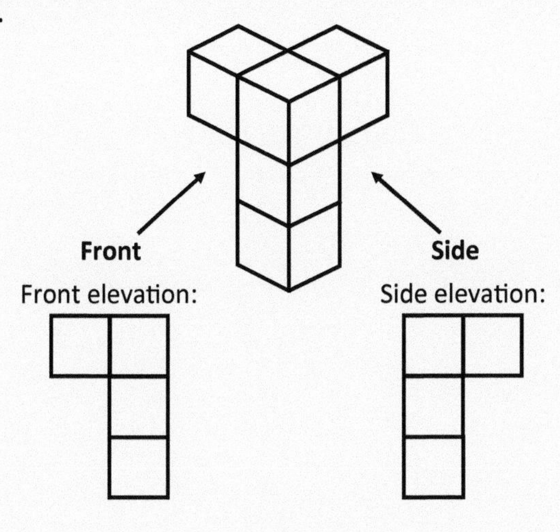

Test yourself

1. Draw the side and front elevation of a cube.

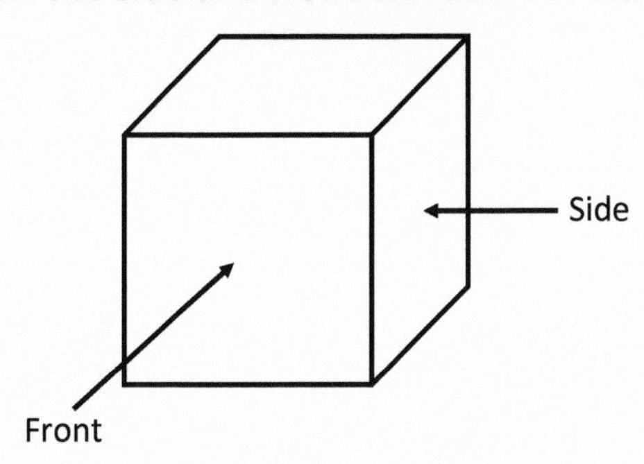

Challenge yourself

1. The diagram below shows the plan and elevations of a three-dimensional shape made up of smaller cubes. How many smaller cubes are there?

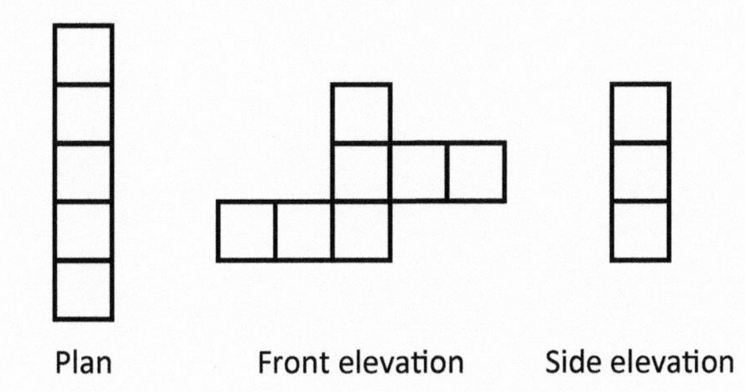

2. The diagram below shows the plan and elevations of a three-dimensional shape made up of smaller cubes. How many smaller cubes are there?

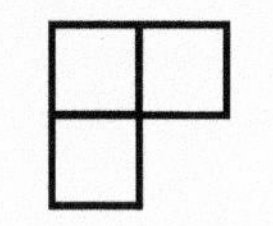

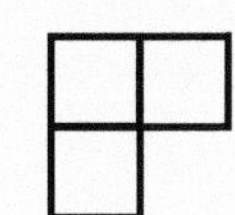

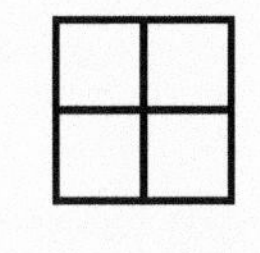

Plan Front elevation Side elevation

ellipse

See *oval*.

***

enlargement

A type of *transformation* in which the size of an object, and its position from a given point, change by the same *ratio*. See also *transformation*.

e.g.

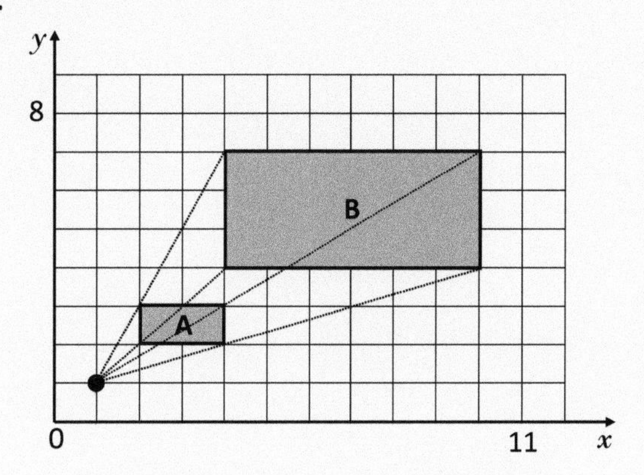

Shape A has been enlarged to shape B by a scale factor of 3 from point (1, 1).

Test yourself

1. Which of the shapes below is an enlargement of shape D?

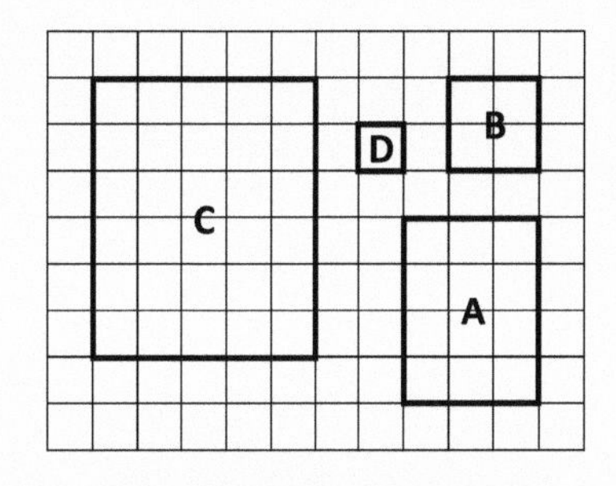

Challenge yourself

1. Identify the shapes that are an enlargement of shape A.

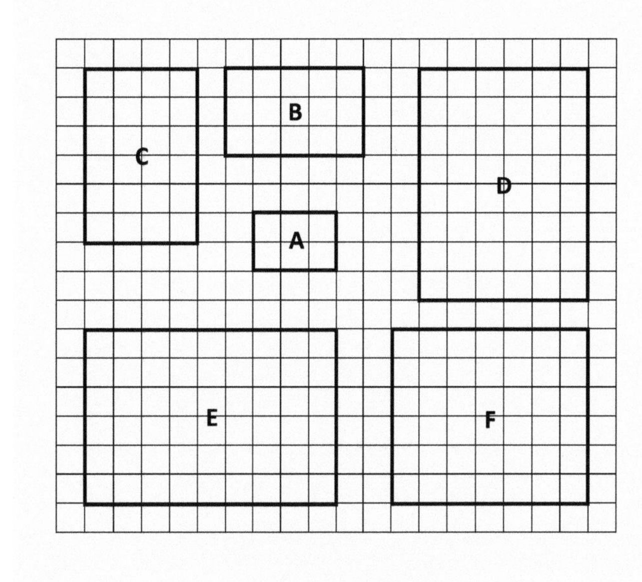

A B C D E F G H I J K L M N O P Q R S T U V W X Y Z

A B C D E F G H I J K L M N O P Q R S T U V W X Y Z

equally likely

When two or more *events* have the same *chance* (*probability*) of occurring. See also *fifty-fifty*.
e.g. When a die is rolled, an even number and an odd number are equally likely outcomes.

Test yourself

1. The chance of rain on a particular day is equally likely as the chance of snow. If the probability of snow is 0.3, how likely is it to rain?

2. If a fair coin is tossed, is the chance of the coin landing on either heads or tails equally likely?

Challenge yourself

1. An event P has a probability of 0.75. Which of the arrows A, B or C shows the best position on the probability line for an event that is equally likely to occur as event P?

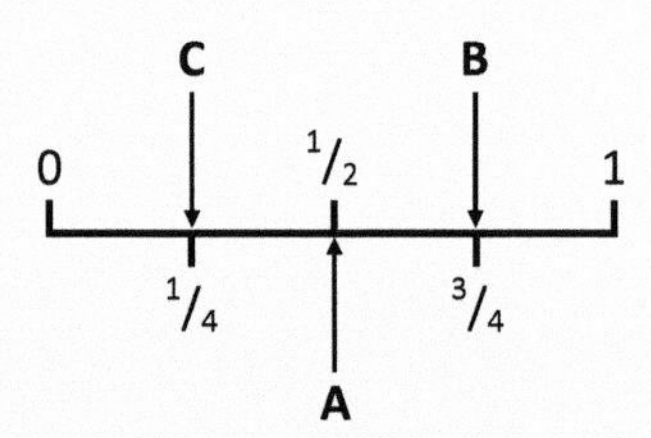

equals

This is when one amount is the same as another. It has the symbol '='.
e.g. If $x = 3 + 7$ and $y = 1 + 9$, both x and y are equal to 10, i.e. $x = y$.

Test yourself

1. Is the sum 6 + 3 + 1 equal to 10?

2. Is 5 - 2 + 2 equal to 9?

Challenge yourself

1. $7x + 4y - 3z = 10$. Given that $x = 5$ and $y = -7$, what is the value of z?

2. $5x - 4y - 3z = -12$. Given that $x = 5 + y$ and $y = -7$, what is the value of z?

equation

A statement containing an *equals* sign, showing that two or more *expressions* are the same. An equation that contains a *variable*, such as x, is known as an algebraic equation.
e.g. $1 + 3 = 4$ and $x + 3x = 4x$.

Test yourself

1. Solve the equation $x = 4 + 6$.

2. Solve the equation $y = 10 + 3$.

Challenge yourself

1. If $11x - 8 = 10 + 2x$, what is the value of x?

2. If $x = 4 \times 15 - 8 \div 2$, what is the value of x?

equidistant

When two or more points are the same *distance* from a common point.
e.g.

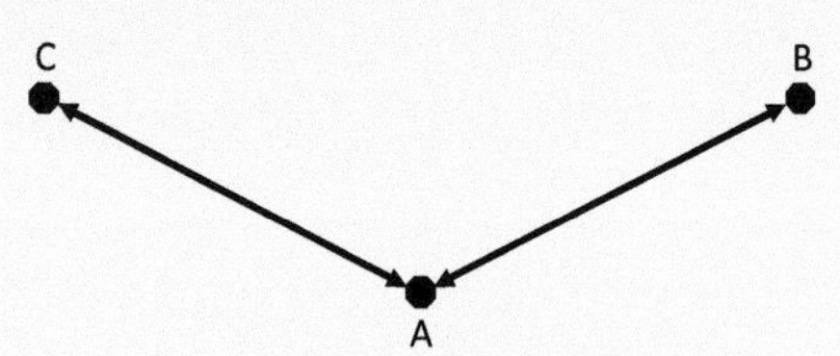

Points B and C are equidistant from point A.

Test yourself

1. From which point are points D and E equidistant?

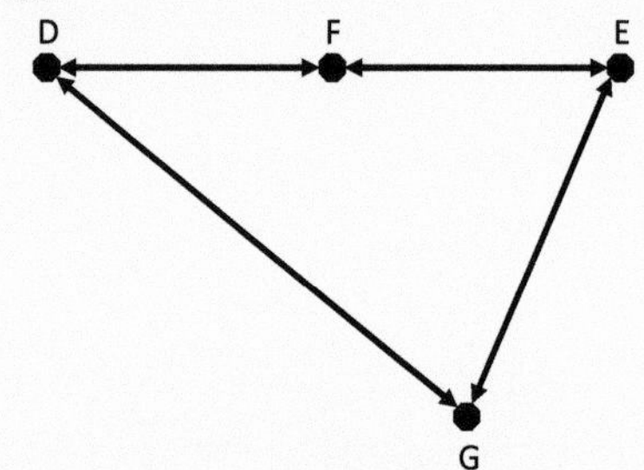

Challenge yourself

Answer the following questions using the graph below.

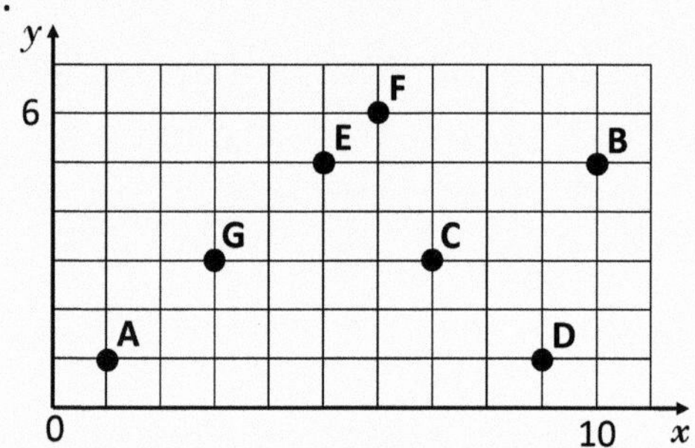

1. From which point are points A and D equidistant?

2. From which point are points C and G equidistant?

3. Which points are equidistant from point G?

equilateral triangle

A three-sided *polygon* (*triangle*) with three *equal angles* and three *sides* of equal *length*.

e.g.

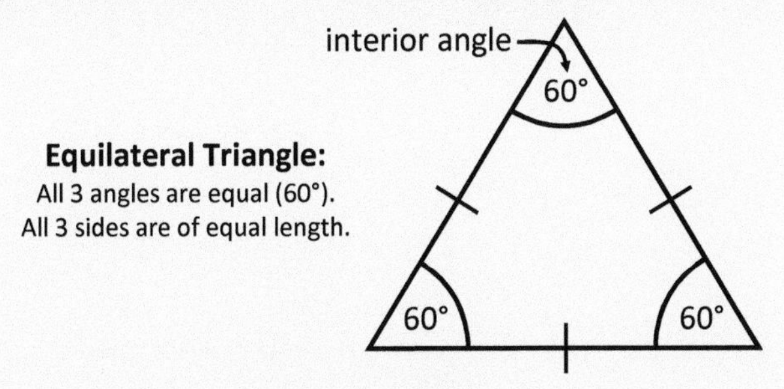

Test yourself

1. What is the sum of all the interior angles of an equilateral triangle?

2. If one side of an equilateral triangle is 2cm, what is the sum of all the sides?

Challenge yourself

1. Given that an equilateral triangle has a perimeter of 144mm, what is the length of each side in mm?

2. Look at the diagram below. Given that the perimeters of the square and the equilateral triangle are 240cm and 123cm respectively, what is the value of x in metres?

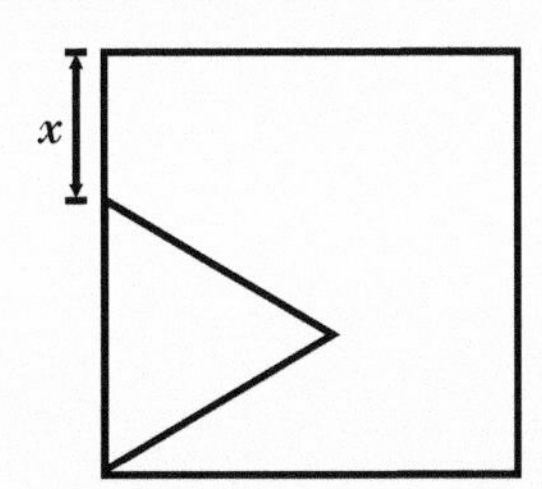

equivalent

This is when something is the same as something else. See also *equivalent fractions*, *equivalent ratios*.

e.g. 17:30 is equivalent to 5.30pm.

Test yourself

1. Is 100 pence equivalent to a pound (£)?

2. Is the time 16:00 equivalent to 6.00pm?

3. Is the ratio 2:10 equivalent to 1:5?

4. Is the fraction $^2/_8$ equivalent to $^2/_4$?

Challenge yourself

1. Which of the following fractions are equivalent to $^2/_3$?

$^1/_2$, $^4/_5$, $^{10}/_{15}$, $^{200}/_{30}$, $^{40}/_{60}$

2. Convert 19:21 into 12-hour clock format.

equivalent fractions

Fractions with the same *value*, but written using a different *numerator* and *denominator*. They refer to the same proportion of a *whole* and should all give the same fraction when simplified. See also *simplify*.

e.g. $^5/_{10}$, $^4/_8$, $^3/_6$, $^2/_4$ and $^1/_2$ are all equivalent fractions.

Test yourself

1. Is $^1/_2$ equivalent to $^4/_6$?

2. Is $^1/_3$ equivalent to $^3/_9$?

Challenge yourself

1. Which of the following fractions are equivalent to $^5/_4$?

$^{10}/_6$, $^{350}/_{280}$, $^{1000}/_{80}$, $^{200}/_{40}$, $^4/_5$

2. Which of the following fractions are equivalent to $^1/_4$?

$^1/_{25}$, $^{25}/_{100}$, $^{10}/_{80}$, $^{20}/_{40}$, $^{10}/_{40}$

equivalent ratios

Ratios that refer to the same proportion of a *whole* and should all give the same ratio when simplified. See also *simplify*.

e.g. 5:10, 4:8, 3:6, 2:4 and 1:2 are all equivalent.

Test yourself

1. Is 2:6 equivalent to 1:3?

2. Is 1:10 equivalent to 10:20?

Challenge yourself

1. Simplify 124:66.

2. If there are 96 black balls and 84 pink balls in a box, what is the ratio of pink to black balls?

A B C D E F G H I J K L M N O P Q R S T U V W X Y Z

estimation

See *approximation*.

***

Euler's polyhedral formula

For a *polyhedron* that does not intersect with itself, Euler's formula states that the number of *faces plus* the number of *vertices minus* the number of *edges* is always *equal* to two.

faces + vertices - edges = 2

e.g. A triangular pyramid has 6 edges, 4 faces and 4 vertices. This satisfies Euler's theorem.

Triangular Pyramid (Tetrahedron):
It has 4 faces.
It has 4 vertices.
It has 6 edges.

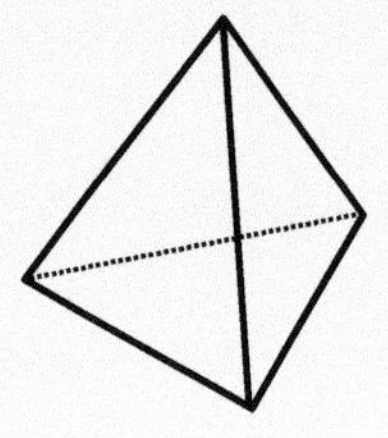

<u>Test yourself</u>

1. Look at the triangular prism below. Does the shape satisfy Euler's theorem?

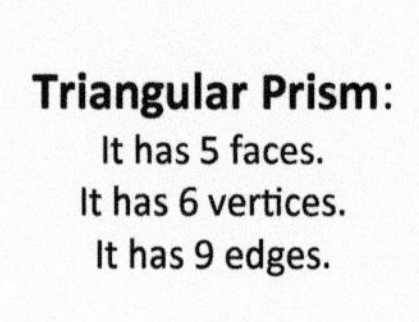

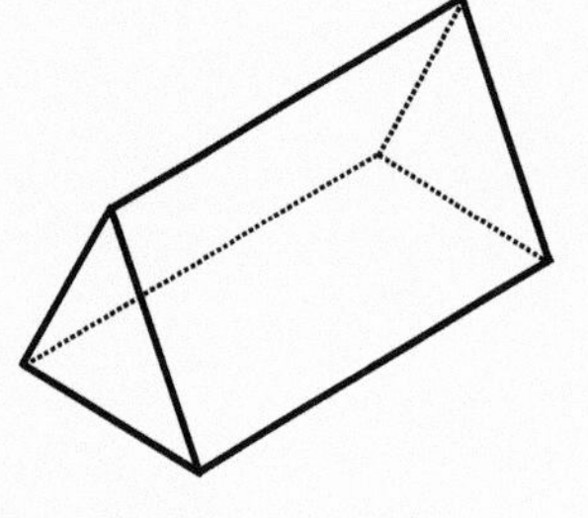

<u>Challenge yourself</u>

1. A shape has 8 faces and 12 edges. According to Euler's theorem, how many vertices should the shape have?

2. A shape has 5 faces and 5 vertices. According to Euler's theorem, how many edges should the shape have?

3. Look at the octahedron below. Does the shape satisfy Euler's theorem?

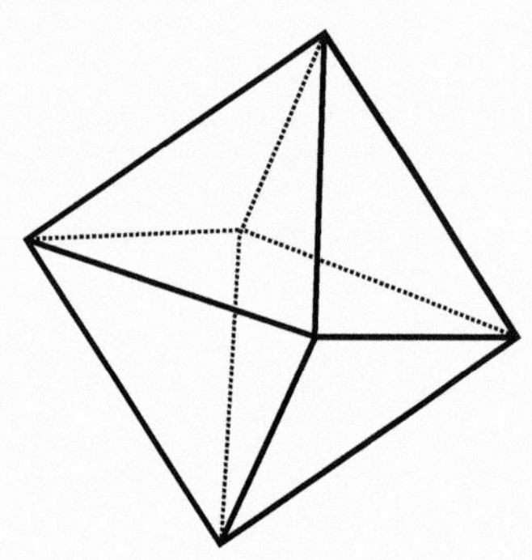

evaluate

To calculate the *value* of something.
e.g. Evaluating 5 + 5 gives 10.

<u>Test yourself</u>

1. Evaluate 11 + 12.

2. Evaluate 7 × 6.

<u>Challenge yourself</u>

1. Evaluate the value of x in the algebraic equation $x + 15x + 5 = 17x - 10$.

2. Evaluate the value of y in the equation below.
$y - 82 - 3y = 0$.

even chance

See *equally likely*.

***

even number

Any *integer divisible* by 2. In other words, the *remainder* is *zero* when an *even number* is divided by 2.
<u>Note:</u> *Zero* is an even number.
e.g. 8 is an even number as it is divisible by 2 to give 4.

<u>Test yourself</u>

1. List the first five even numbers.

2. What is the sum of the first five even numbers?

<u>Challenge yourself</u>

1. Is 26,156 an even number?

2. Is the product of 5529 × 54 an even number?

3. Is the product of 86 × 1.5 an even number?

event

This is something that happens at a given time.
e.g. Picking a marble at random from a bag.

<u>Test yourself</u>

1. Describe an event that has a probability of 50%.

2. If an event has a probability of 0.1, is it likely or unlikely to occur?

Challenge yourself

1. In an event, a yellow marble is picked from a bag that contains 15 yellow and 11 white marbles; it is not replaced. What is the likelihood of picking another yellow marble from the same bag?

2. What is the probability of an event in which a fair coin lands on heads 5 times consecutively?

explanatory variable

See *independent variable*.

***

exponent

See *power*.

***

expression

A mathematical statement that contains a number and/or a single letter (a *variable*). An expression can include *addition*, *subtraction*, *multiplication*, *division* and *powers*; however, it does not include an *equals* sign.
e.g. If an apple costs 30 pence and a banana costs 20 pence, an expression for the total cost of x number of apples and y number of bananas in pence is $30x + 20y$.

Test yourself

1. Which of the following options is not an expression?
   a. $x + y$ b. $3x = 2$ c. $10y$

Challenge yourself

1. Evaluate $1^2 - 2^2 + 3^2 - 4^2 + 5^2$.

2. Given that $x = \sqrt{157}$, evaluate $x^2 + 52$.

3. A large smoothie costs double that of a small smoothie. Write an expression for the total cost in pounds if one of each was bought, in terms of S only, where S represents the cost of a small smoothie.

exterior angle (external angle)

The *angle* formed between the *side* of a *polygon* and a straight line which extends from the adjacent side.

Note: For any polygon, the *sum* of all its exterior angles will always be *equal* to 360°.
e.g.

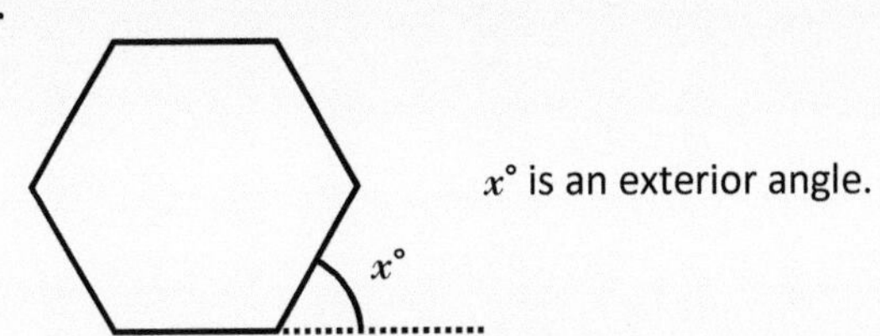

For a regular hexagon, the size of each exterior angle is $6x° = 360°$; $x° = 60°$.

Test yourself

1. What is the size of the exterior angle of the regular pentagon shown below?

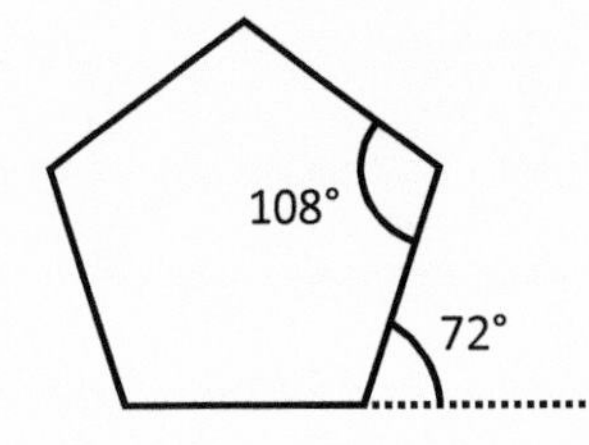

2. What is the size of the exterior angle of the regular octagon shown below?

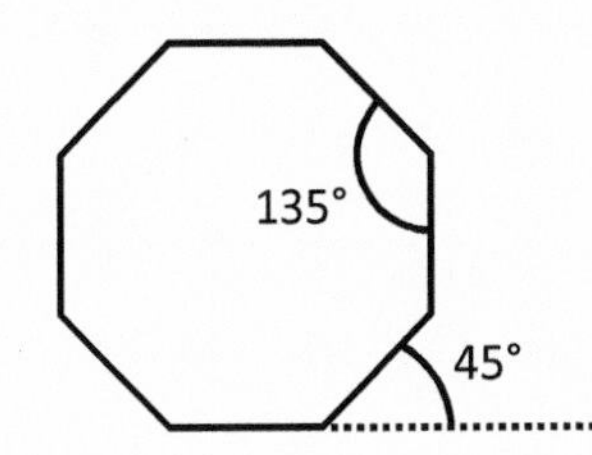

Challenge yourself

1. What is the sum of all the exterior angles of a hexagon?

2. How many exterior angles are found on a nonagon?

3. What is the size of an exterior angle found on a regular decagon?

external angle

See *exterior angle*.

***

face
An individual *surface* of a *two-dimensional* or *three-dimensional* shape. See also *side*.
Note: All two-dimensional shapes have one face.
e.g.

Pentagonal Prism:
It has 7 faces.
It has 10 vertices.
It has 15 edges.

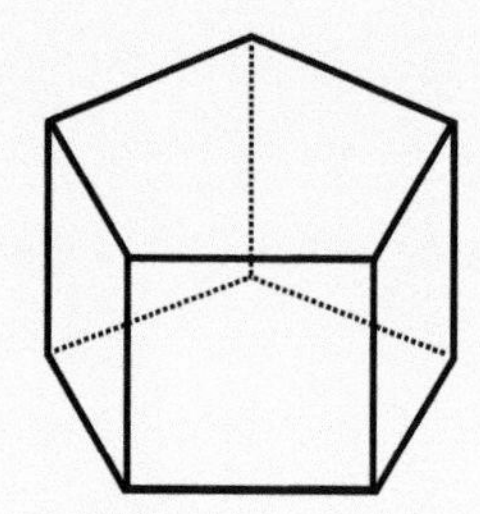

Test yourself
1. A pentagonal prism is shown in the example above. How many faces does it have?

2. How many faces does a cuboid have?

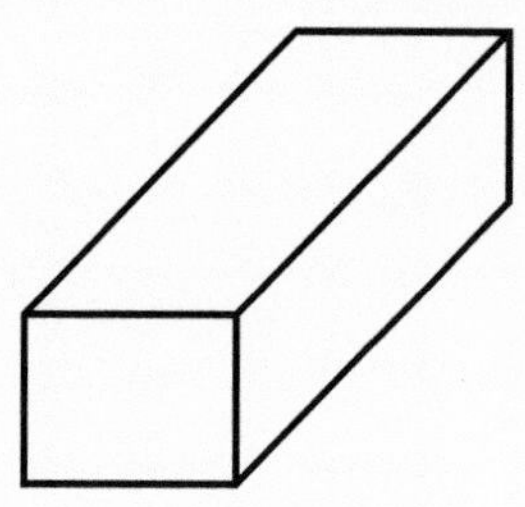

Challenge yourself
1. How many faces does a triangular prism have?

2. How many faces does a hexagonal prism have?

3. How many faces does a square pyramid have?

4. How many faces does a sphere have?

factor
A *whole number* that divides exactly into another whole number.
e.g. The factors of 12 are 1, 2, 3, 4, 6 and 12.

Test yourself
1. Find all the factors of 3.

2. What are the factors of 6?

3. What are the factors of 10?

Challenge yourself
1. Find all the factors of 32.

2. What is the sum of all the factors of 21?

3. How many factors does 18 have in total?

factorise
To write a number or an *expression* as a *product* of its *factors*.
e.g. $4x + 8y$ can be factorised into $4(x + 2y)$.

Test yourself
1. Given that the highest common factor (HCF) of 8 and 12 is 4, factorise $8x + 12$ by taking the HCF of 8 and 12 out of the expression.

2. Factorise $8x + 2$ by taking 2 out of the expression.

Challenge yourself
1. Factorise $36y + 18x$.

2. Factorise $2x^3 + 6x^2$.

fair
An item or *event* that is free from *bias*, i.e. it is impartial.
e.g. The probability that a die, numbered 1 to 6, lands on a four is $^1/_6$, only if the die is fair.

Test yourself
1. If the probability of a six-sided die, numbered 1 to 6, landing on 3 is $^5/_6$, is the die fair?

Challenge yourself
1. A fair die is rolled two times consecutively. What is the chance of the die landing on an even number and then on an odd number? Give your answer as a fraction.

2. A fair twenty-sided die is labelled from 5 to 24. What is the probability of the die landing on an even number twice in a row?

F-angles
See *corresponding angle*.

***

Fibonacci sequence

The Fibonacci sequence: (0,) 1, 1, 2, 3, 5, 8, 13,...
A sequence in which each *consecutive term* is calculated by adding the previous two numbers together, starting either from 0 or 1.
Note: Other sequences that follow this pattern can also be described as following the rule of the Fibonacci sequence.
e.g. 5, 10, 15, 25, 40,...

Test yourself

1. Two adjacent terms of a sequence are 5 and 6. If the sequence follows the rule of the Fibonacci sequence, calculate the value of the next term.

2. Two adjacent terms of a sequence are 9 and 23. If the sequence follows the rule of the Fibonacci sequence, calculate the value of the next term.

Challenge yourself

1. Fill in the spaces below so that the pattern stays the same.

10	10	20		50		

2. Fill in the spaces below so that the pattern stays the same.

4	4		12		32	

fifty-fifty

i. Dividing into two *equal* halves.
e.g. A fifty-fifty split of £270 is £135 and £135.

ii. In probability, see *equally likely*.

***

Test yourself

1. What is a fifty-fifty split of £10?

2. If a biased coin is tossed, is the chance of the coin landing on heads fifty-fifty?

Challenge yourself

1. If Natasha and Jenny were to carry out a fifty-fifty split of £850, how much would each person receive?

2. Express a fifty-fifty chance as a decimal.

3. Express a fifty-fifty chance as a percentage.

figure

i. In *geometry*, a figure is a shape or an object.
e.g. A plane 4-sided figure is known as a quadrilateral.

Quadrilateral:
It has 4 vertices.
It has 4 edges.
It has 4 interior angles.

ii. In the numeral system, a figure is an element that forms a *value*.
e.g. In the number 1234, the figure 1 represents 1000.

Test yourself

1. Draw a two-dimensional figure with five sides of equal length.

2. In the number 21, what value does the figure 2 represent?

Challenge yourself

1. What is the name given to a figure with two pairs of equal sides, one pair of equal and opposite angles, and diagonals that intersect at right angles?

2. What is the name given to a 4-sided figure with one pair of parallel sides?

3. In the number 581.21, what value does the figure 8 represent?

4. In the number -12.581, what value does the figure 8 represent?

finite decimal

A *decimal* with a limited number of *digits* after the *decimal point*, i.e. it can be expressed as an exact decimal number. See antonym *infinite decimal*.
e.g. One half ($^1/_2$) is a finite decimal as it can be written as 0.5.

Test yourself

1. Can $^2/_5$ be written as a finite decimal?

2. Can $^1/_3$ be written as a finite decimal?

A B C D E F G H I J K L M N O P Q R S T U V W X Y Z

<u>Challenge yourself</u>

1. Show that $^3/_4$ is finite by expressing it as a decimal.

2. Show that $^{240}/_{16}$ is finite by expressing it as a whole number.

3. Which of the expressions below are not finite decimals?

A	B	C	D	E
$^{58}/_8$	π - 3	√2	0	3.33

flat angle (straight angle)

The *angle* formed on a straight line, i.e. half a full turn, which is exactly 180°.

e.g.

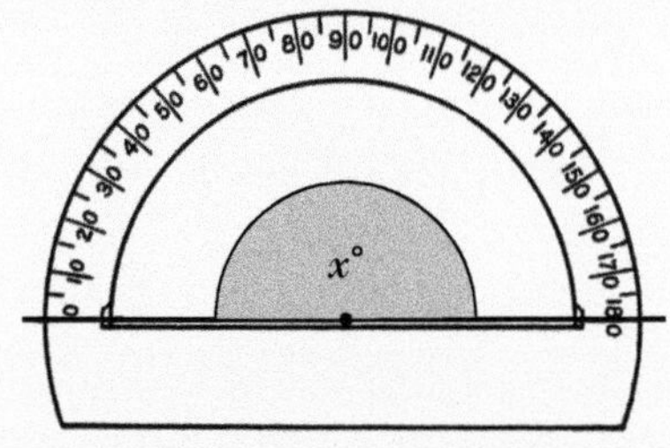

Angle x° is equal to 180°.
Therefore, it is a straight angle.

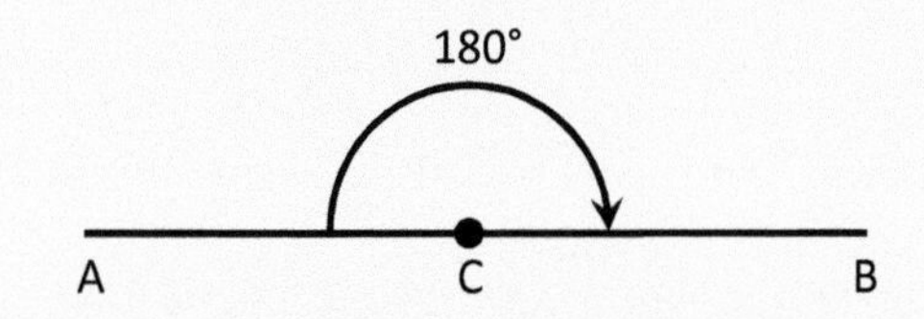

Line ACB is a straight line, hence angle AĈB is a flat angle and is equal to 180°.

<u>Test yourself</u>

1. A flat angle is always 180°. How many right angles (90°) are there in a flat angle?

<u>Challenge yourself</u>

1. If I am facing north-east and I turn 180°, in what direction am I now facing?

2. How many flat angles are there in a clockwise turn from south-east to north-east? Give your answer as an improper fraction.

flow chart

A diagram illustrating an *order of operations*. See also *number machine*.

e.g.

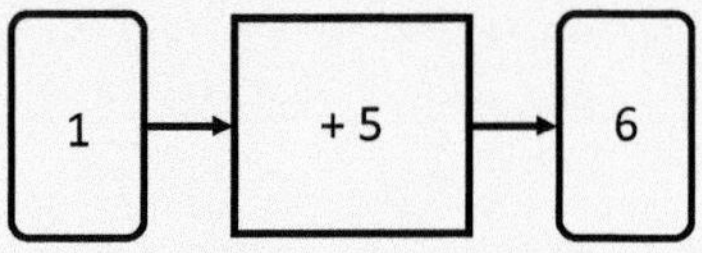

1 → + 5 → 6

Here, the input is 1, the operation is '+ 5' and the output is 6.

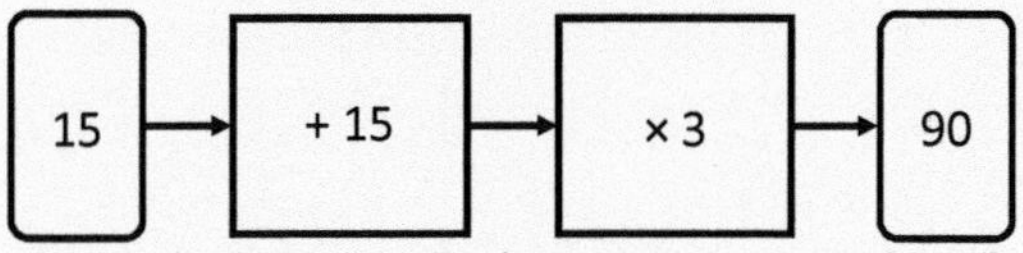

15 → + 15 → × 3 → 90

Here, the input is 15, the operations are '+ 15' followed by '× 3', and the output is 90.

<u>Test yourself</u>

1. A flow chart has an output of 20 and an operation of '÷ 2'. What is the input?

2. Calculate the input, x, of the flow chart below.

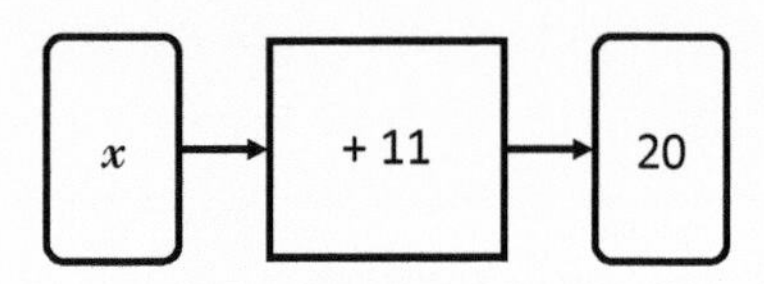

<u>Challenge yourself</u>

1. Work out the missing operation in the flow chart below.

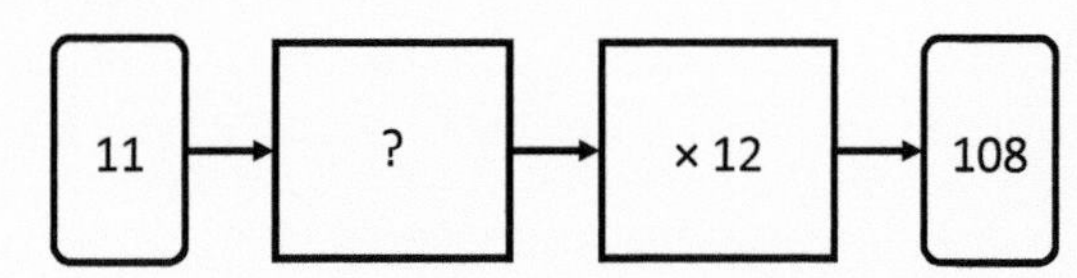

2. Calculate the output, y, of the flow chart below.

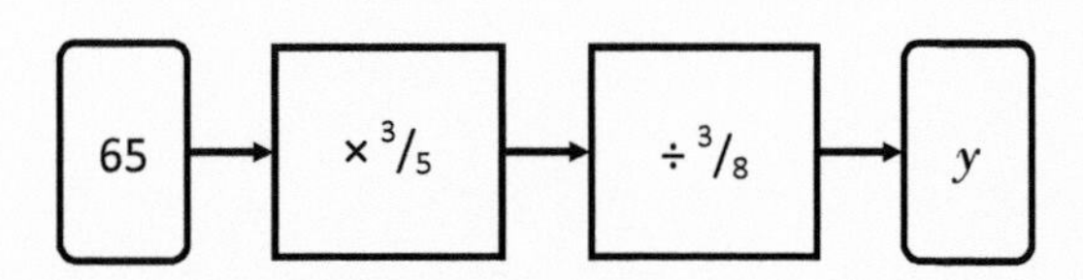

foot (ft or ') (plural: feet)

An *imperial unit* of *length equal* to 12 *inches* or one-third of a *yard*. (1ft = 30.48cm)

e.g. 2 feet is equivalent to 24 inches.

<u>Test yourself</u>

1. How many inches are there in 2 feet?

2. How many feet are there in 2 yards?

<u>Challenge yourself</u>

1. How many inches are there in 11 feet?

2. Approximate 4 feet, in centimetres, to the nearest cm.

formula (plural: formulae)

An *equation* that expresses a mathematical relationship between two or more *variables*.
e.g. The formula for converting feet (ft) into yards (yd) is yd = $^{1}/_{3}$ × ft.

Test yourself

Answer the following questions using the formula for the volume of a cuboid below.
Volume = length (l) × width (w) × height (h)
1. Calculate the volume of a cuboid of length 2cm, width 4cm and height 1cm.

2. Calculate the volume of a cuboid of length 4mm, width 5mm and height 2mm.

3. Calculate the volume of a cuboid of length 7cm, width 10cm and height 2cm.

Challenge yourself

1. Rearrange $3x - y = x + d$ to make x the subject of the formula.

2. Rearrange $r - 4r + t = {}^{t}/_{6}$ to make r the subject of the formula.

3. Using the formula for converting feet (ft) into yards (yd), convert 462 feet into yards.

4. Using the formula for converting feet (ft) into yards (yd), convert 23 yards into feet?

fraction

A part of a *whole* expressed in the form $^{n}/_{d}$, where n is the *numerator* and d is the *denominator*.
Note: A fraction can also be expressed as a *decimal* or *percentage*.
e.g.

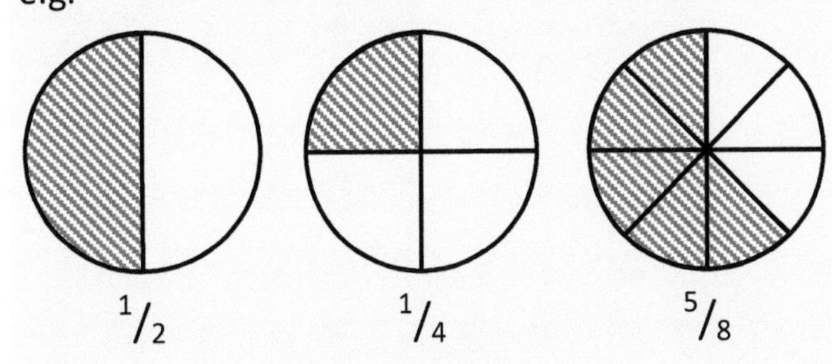

Test yourself

1. Express one-third as a fraction.

2. Express three-quarters as a fraction.

Challenge yourself

1. What is $^{5}/_{8} + {}^{11}/_{12}$ as an improper fraction?

2. Calculate $^{14}/_{15} \times {}^{3}/_{7}$.

3. Calculate $^{4}/_{9} \div {}^{2}/_{3}$.

frequency

The number of observations in a given time period.
Note: An observation is the occurrence of a given *event*.
e.g. A frequency distribution table showing exam results.

Mark	0 - 20	21 - 40	41 - 60	61 - 80	81 - 100
Frequency	10	5	17	20	7

The table above shows that there were 17 students who scored between 41 and 60 marks.

Test yourself

Answer the following questions using the table in the example above.
1. How many students scored between 0 and 20 marks?

2. How many students scored between 81 and 100 marks?

Challenge yourself

Answer the following questions using the table in the example above.
1. How many students took the test?

2. Calculate the number of students who scored over 40 marks.

frequency distribution table

A table or chart used to show the number of times an *event* or *value* occurs.
e.g. A frequency distribution table illustrating the number of goals conceded by football teams during a league season.

No. of goals	16	17	18	19	20
Frequency	4	6	2	2	6

A B C D E F G H I J K L M N O P Q R S T U V W X Y Z

Test yourself

Answer the following questions using the table in the example.

1. What was the most number of goals conceded by a team?

2. How many teams conceded 18 goals?

Challenge yourself

Answer the following questions using the table in the example.

1. How many teams played in the league this season?

2. In total, how many goals were conceded?

3. Calculate the mean number of goals conceded during the season by a team.

full turn (full rotation)

See *revolution*.

***

function

A function is a rule that is applied to a *set* of *values* (*inputs*) to obtain another set of values (*outputs*). See also *inverse function*.

e.g. Multiplying a number by 10 is a simple function.

Test yourself

1. A function which multiplies a number by five is applied to an input value of 5. What is the value of the output?

2. Using the function $y = x$, what is the value of y when $x = 2$.

Challenge yourself

1. The relationship between the radius (r) and the area (A) of a circle is given by the function $A = \pi r^2$. Assuming π is equal to 3.14, if the radius of a circle is 3cm, what is its area?

2. The relationship between the radius (r) and the circumference (C) of a circle is given by the function $C = 2\pi r$. Assuming π is equal to 3.14, if the radius of a circle is 100mm, what is its circumference?

G

gallon (gal)

An *imperial unit* of *volume*. A gallon is *equal* to 8 *pints*.

e.g. Half a gallon is equal to 4 pints.

Test yourself

1. What is a quarter of a gallon in pints?

2. What is 12 pints expressed in gallons?

Challenge yourself

1. Convert 3.5 gallons into pints.

2. Convert 50 pints into gallons, giving your answer as a fraction.

geometric sequence

A number *sequence* in which each *consecutive term* is obtained by multiplying the previous *term* with a *constant*, i.e. it has a *common ratio*.

e.g. 10, 20, 40, 80, 160 has a common ratio of +2.

Test yourself

1. Calculate the common ratio of the following geometric sequence: 1, 3, 9, 27, 81.

2. Calculate the common ratio of the following geometric sequence: 1, 5, 25, 125, 625.

Challenge yourself

1. Calculate the common ratio of the following geometric sequence: 80, -40, 20, -10, 5.

2. Complete the geometric sequence below so that the pattern stays the same.

2	-10	50	-250	1250		

3. Complete the geometric sequence below so that the pattern stays the same.

	144		4	$^{2}/_{3}$		$^{1}/_{54}$

geometry

The study of shapes and their properties. See also *dimension, two-dimensional, three-dimensional.*

e.g.

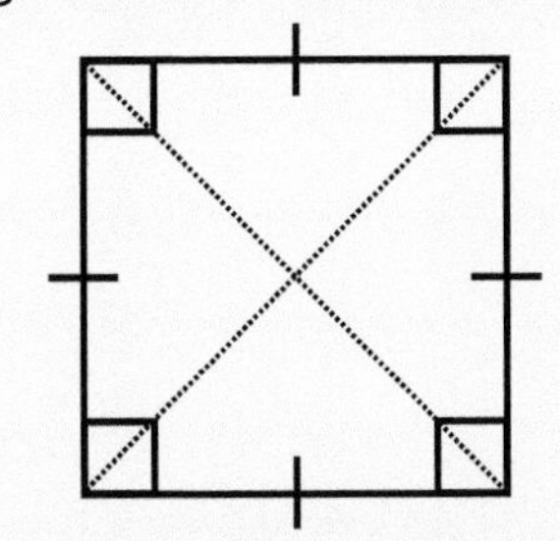

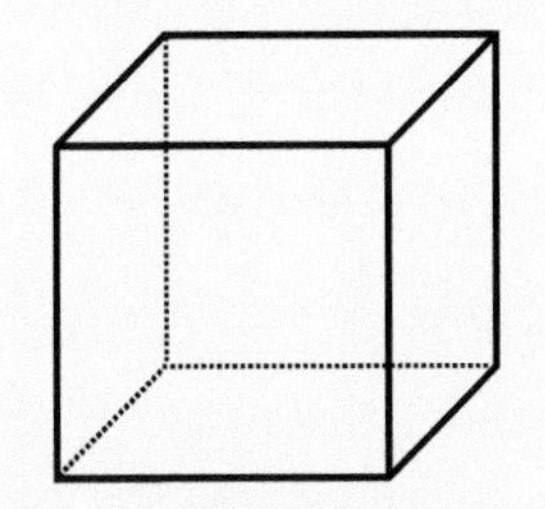

Square:
All 4 angles are equal (90°).
All 4 sides are of equal length.
It has 4 vertices.
The diagonals bisect each other at 90°.

Cube:
It has 6 faces.
It has 8 vertices.
It has 12 edges.

A square has two dimensions: length and width.
A cube has three dimensions: length, width and height.
Therefore, a square is a two-dimensional shape and a cube is a three-dimensional shape.

<u>Test yourself</u>

1. Is a rectangle a two-dimensional shape?

2. Is a square pyramid a two-dimensional shape?

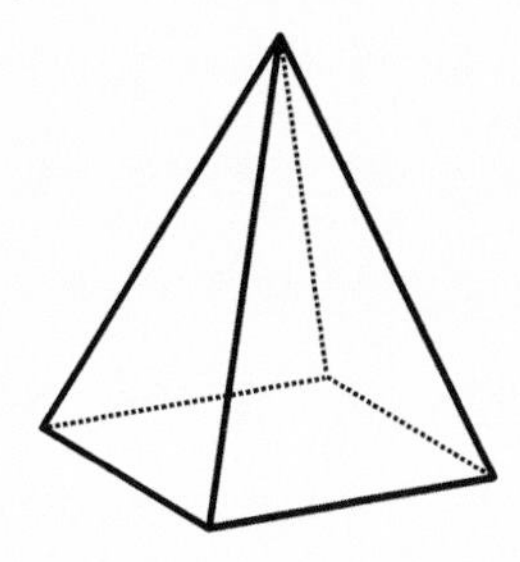

<u>Challenge yourself</u>

1. How many lines of symmetry does a hexagon have?

2. How many vertices does an octahedron have?

gradient (slope)

A measure of the steepness of a straight line, i.e. the rate at which y increases or decreases compared with x between two points on a *graph*.
<u>Note:</u> A *horizontal* line has a gradient of *zero*, and a *vertical* line is not defined (it is *infinite*).
Additionally, a gradient can be either positive or negative, and can be calculated using:

$$\text{gradient} = (y_2 - y_1) \div (x_2 - x_1),$$

where (x_1, y_1) and (x_2, y_2) are the *coordinates* of the two points that lie on the straight line.

e.g. A graph depicting the walking speed of three people using positive gradients.

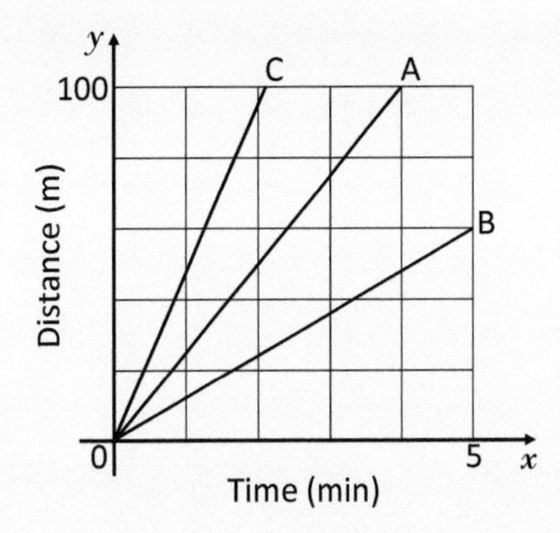

Line A is steeper than line B.
Therefore, line A has a higher gradient than line B.

<u>Test yourself</u>

Answer the following questions using the graph in the example above.

1. Is person C walking faster than person A?

2. Is person C walking faster than person B?

3. Which person is walking the slowest?

<u>Challenge yourself</u>

Answer the following questions using the graph in the example above.

1. What is the walking speed of person A? Give your answer in metres per minute.

2. What is the walking speed of person B? Give your answer in metres per minute.

3. Draw a straight line that represents a walking speed of 40 metres per minute.

gram (g)

A *metric unit* of *mass equal* to one-*thousandth* of a *kilogram*.

e.g. 1000g is equivalent to 1kg.

<u>Test yourself</u>

1. How many grams are there in 3 kilograms?

2. What is 500g in kilograms?

<u>Challenge yourself</u>

1. What is 5812 grams in kilograms?

2. What is 0.351 kilograms in grams?

A B C D E F G H I J K L M N O P Q R S T U V W X Y Z

graph

A visual illustration of the relationship between two *variables,* plotted with reference to a set of *axes*. See also *bar graph, linear graph, conversion graph, distance-time graph, scatter graph.*

e.g.

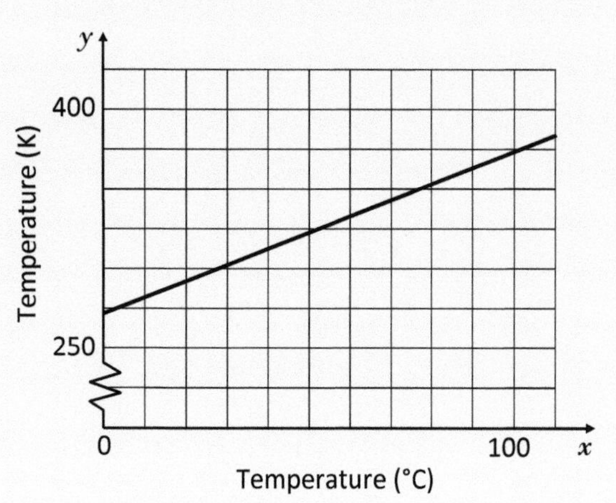

<u>Test yourself</u>

Answer the following questions using the graph in the example above.

1. Which variable is represented by the x-axis?

2. Which variable is represented by the y-axis?

<u>Challenge yourself</u>

Answer the following questions using the graph in the example above.

1. Is the relationship between the temperature measured in Kelvin and temperature measured in degrees Celsius linear?

2. Using the conversion graph above, approximate 40°C in Kelvin.

greater than

When one quantity is larger than another. It has the symbol '>'. See also *inequality, less than.*

e.g. 2 is greater than 1, i.e. $2 > 1$.

<u>Test yourself</u>

1. Is 10 greater than 5?

2. Is the inequality $4 > 8$ true?

3. Is the inequality $1 > 0$ true?

<u>Challenge yourself</u>

1. Is $^5/_9$ greater than $^3/_7$?

2. Given that $a > b > 0 > c$, is $^b/_c > {^a/_c}$ true?

3. Given that $a > 0 > b > c$, is $^a/_b > {^b/_c}$ true?

greater than or equal to

When one quantity is larger than or the same as another. It has the symbol '≥'. See also *inequality, less than or equal to.*

e.g. 5 is greater than or equal to 2, i.e. $5 \geq 2$. Also, 2 is greater than or equal to 2, i.e. $2 \geq 2$.

<u>Test yourself</u>

1. Is the inequality $3 \geq 6$ true?

2. Is the inequality $4 \geq 4$ true?

<u>Challenge yourself</u>

1. If $5x \geq 20$, what is the smallest value x can be?

2. If $4x + 4 \geq 24$, what is the smallest value x can be?

greatest common factor

See *highest common factor.*

***

greatest value (maximum value)

The largest possible amount or quantity.

e.g. In the dataset {1, 2, 4, 6}, the greatest value is 6.

<u>Test yourself</u>

1. What is the greatest value in the dataset below?

{1, 5, 8, 11, 16}

2. What is the maximum value in the dataset below?

{-100, 51, 0, 1, 0.587, 0.99}.

<u>Challenge yourself</u>

1. If $54 \geq 2x$, what is the maximum value of x?

2. Given that $y = -x^2 - 5$ and $x = \{0, 11, -1, 20\}$, what is the greatest value y can be?

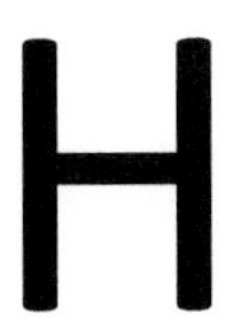

height

The *distance* between the *base* of a *two-dimensional* or *three-dimensional* shape and its tallest point.
Note: The height is always *perpendicular* to the *base* of the shape.
e.g. Isosceles triangle

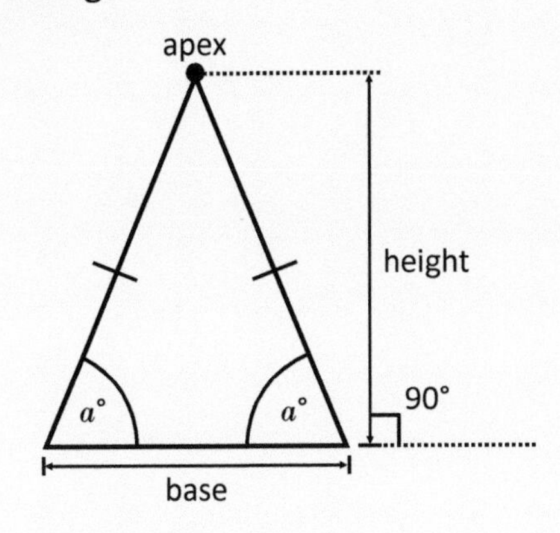

Test yourself

1. Look at the cylinder below. Which letter represents the height of the cylinder?

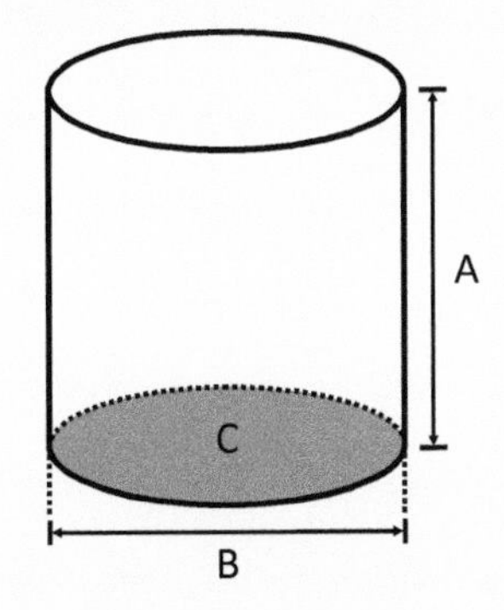

Challenge yourself

1. The area of an isosceles triangle is 27cm^2. What is the height of the triangle if the base is 9cm?

2. If the volume of a cylinder is 300mm^3 and the cross-sectional area is 15mm^2, what is its height?

3. Calculate the height of the scalene triangle below if its area is 255cm^2.

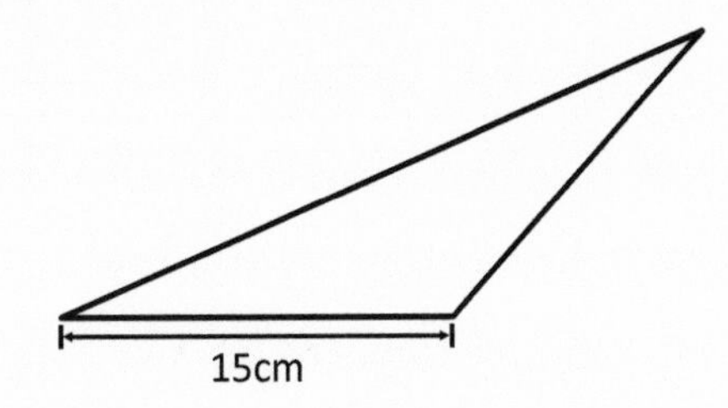

hemisphere

One half of a *sphere*.
e.g.

Hemisphere:
It has 1 flat face (base).
It has 1 curved face.
It has 1 curved edge.

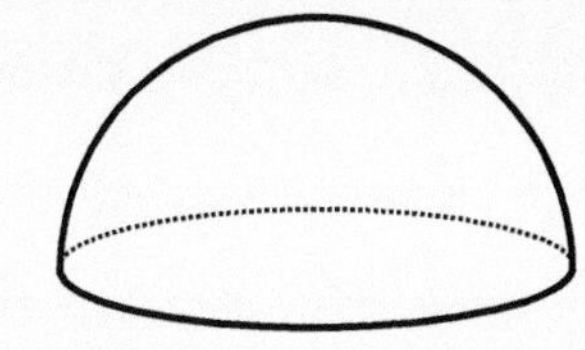

Test yourself

1. How many hemispheres are required to make a sphere?

Challenge yourself

1. If the volume of a sphere is 5842cm^3, what is the volume of a hemisphere with the same radius? Give your answer in cm^3.

2. The surface area of a sphere is 6348cm^2 and its radius is 23cm. Taking π to be 3 and the radius as 23cm, what is the surface area of a hemisphere including its base?

heptagon (septagon)

A seven-sided *polygon*.
e.g.

Regular Heptagon:
All 7 angles are equal.
All 7 sides are of equal length.
The sum of the interior angles is 900°.

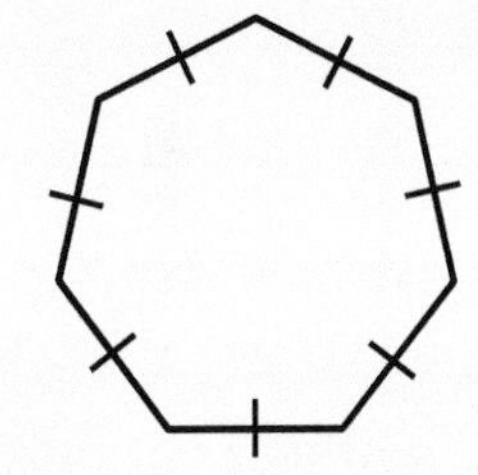

Test yourself

1. Is the shape below a heptagon?

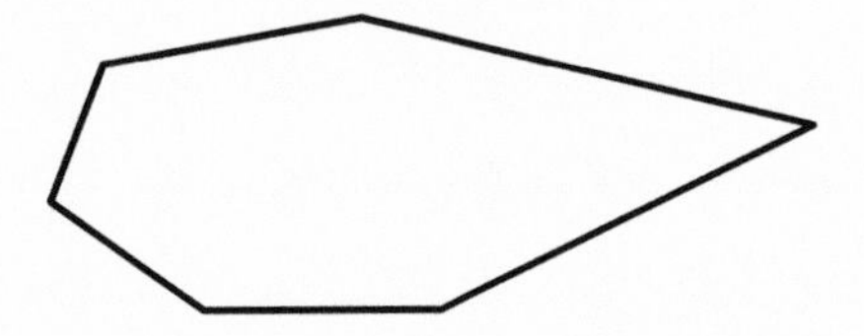

2. If one side of a regular heptagon measures 2cm, what is the total length of the seven sides?

Challenge yourself

1. Calculate the interior angle of a heptagon correct to 1 decimal place.

2. If the apothem of a regular heptagon is 5cm and its perimeter measures 35cm, what is its area? Give your answer in cm^2.

A
B
C
D
E
F
G
H
I
J
K
L
M
N
O
P
Q
R
S
T
U
V
W
X
Y
Z

hexagon

A six-sided *polygon*.

e.g.

Regular Hexagon:
All 6 angles are equal.
All 6 sides are of equal length.
The sum of the interior angles is 720°.

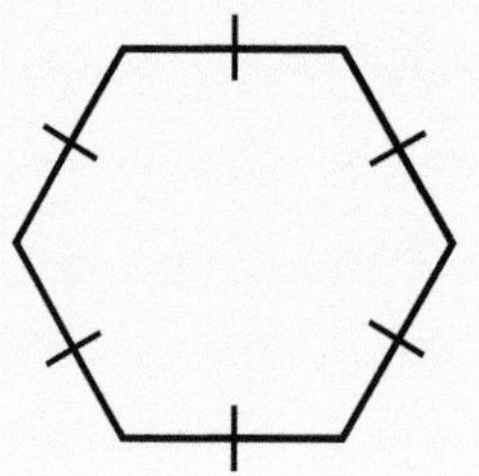

Test yourself

1. Is the shape below a hexagon?

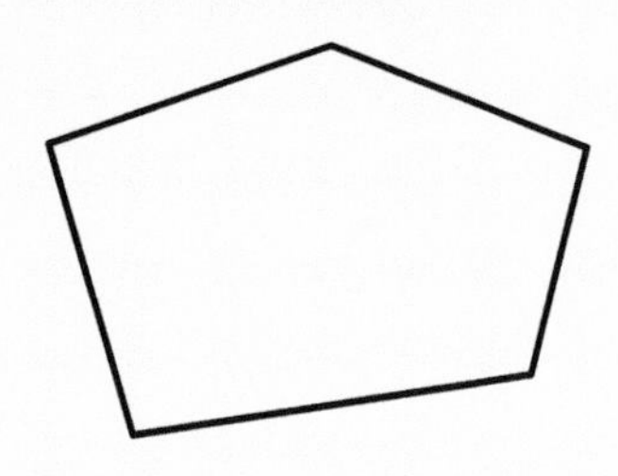

2. If one side of a regular hexagon measures 3cm, what is the total length of the six sides?

Challenge yourself

1. Calculate the interior angle of a hexagon.

2. If the apothem of a regular hexagon is 7mm and its perimeter measures 42mm, what is its area? Give your answer in mm^2.

highest common factor (HCF)

The largest *factor* that is common between two or more given numbers.

Note: The synonym of HCF is *greatest common factor*.

e.g. The factors of 10 are 1, 2, 5 and 10, and the factors of 25 are 1, 5 and 25. Hence, the HCF is 5.

Test yourself

1. What is the highest common factor of 2 and 6?

2. What is the highest common factor of 6 and 8?

Challenge yourself

1. What is the highest common factor (HCF) of 52 and 18?

2. Oliver and Natasha collect stamps. If Oliver has 42 and Natasha has 77, what is the highest common factor (HCF) of the number of stamps collected?

histogram

A diagram which shows the *frequency* distribution for a range of different *intervals*.

Note: The *area* of each bar is *equal* to the frequency in that category and the *height* of each bar is known as the frequency density.

e.g.

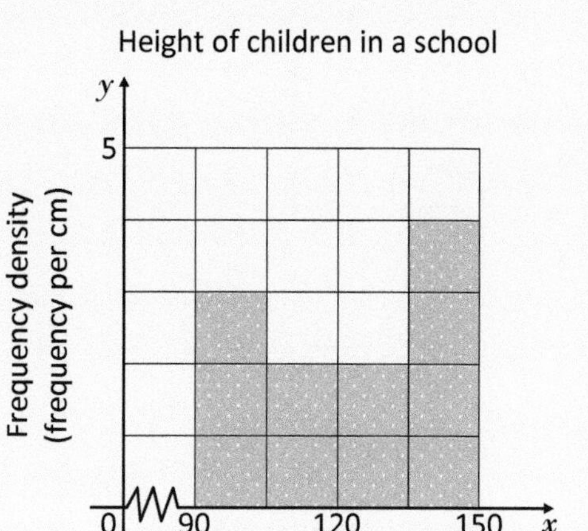

Test yourself

Answer the following questions using the histogram in the example above.

1. What could be the height of the tallest child?

2. What could be the height of the shortest child?

Challenge yourself

Answer the following questions using the histogram in the example above.

1. How many people have a height between 90cm and 105cm?

2. How many people have a height between 105cm and 135cm?

horizontal

Parallel to the horizon, i.e. at a *right angle* to the *vertical*. See antonym *vertical*.

e.g.

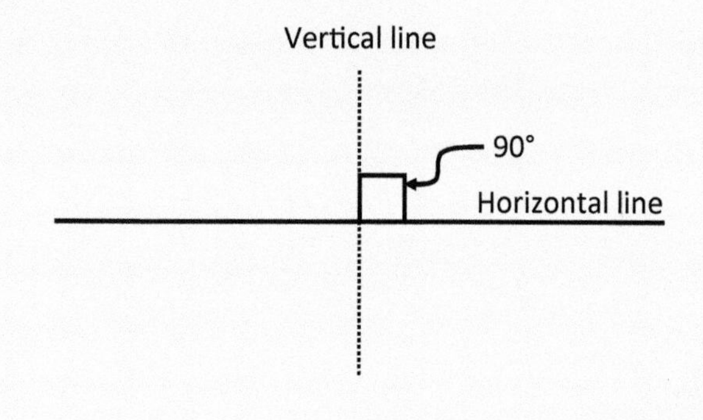

Test yourself

1. Draw two horizontal lines to show that parallel lines never intersect.

Challenge yourself

1. A horizontal line is divided by a vertical line in a ratio 5 : 7. If the length of the horizontal line is 96cm, what is the length of the longer side in cm?

2. A straight line which makes an angle of 45° above the horizontal is rotated anticlockwise until the line is at right angle to the vertical. Calculate the two possible angles by which the straight line can be rotated?

hour (hr)

A period of time consisting of 60 *minutes* and *equal* to $^1/_{24}$th of a *day*.
e.g. 900 minutes is equivalent to 900 ÷ 60 = 15 hours.

Test yourself

1. What is 120 minutes expressed in hours?

2. How many minutes are there in half an hour?

Challenge yourself

1. How many hours are there in a week?

2. What is 1020 minutes expressed in hours?

3. How many seconds are in 2 hours?

hundredth

i. A single part of something that has been divided into one hundred *equal* parts. It is expressed as $^1/_{100}$.
e.g. A hundredth of £1500 is $^1/_{100}$ × £1500 = £15.

ii. The *ordinal number* (numerical order) of one hundred, i.e. 100th.
e.g. Ranking one hundredth in a marathon.

Test yourself

1. Calculate $^1/_{100}$ × £500.

2. What is the hundredth positive integer on a number line?

Challenge yourself

1. What is a hundredth of £8421?

2. What is the hundredth square number?

3. Considering zero is the first even number, what is the hundredth?

hypotenuse

The longest *side* of a *right-angled triangle* which is the side found opposite the *right angle*.
e.g.

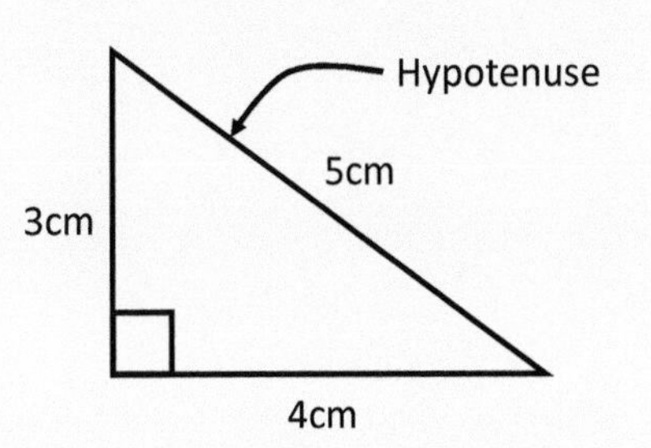

Test yourself

1. What is the length of the hypotenuse of the right-angled triangle in the example above?

Challenge yourself

Answer the following questions using the graph below.

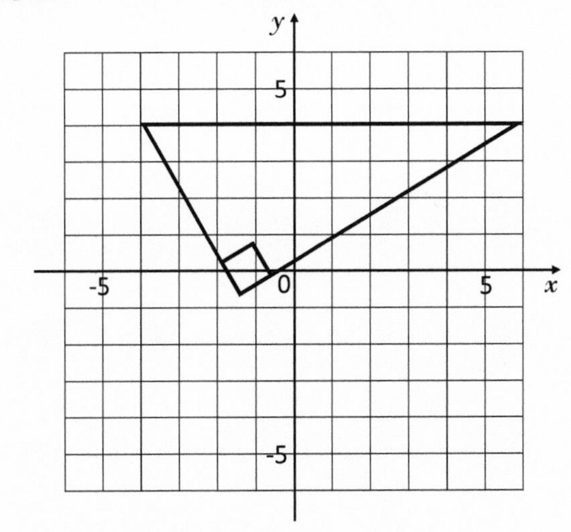

1. What is the length of the hypotenuse of the triangle shown above?

2. What are the coordinates of the midpoint of the hypotenuse?

3. The hypotenuse of the triangle above is divided into two by the y-axis. What is the ratio of the shorter length to the longer length?

A B C D E F G H I J K L M N O P Q R S T U V W X Y Z

I

identical

If something is identical, it is exactly alike.

e.g.

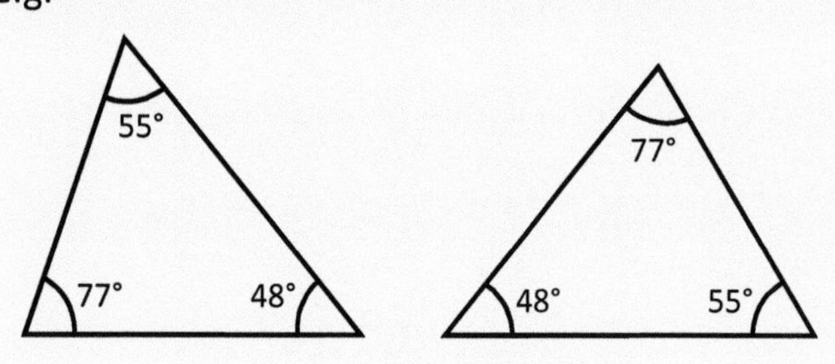

These two triangles are identical.

Test yourself

1. The two triangles below are identical. What is the size of angle x°?

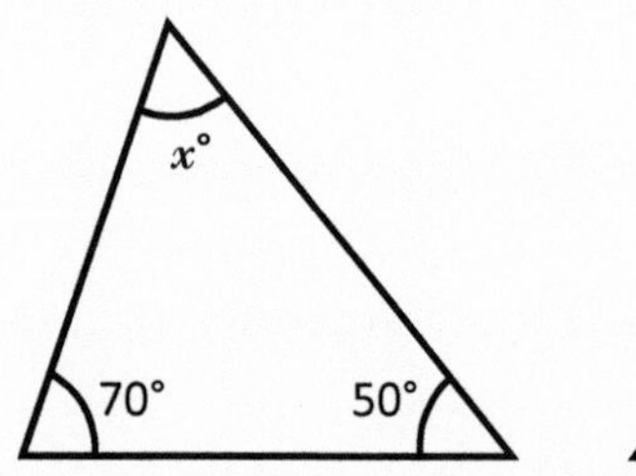

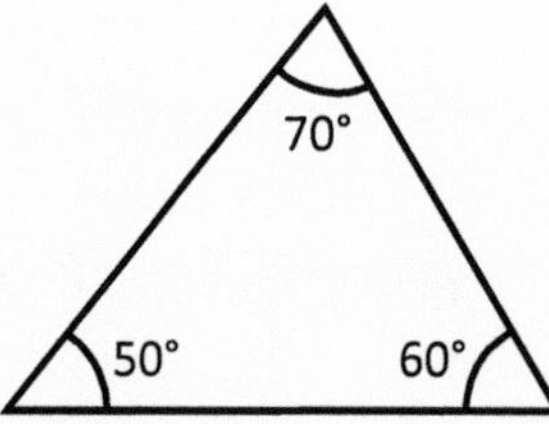

Challenge yourself

1. The shape below consists of two identical right-angled triangles. What is the size of angle x°?

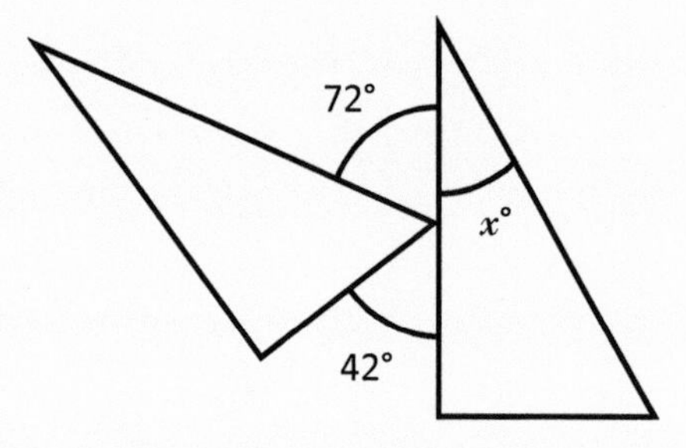

2. The shape below is made up of four identical rectangles. What is the length of l?

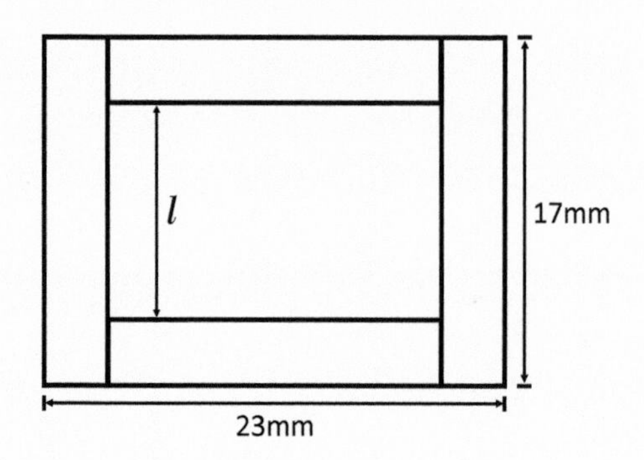

image

The new position of a point, line or a *figure* following a *transformation*.

e.g.

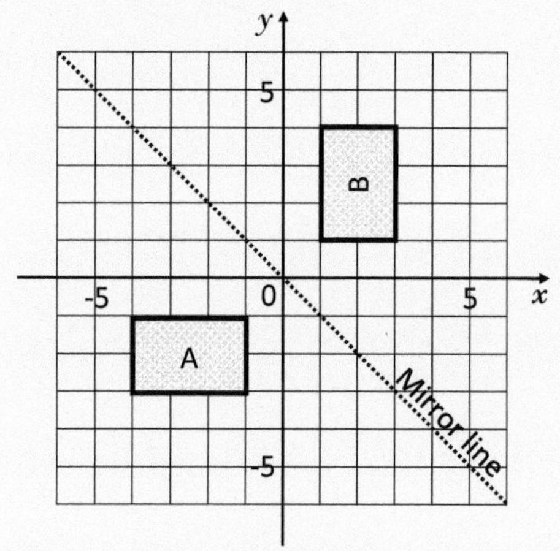

Shape A is reflected across the mirror line to produce image B.

Test yourself

1. Shape C below is reflected across the mirror line to produce D. Is shape D an image of C?

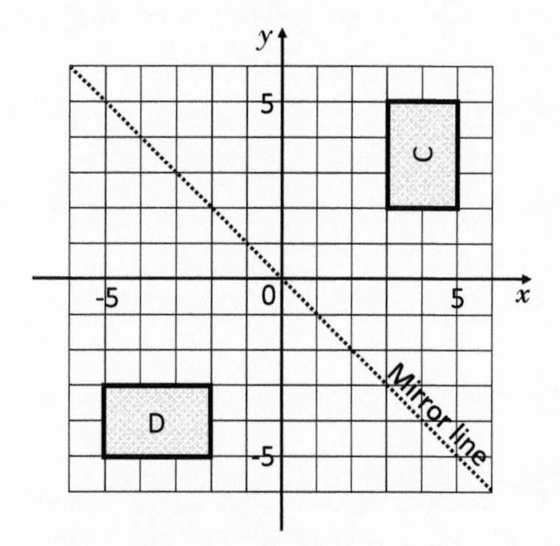

Challenge yourself

1. Shape A is reflected to produce image B. On the graph below, draw the mirror line.

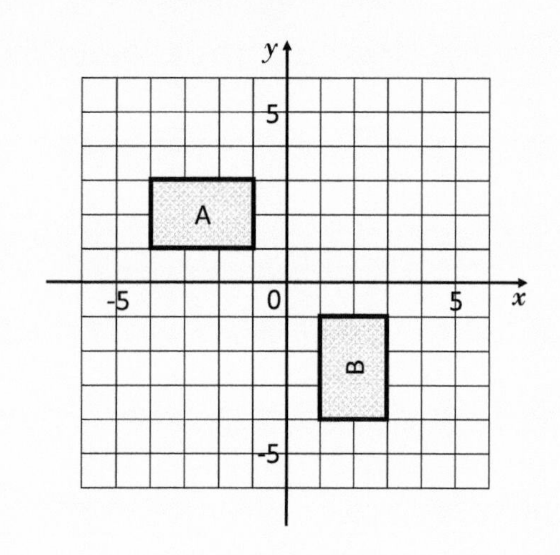

imperial units

The system of *units* first defined in the British Weights and Measures Act.
e.g. Inch, foot and mile.

Units of length	Units of mass	Unit of volume
Inch (in or ")	Ounce (oz)	Fluid ounce (fl. oz)
Foot (ft or ')	Pound (lb)	Pint (pt)
Yard (yd)	Stone (st)	Gallon (gal)
Mile	Ton	

Test yourself

1. Is a yard an imperial unit of length?

2. Is a pound an imperial unit of mass?

3. Is a pint an imperial unit of volume?

Challenge yourself

1. Given that a mile is equivalent to 1600 metres, convert 1mph to metres per second.

2. Given that a foot is equivalent to 30.5cm, convert 11ft to metres.

3. If a gallon is approximately equivalent to 4 litres, how many litres are there in 81 gallons?

impossible

An *event* that is not capable of occurring, i.e. an event that has a *probability* of *zero*.
e.g. It is impossible to pick a black cube from a bag which contains three red cubes and two yellow cubes.

Test yourself

Are the following statements true or false?
1. It is impossible for a six-sided die labelled 1 to 6 to land on number 9.

2. It is impossible to score 100% in an exam.

Challenge yourself

Are the following statements true or false?
1. The probability of an impossible event occurring is zero.

2. Picking a red marble from a bag containing 999 black marbles and one red marble is impossible.

improbable

See *unlikely*.

***

improper fraction (top-heavy fraction)

A *fraction* where the *numerator* is larger than the *denominator*.
e.g. $^{7}/_{5}$ and $^{3}/_{2}$ are improper fractions because the number at the top of the fraction is greater than the number at the bottom.

Test yourself

1. Circle all the improper fractions below.

$^{1}/_{2}$ $^{5}/_{5}$ $^{4}/_{3}$ $^{9}/_{5}$ $^{1}/_{5}$

2. Simplify the improper fraction $^{18}/_{8}$.

Challenge yourself

1. Express $^{58}/_{7}$ as a mixed fraction.

2. Express $4\,^{8}/_{9}$ as a improper fraction.

3. What is $3\,^{7}/_{10} + 2\,^{4}/_{5}$ as an improper fraction?

4. What is $6\,^{1}/_{2} - 2\,^{5}/_{6}$ as an improper fraction?

inch (in or ")

An *imperial unit* of *length equal* to one twelfth of a *foot*. (1in = 2.54cm).
e.g. 1 inch is equivalent to $^{1}/_{12}$ft.

Test yourself

1. Is an inch an imperial unit of length?

2. Is an inch greater than a centimetre?

Challenge yourself

1. How many inches are there in 15ft?

2. Given that 1in is equal to 2.54cm, convert 17in to centimetres.

increase

To make the *value* or quantity of something larger.
e.g. The price of a £10 football was increased by 10%. Because 10% of £10 is £1, the new price of the football is £10 + £1 = £11.

A B C D E F G H I J K L M N O P Q R S T U V W X Y Z

A B C D E F G H I J K L M N O P Q R S T U V W X Y Z

Test yourself

1. There were 20 vehicles in a car park. After 2 hours there were 25 vehicles. What is the increase in the number of vehicles?

2. The price of a handbag was £20. If the price of the handbag is increased by 20%, what would be the new price?

Challenge yourself

1. Increase 152.2 by 94.49.

2. Increase $^5/_8$ by 8 $^4/_7$.

3. House prices in Harrow have increased by 17% in the last ten years. If a house in Harrow was £250,000 ten years ago, how much is it worth now?

4. The population of a small village has increased by a factor of $^5/_4$ over the last five years. If the population was 12,000 five years ago, what is the population now?

increasing order

See *ascending order*.

***

independent event

An *event* that has an *outcome* which is not affected by any other event.

e.g. When you toss a coin twice, the outcome of the second toss is not affected by the outcome of the first toss, i.e. the probability of getting tails is $^1/_2$ for both attempts.

Test yourself

1. The probability of getting heads when a coin is tossed is 0.5. Given that this is an independent event, what is the probability of getting heads again?

Challenge yourself

1. Which of the following can be described as being an independent event?

a. Picking five hearts from a deck without replacing them.

b. Picking 2 red marbles from a bag of 5 black and 3 red marbles without replacing them each time.

c. Getting a head on the 20th toss of a fair coin.

independent variable

A *variable* whose *value* is not determined by the value of other variables, i.e. its value does not depend on that of another.

e.g. When you are measuring the distance travelled by a bus between certain time intervals, the time is the independent variable because the measurement of time does not depend on the speed of the bus.

Test yourself

1. If a variable has a fixed number of values, is it an independent variable?

Challenge yourself

For each experiment described below, state which variable is independent.

1. Measuring the speed of an airplane between certain time intervals.

2. Measuring the speed of a bus over a certain distance.

index (plural: indices)

See *power*.

***

indivisible

A given number is indivisible by another number if it cannot be divided by the other number to give a *whole number*.

Note: *Prime numbers* are always indivisible.

e.g. 11 is indivisible by 2.

Test yourself

1. Given that 10 ÷ 2 = 5, is 10 indivisible by 2?

2. Given that 12 ÷ 2 = 6, is 12 indivisible by 2?

Challenge yourself

121 584 65 78 49 10

1. Which of the numbers shown above are indivisible by 2?

2. Which of the numbers shown above are indivisible by 5?

inequality (<, >, ≤, ≥, ≠)

A mathematical statement that relates numbers and/or *expressions* to one another. Usually used when two quantities are not *equal*. See also *greater than, greater than or equal to, less than, less than or equal to*.

e.g. The statement '3 is less than 5' can alternatively be written as: $3 < 5$ and $5 > 3$.

Test yourself

1. Which of the following inequalities are true?

a. $5 < 6$
b. $7 < 3$
c. $8 > 1$
d. $10 < 3$

Challenge yourself

1. Which of the following inequalities are true?

a. $-50 + 38 < 2 - 27$
b. $520 \div 52 \leq 2 \times 5$
c. $5\,{}^{3}/_{8} \geq {}^{58}/_{6}$
d. $12 \times 13 \neq 4 \times 17$

infinite decimal

A *decimal* with an unlimited number of *digits* after the *decimal point*, i.e. it cannot be written as an exact decimal number.

e.g. ${}^{1}/_{3} = 0.33333...$ (3 repeats infinitely)

Test yourself

1. Given that ${}^{1}/_{4} = 0.25$, can ${}^{1}/_{4}$ be expressed as an infinite decimal?

2. Give that ${}^{1}/_{8} = 0.125$, can ${}^{1}/_{8}$ be expressed as an infinite decimal?

3. Given that ${}^{1}/_{6} = 0.166666...$, can ${}^{1}/_{6}$ be expressed as an infinite decimal?

Challenge yourself

$\pi \quad 3^{999} \quad \sqrt{2} \quad 0 \quad {}^{985}/_{5} \quad {}^{0}/_{3}$

1. Which numbers above have an infinite number of decimal places?

2. Can ${}^{1}/_{9}$ be expressed as an infinite decimal?

3. Can ${}^{1}/_{6} + {}^{1}/_{10}$ be expressed as an infinite decimal?

infinity (infinite)

An abstract concept describing something that has no end; that is, the state of being infinite. It has the symbol '∞'. See also *infinite decimal*.

e.g. A circle has infinite lines of symmetry.

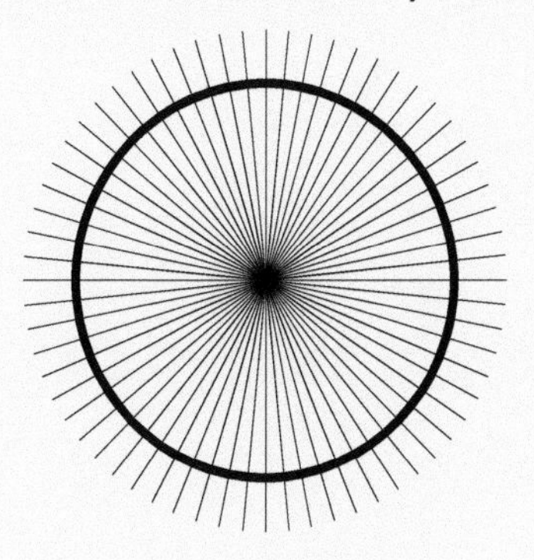

Challenge yourself

1. What is the order of rotational symmetry of a circle?

input

Information that is put into a system.

e.g.

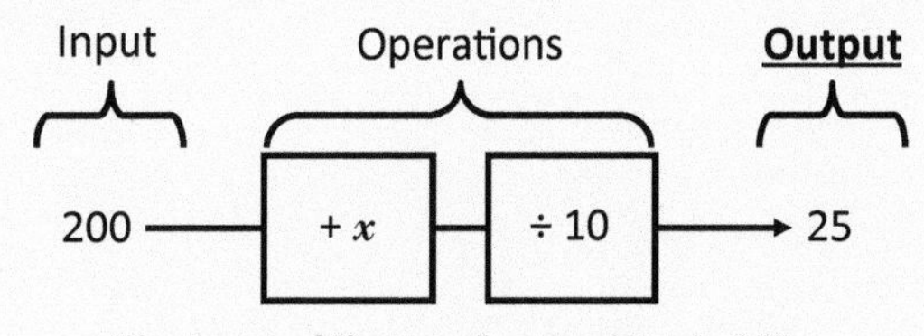

The input of the number machine is 200.

Test yourself

1. Identify the input of the number machine below.

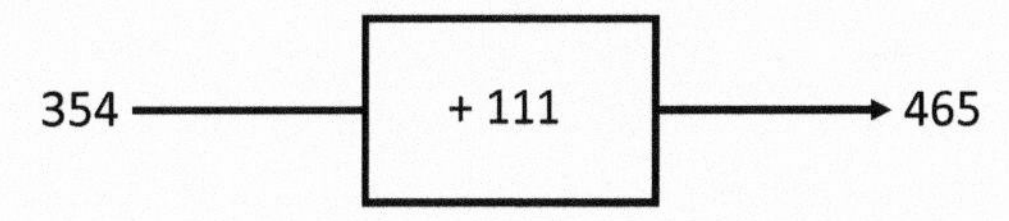

Challenge yourself

1. Calculate the input x.

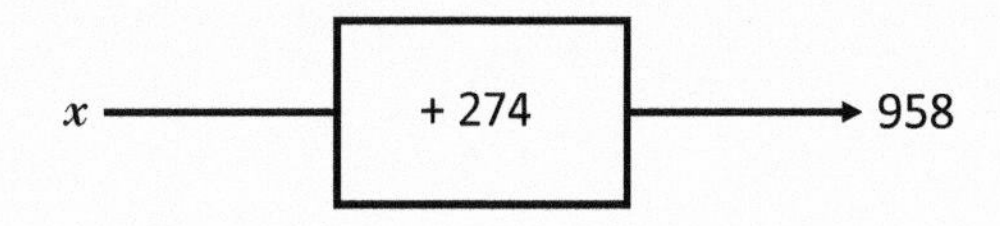

2. Calculate the input x.

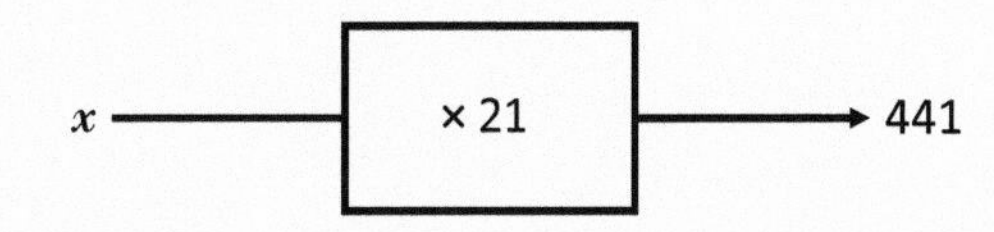

3. A number machine has an output of 372 and an operation of '× 1.5'. What is the input?

A B C D E F G H I J K L M N O P Q R S T U V W X Y Z

A B C D E F G H I J K L M N O P Q R S T U V W X Y Z

integer

The name for any *whole number*, either positive or negative, including *zero*. See also *positive number*, *negative number*, *whole number*.

e.g. -3, -2, -1, 0, 1, 2, 3

Test yourself

1. Is 5 an integer?

2. Is -10 an integer?

Challenge yourself

1. What is $^{548}/_{3}$ to the nearest integer?

2. What is the sum of the first four consecutive triangular numbers and the first four consecutive positive even integers?

intercept

The point at which a line crosses an *axis* on a graph. See also *intersection*.

e.g.

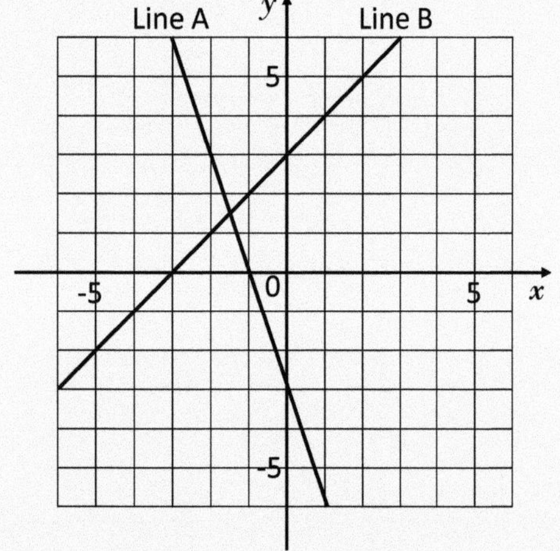

The y-intercept of line A is at the point (0, -3).
The x-intercept of line A is at the point (-1, 0).

Test yourself

Answer the following question using the graph in the example above.

1. How many intercepts are there? Circle all the intercepts.

Challenge yourself

Answer the following question using the graph in the example above.

1. Where does line B intercept the y-axis?

2. Where does line B intercept the x-axis?

interest

i. Interest is the additional amount of money that has to be paid back when money is borrowed (loan).

interest (£) = interest rate (%) × loan (£)

e.g. With an annual interest rate of 5%, if £500 is borrowed, the interest that has to be paid back in a year is £25 because 5% of £500 is £25.

ii. Interest is also the amount of money the bank pays you when you put money into a savings account.

interest (£) = interest rate (%) × total amount (£)

e.g. With an annual interest rate of 2%, if £1000 is put into a savings account, the amount of interest received in the first year is £20 because 2% of £1000 is £20. The amount of interest received in the second is 2% of £1020 which is £20.40.

Test yourself

1. If the interest rate is 2% and £100 is borrowed, what is the amount of interest that has to be paid back?

2. If the annual interest rate is 5% and £100 is put into a savings account, what is the amount of interest received in the first year?

Challenge yourself

1. Tahnia deposits £556 into her savings account with an interest rate of 4% per year. How much money does she have after the first year?

2. Olivia borrows £221 from a bank with an interest rate of 6% annually. How much money does she have to pay back in a year?

interior angle (internal angle)

An *angle* inside a *polygon* between a *side* and its adjacent side.

The *sum* of the interior angles in an *n*-sided polygon is given by:

$180° \times (n - 2)$.

The size of a single interior angle of an *n*-sided *regular* polygon is given by:

$^{180° \times (n - 2)}/_{n}$.

e.g.

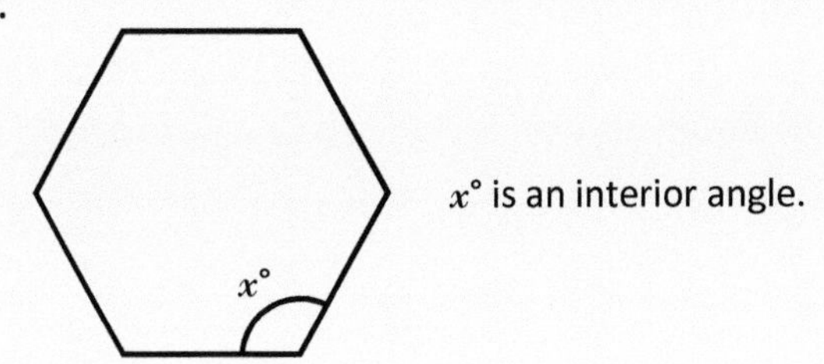

Test yourself

1. Which of the angles, $x°$ or $y°$, is an interior angle of the polygon below?

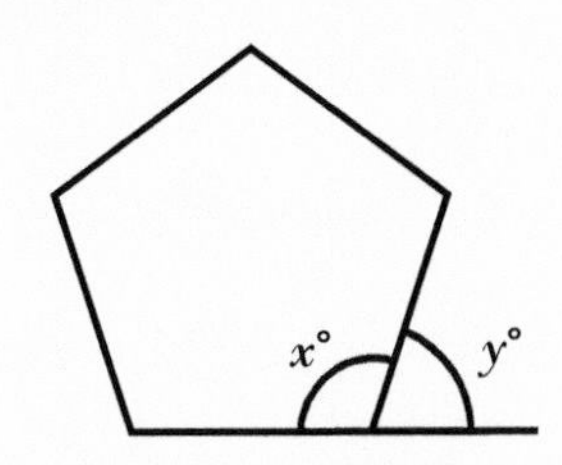

Challenge yourself

1. How many interior angles does a regular decagon have?

2. What is the size of the interior angle found within a regular nonagon?

3. What is the sum of the interior angles in a regular hexagon?

internal angle

See *interior angle*.

***

intersection

A common point at which two or more lines either cross or meet. See also *intercept*.

e.g.

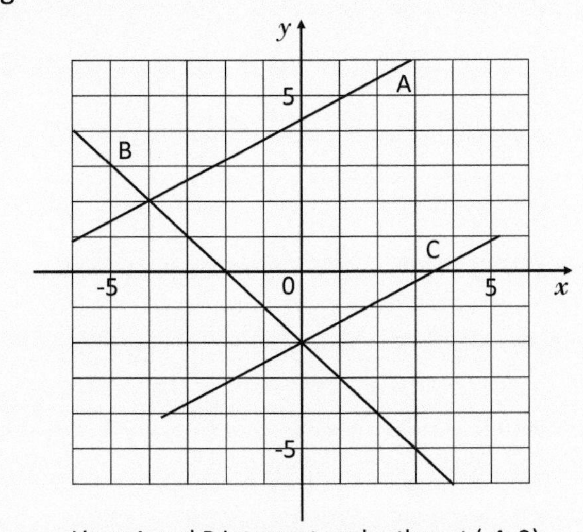

Lines A and B intersect each other at (-4, 2)

Test yourself

1. In the graph in the example, how many intersections are there in total?

Challenge yourself

1. Using the graph in the example, identify the coordinates where lines B and C intersect.

interval

i. A period of time between two instants.

e.g. Between 17:10 and 17:30, there is an interval of 20 minutes.

ii. A space between two points.

e.g. Trees were planted at intervals of 10 metres.

Test yourself

1. What is the time interval between 12:10 and 12:20?

2. How many 200m intervals are there in 2km?

Challenge yourself

1. What is the time interval between 14:54 and 21:16?

2. A scale is shown below. What is the size of each interval?

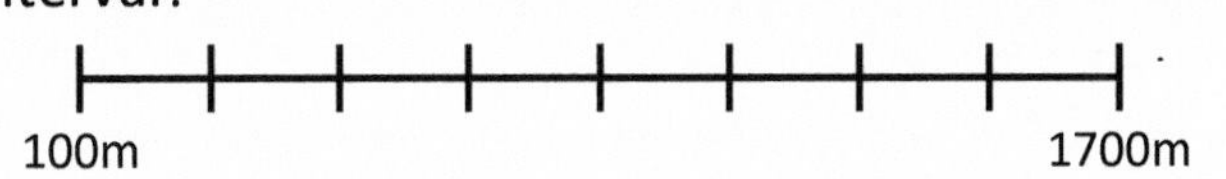

inverse function

A *function* that reverses a given function, i.e. a function that has the opposite effect of another.

e.g. Dividing by 3 is the inverse function of multiplying by 3, and subtracting 3 is the inverse function of adding 3.

Test yourself

1. What is the inverse function of '+ 3'?

2. What is the inverse function of '× 2'?

Challenge yourself

1. Given that the missing operation '?' is multiplication, identify the value of x.

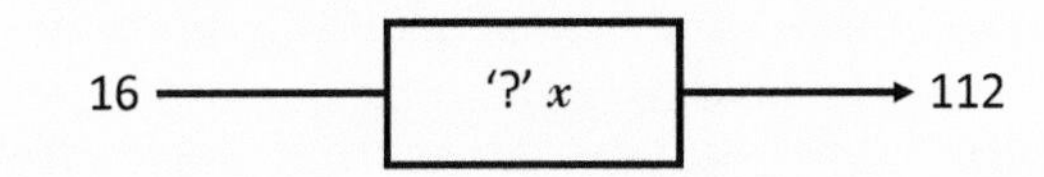

A B C D E F G H I J K L M N O P Q R S T U V W X Y Z

A B C D E F G H I J K L M N O P Q R S T U V W X Y Z

irrational number

A *real number* that cannot be written as a *fraction*, i.e. it cannot be expressed as a *ratio* of two *integers*.

e.g. pi (π) and √2 are examples of irrational numbers.

Test yourself

1. Is 10 an irrational number?

2. Is $^1/_2$ an irrational number?

Challenge yourself

1. Is 0.1 an irrational number?

2. Circle all the irrational numbers.

√12 $^4/_9$ 0.5489 √1 √49

irregular polygon

A *polygon* that has unequal *sides* and unequal *angles*.

e.g.

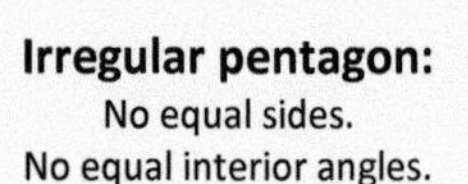

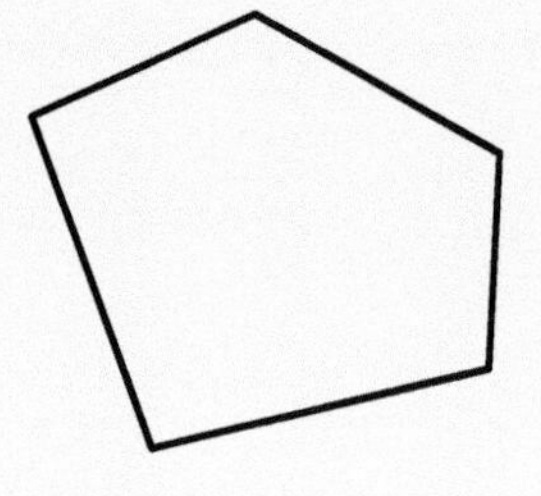

Test yourself

1. Which of the shapes are irregular polygons?

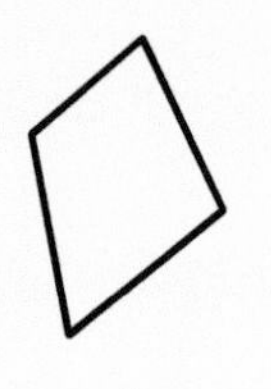

A

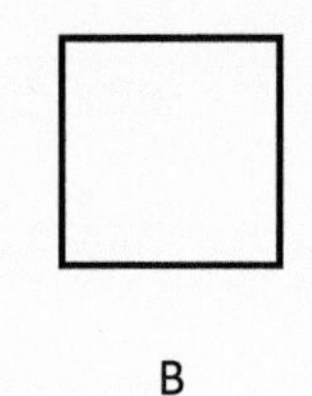

B

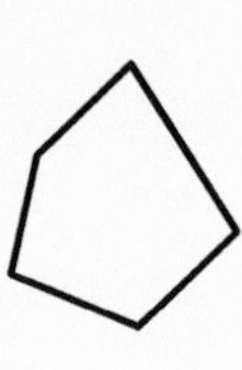

C

Challenge yourself

1. Calculate the sum of all the exterior angles of an *n*-sided polygon.

2. What is the name of the polygon below?

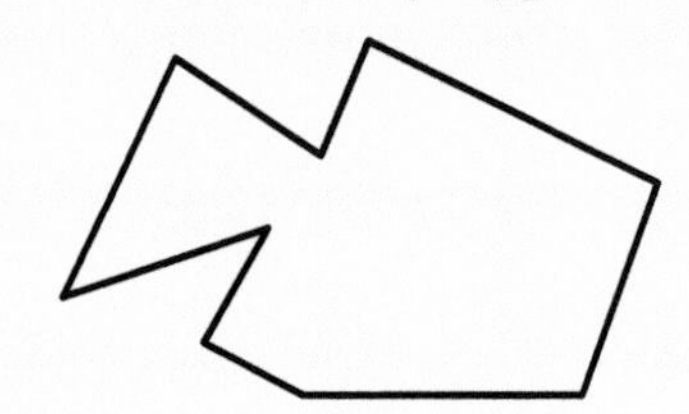

isosceles trapezium

A *trapezium* that has one *line of symmetry*, two pairs of *equal angles* and one pair of *parallel sides*.

e.g.

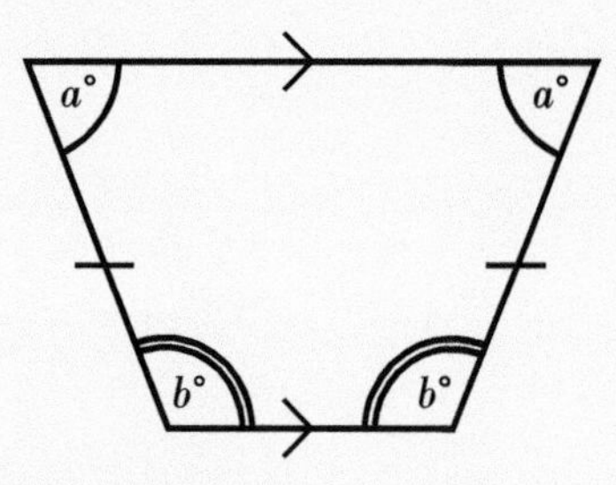

Test yourself

1. Is the shape below an isosceles trapezium?

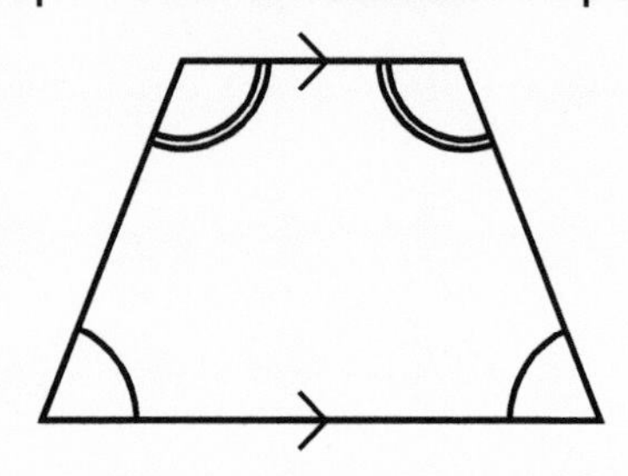

2. What is the sum of the number of vertices and lines of symmetry of an isosceles trapezium?

Challenge yourself

1. If the size of angle $a°$ below is 74°, what is the size of angle $b°$?

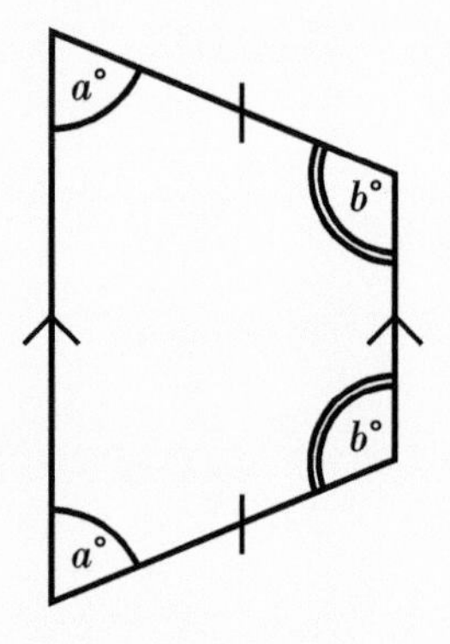

2. What is the sum of all the interior angles of an isosceles trapezium?

3. If the combined length of the parallel sides of an isosceles trapezium is 78cm, and the total perimeter is 186cm, what is the length of one of the slanted sides? Give your answer in cm.

4. If the combined length of the parallel sides of a trapezium is 25m, and they are 8m apart, what is the area of the trapezium in m^2?

isosceles triangle

A *triangle* with two equal *sides* and two equal *angles*.

Note: The two *equal* angles are situated opposite the two equal sides.

e.g.

Isosceles Triangle:
2 angles are equal.
2 sides are of equal length.

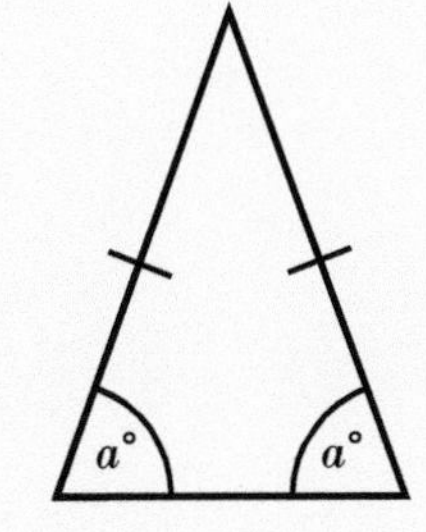

Test yourself

1. Is the shape below an isosceles triangle?

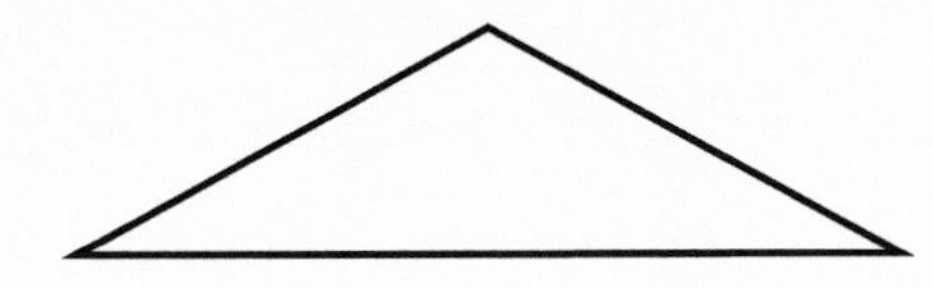

2. What is the sum of the numbers of equal sides and vertices of an isosceles triangle?

Challenge yourself

1. If the angle $a°$ below is 63°, what is the value of the angle at the apex?

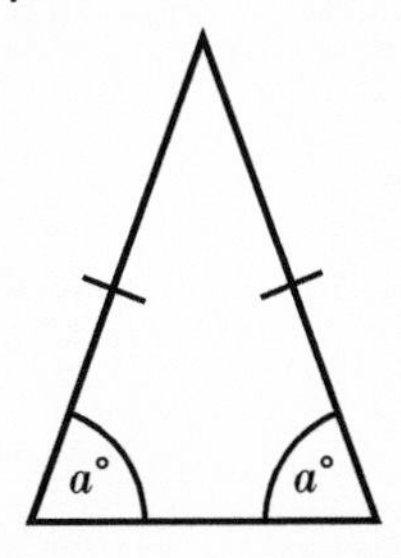

2. If the perimeter of an isosceles triangle is 487mm and its base measures 120mm, what is the length of one of the adjacent sides? Give your answer in cm.

3. If the base of an isosceles triangle is 52mm and the height is 1.7cm, what is the area in mm^2?

J

join

When two or more points are connected together with a straight line.

e.g.

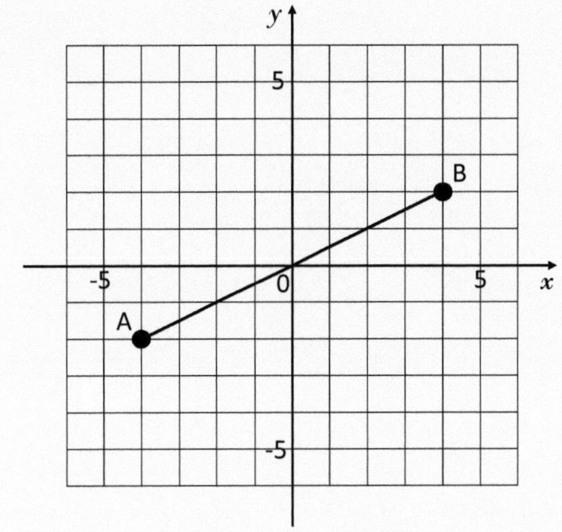

Points A and B are joined with a straight line.

Test yourself

1. Draw a straight line to join points D and F.

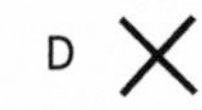

Challenge yourself

Answer the following question using the graph in the example above.

1. Given that the coordinates of C are (2, 5), what is the name given to the shape produced when straight lines are drawn to join the three points?

A B C D E F G H I J K L M N O P Q R S T U V W X Y Z

K

kilogram (kg)

A *metric unit* of *mass equivalent* to 1000 *grams*.
e.g. 2kg is equivalent to 2000g.

Test yourself

1. How many grams are there in 3 kilograms?

2. What is 2000 grams expressed in kilograms?

Challenge yourself

1. Convert 5.78kg to grams.

2. Convert 986g to kilograms.

3. The combined weight of 10 empty sacks weigh 100 grams and each sack can hold 500 grams of rice. How heavy are 10 full sacks of rice in grams?

4. The mass of a baby elephant is 50kg and increases at a rate of 900 grams per year for 5 years. After 5 years the elephant contracts a disease causing it to lose weight at a rate of 0.1 kilograms per year. What is the elephant's weight, in kg, after 7 and a half years?

kilolitre (kl)

A *metric unit* of *volume equivalent* to 1000 *litres*.
e.g. 3000l is equivalent to 3kl.

Test yourself

1. How many litres are there in 2 kilolitres?

2. What is 4000 litres expressed in kilolitres?

Challenge yourself

1. Convert 78.8kl to litres.

2. Convert 9286l to kilolitres.

3. If a swimming pool has the capacity of 375 litres, how many swimming pools can be filled from a one kilolitre tank of water?

4. What is the volume of water (in kl) that can be held by 5 buckets if each has a capacity of 2 litres?

kilometre (km)

A *metric unit* of *length equivalent* to 1000 *metres*.
e.g. 7000m is equivalent to 7km.

Test yourself

1. How many metres are there in 4 kilometres?

2. What is 2000 metres expressed in kilometres?

Challenge yourself

1. Convert 0.0307km to metres.

2. Convert 2.005m to kilometres.

3. If a car drives at a speed of 80 kilometres per hour, how long will it take to travel 1000 kilometres? Give your answer to the nearest hour.

4. The national speed limit is 90,000 metres per hour and Ayush drives 240 kilometres in 3 hours. What is his average speed and does he exceed the speed limit?

kilometres per hour (km/h)

A *metric unit* of *speed* expressing the number of *kilometres* travelled by a body in an *hour*.
e.g. A car travelling at a speed of 2km/h will have covered a distance of 10km in 5 hours.

Test yourself

1. Write forty-eight kilometres per hour.

2. If a car is travelling at a speed of 3km/h, how far has it travelled in 2 hours?

3. If a car covers a distance of 100m in 20 seconds, at what speed is it travelling?

Challenge yourself

1. Convert 40km/h to metres per second.

2. A bus is travelling at 50 kilometres per hour. How far does the bus travel in 5.1 hours? Give your answer in km.

3. A car is travelling at 20 kilometres per hour. How far does the car travel in 21 minutes? Give your answer in km.

kite

A *quadrilateral* with two pairs of *equal* adjacent *sides*, and a pair of equal opposite *angles*. It has no *parallel* sides and the *diagonals* cross (intersect) at *right angles* (90°).
e.g.

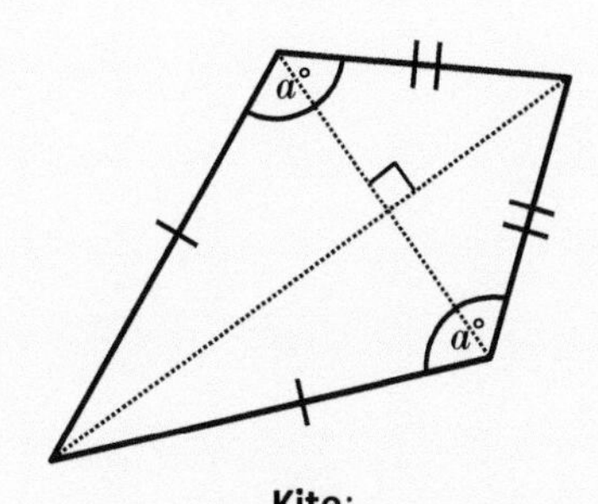

Kite:
2 pairs of adjacent sides are of equal lengths.
1 pair of opposite angles is equal.
The two diagonals intersect at 90°.

<u>Test yourself</u>

1. Is the shape below a kite?

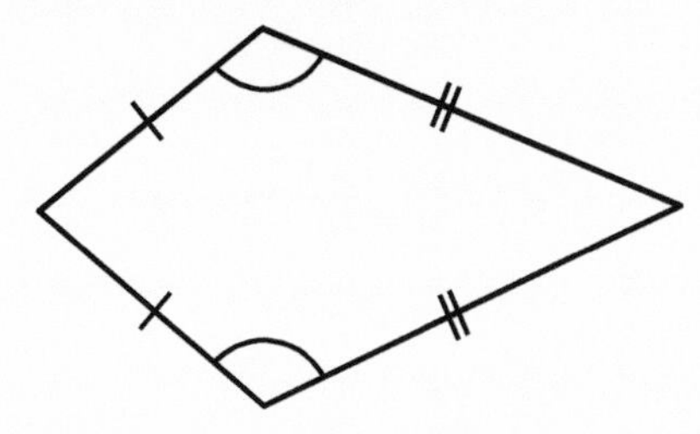

2. What is the sum of the number of edges and the number of pairs of equal angles?

<u>Challenge yourself</u>

1. How many lines of symmetry does a kite have?

2. What is the order of rotational symmetry of a kite?

3. A side of a kite has a length of 5.2cm and its adjacent side measures 32mm. What is the perimeter of the kite in cm?

4. If a kite has two angles each of 30°, what is the sum of the other two angles?

label

To assign a name or tag.
e.g.

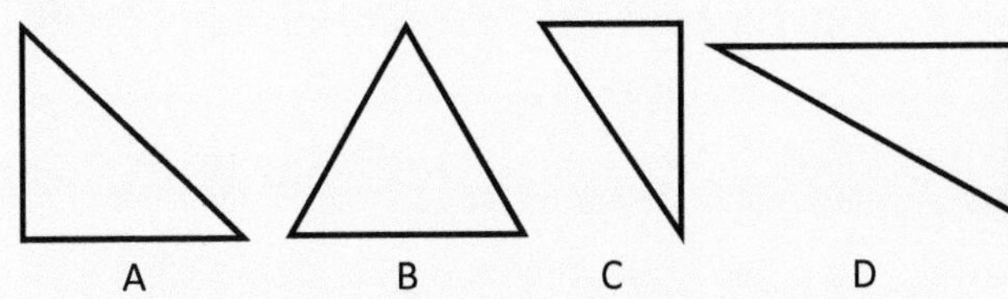

The shape labelled B is the only equilateral triangle above.

<u>Test yourself</u>

1. Label the two axes on the bar graph below?

Average summer rainfall (in mm) in London, England

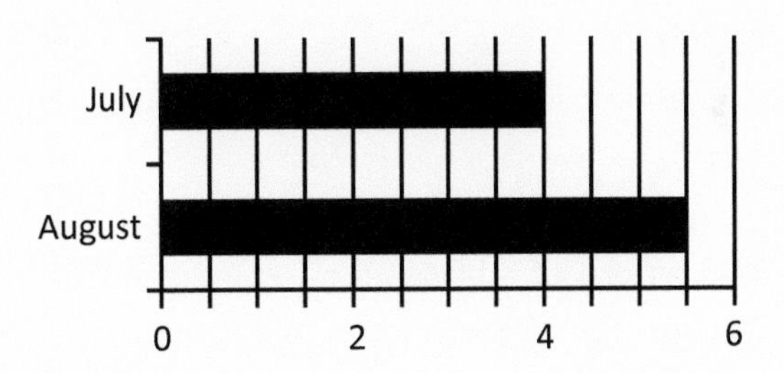

<u>Challenge yourself</u>

1. What is the name given to the shape labelled A, C and D?

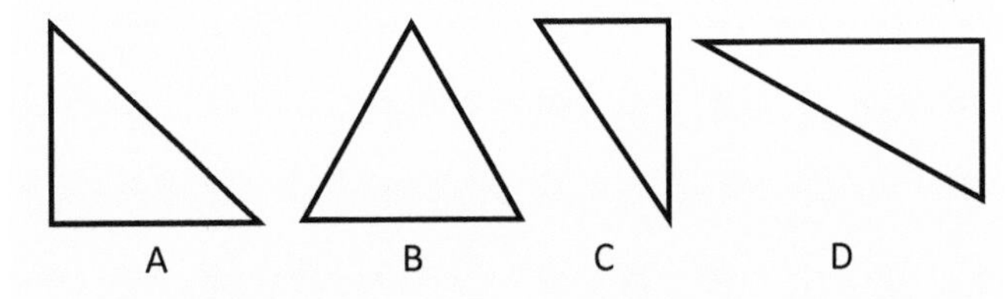

2. Label the shapes below with the correct letters.

A. Hexagon B. Circle C. Square

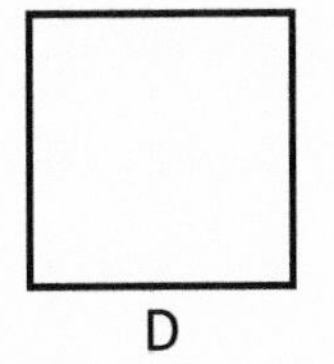

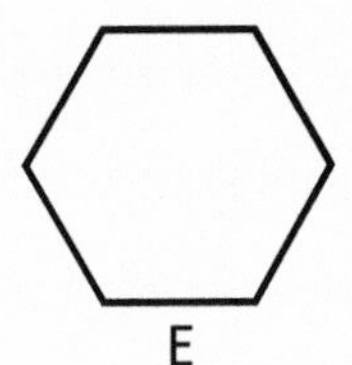

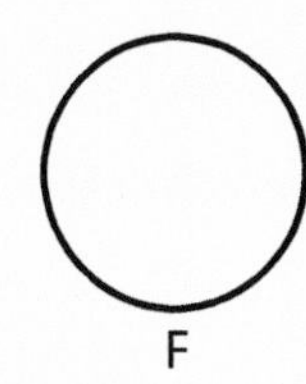

leap year

A calendar year with 366 *days* which includes 29th February. It occurs every fourth *year*.
e.g. The year 2012 was a leap year.

A B C D E F G H I J K L M N O P Q R S T U V W X Y Z

Test yourself

1. How often does a leap year occur?

2. Which month gains a day in a leap year?

Challenge yourself

1. How many days are there in two consecutive years given that one of the years is a leap year?

2. If the date today is 29th February 2016, what will the date be in 366 days time?

3. In a leap year, if February 25th is a Friday, what day will it be on March the 11th that same year?

least value

See *minimum value*.

***

length

The *distance* between two fixed points.

e.g. The length of a football pitch is between 90m and 120m.

Test yourself

1. Using a ruler, measure the length of the straight line AB below. Give your answer in cm.

A ——————————— B

2. Approximately how long is a pen?

A. 20 inches B. 2 inches C. 6 inches

Challenge yourself

1. A straight line joins two points A and B. The coordinates of point A are (5, -12) and the coordinates of point B are (5, 23). What is the length of the line joining the two points?

2. A straight line joins two points C and D. The coordinates of point C are (-2, -18) and the coordinates of point D are (-2, 11). What is the length of the line joining the two points?

less than

When one quantity is smaller than another. It has the symbol '<'. See also *greater than*, *inequality*.

e.g. 1 is less than 2, i.e. $1 < 2$.

Test yourself

1. Is 8 less than 10?

2. Which of the following inequalities are true?

A. $2 < 5$ B. $7 < 5$ C. $1 < 2$

Challenge yourself

1. Is the inequality $^7/_5 < {^8/_6}$ true?

2. Given that $a < b < 0$, is $^a/_a < {^b/_b}$ true?

3. Given that $a < 0 < b < c$, is $^a/_b > {^b/_c}$ true?

less than or equal to

When one quantity is smaller than or *equal* to another. It has the symbol '≤'. See also *greater than or equal to*, *inequality*.

e.g. When $x = \{1, 2, 3\}$, $x^2 = \{1, 4, 9\}$ which is less than or equal to 9, i.e. $x^2 \leq 9$.

Test yourself

1. Is the inequality $5 \leq 5$ true?

2. Which of the following inequalities are true?

A. $3 \leq 10$ B. $8 \leq 4$ C. $2 \leq 2$

Challenge yourself

1. Is the inequality $^{11}/_{12} \leq {^{12}/_{13}}$ true?

2. If $48 \leq 3x$, what is the smallest value x can be?

likelihood

See *probability*.

***

likely

An *event* that has a high *chance* of occurring.

Note: The *probability* of a *likely event* is greater than $^1/_2$ but *less than* 1.

e.g. If a bag contains 5 black balls and 1 red ball, the probability of picking a black ball is likely.

Test yourself

1. Which of the following events is most likely to happen?

a. Finding a 1p coin on a street
b. Finding a £5 note on a street
c. Finding a £10 note on a street

Challenge yourself

1. The probability of event A occurring is 0.4 and the probability of event B occurring is 0.2. What is the probability of event A or event B happening and is this likely?

2. Which of the arrows A, B, C or D shows the best position on the probability line for the event that is likely?

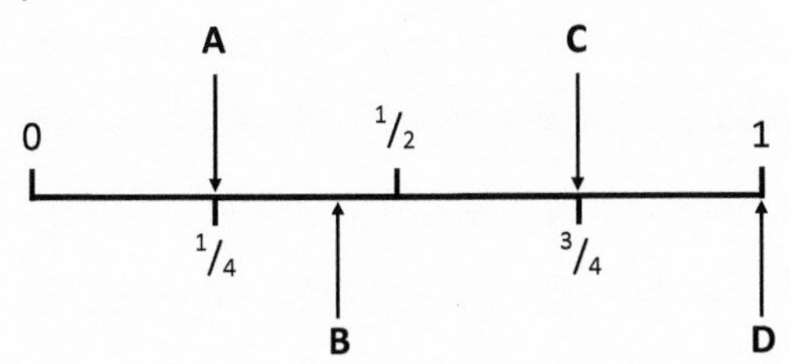

like terms

Terms that are similar in an *algebraic expression*. *Like terms* have the same symbol (*variable*) written after a number. See antonym *unlike terms*.

Note: Like terms can be collected together. Remember that x and x^2 are unlike terms.

e.g. The algebraic expression $4x - 2x + 3y + y$ can be simplified by collecting the like terms to give $2x + 4y$.

Test yourself

Simplify the algebraic expressions below by collecting the like terms.

1. $3x - x$

2. $5y + 2y$

3. $3x - 7x + 3x + y$

4. $2y + 10y - 4x$

Challenge yourself

Simplify the algebraic expressions below by collecting the like terms.

1. $x + 5y - 4x + 11y$

2. $7x - 2y - x + y$

3. $14x + 5y - 41x - 21y$

4. $2(4x + y) - 4x - y$

linear graph

A graph consisting of a straight line that can be written in the form $y = mx + c$.

Note: m is the *gradient*, c is the *constant*, and x and y are the *variables*. The constant can be zero.

e.g.

Linear relationship between mass and volume of water

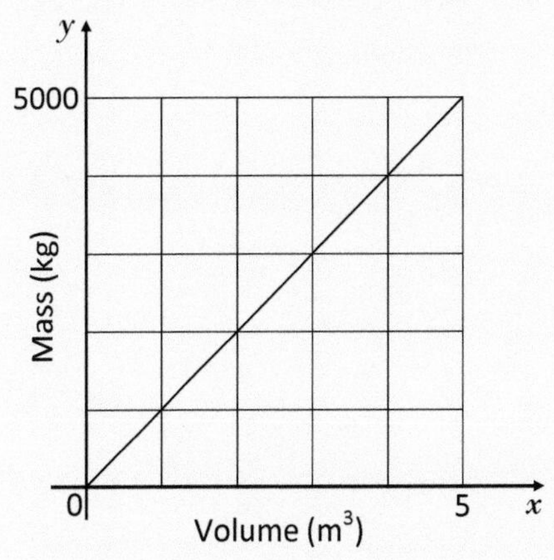

Mass (y) = Density (m) × Volume (x)

For a given substance, the density is constant. In the graph above, the gradient corresponds to the density of water.

Test yourself

Answer the following questions using the graph in the example above.

1. What is the property of a linear graph?

2. If you double the volume of water, does the mass double?

Challenge yourself

Answer the following questions using the graph in the example above.

1. Calculate the gradient of the graph.

2. What is the ratio between the volume and the mass of water?

3. The density of a new substance was examined which gave a straight line with a gradient of +500. Will the second line be steeper than that of water?

4. Using the answer from question 3, how does the density of the new substance differ from that of water?

linear sequence

See *arithmetic sequence*.

***

A B C D E F G H I J K L M N O P Q R S T U V W X Y Z

line graph

In a line graph, all the points of the *data* given are joined using straight lines.

Note: Line graphs do not have to start from the *origin*.

e.g.

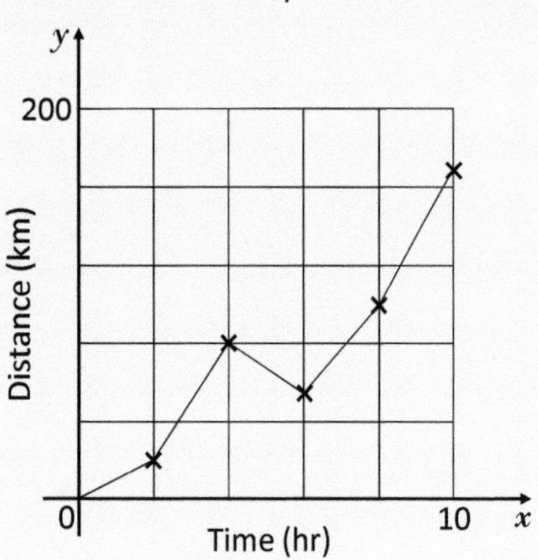

Test yourself

1. Draw straight lines through each point to complete the line graph below.

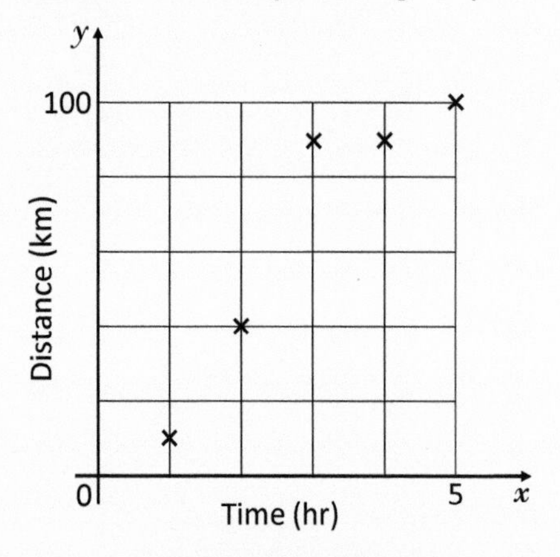

Challenge yourself

Using the line graph in 'Test yourself' above, answer the following questions.

1. How far did the car travel in 3 hours?

2. How far did the car travel between hour 3 and hour 4?

3. If the journey finishes on the 5th hour, how far has the car travelled in total?

line of best fit

A line drawn on a *scatter graph* to show the relationship between two *variables*.

Note: The *gradient* of the line of best fit can be either positive or negative.

e.g.

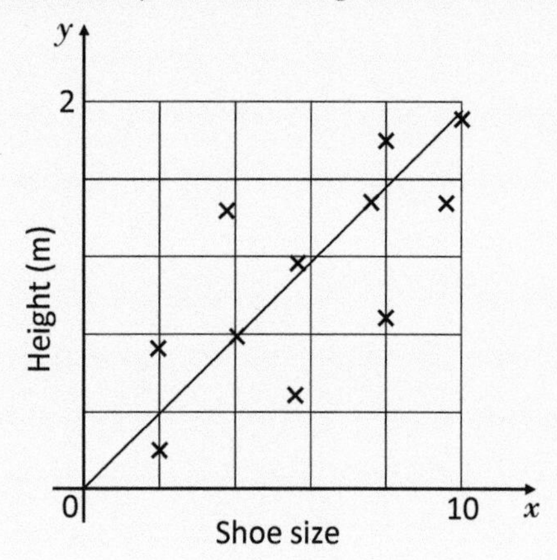

Test yourself

Answer the following questions using the scatter graph below.

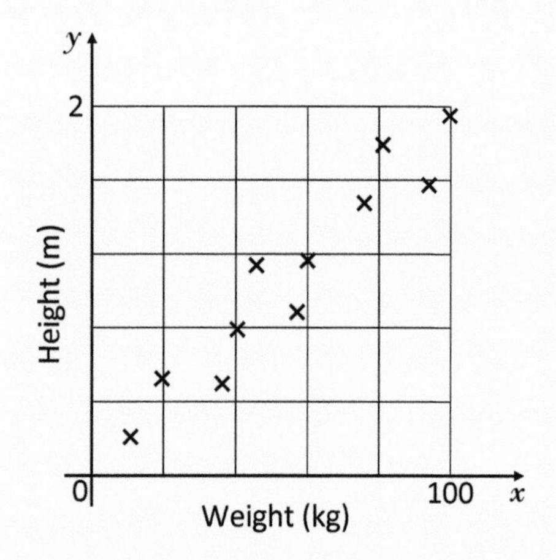

1. Draw the line of best fit on the scatter plot.

Challenge yourself

Answer the following questions using the graph in 'Test yourself' above.

1. Using the line of best fit, estimate the height of a person who weighs 50kg.

2. Using the line of best fit, estimate the weight of a person who is 160cm in height.

3. Is the gradient of the line of best fit negative?

line of symmetry (axis of symmetry)

A line that divides a *figure* into two symmetrical parts, so that when reflected, the figure on one side perfectly *maps* on to the other.

e.g.

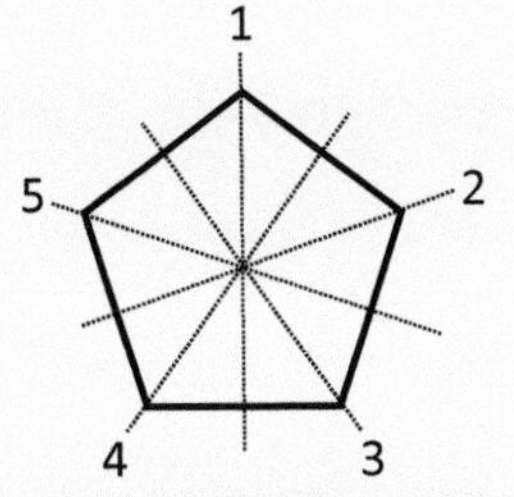

A regular pentagon has 5 lines of symmetry,1 through each vertex.

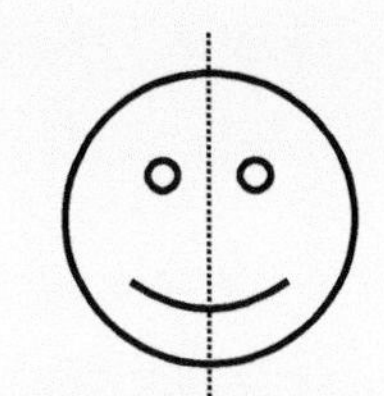

This shape has 1 line of symmetry.

Test yourself

1. The shape shown below has 1 line of symmetry. Draw the line of symmetry.

2. How many lines of symmetry does the shape below have?

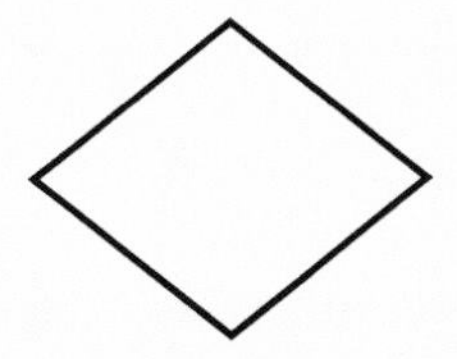

3. How many lines of symmetry does a square have?

Challenge yourself

1. What is the sum of the numbers of lines of symmetry of a scalene triangle and a parallelogram?

2. Which of these shapes has exactly two lines of symmetry?

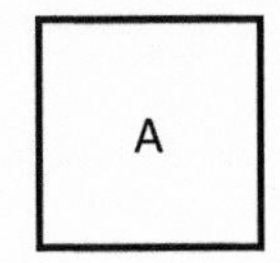

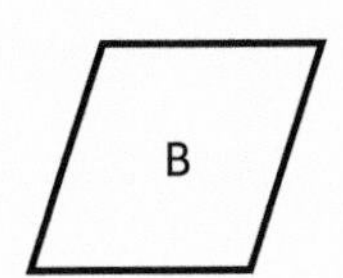

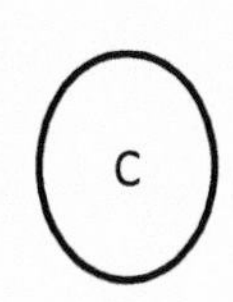

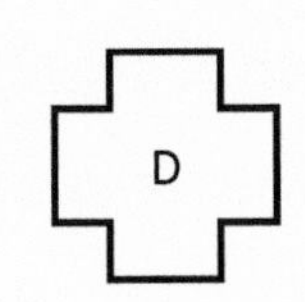

3. Which of these shapes has the most lines of symmetry?

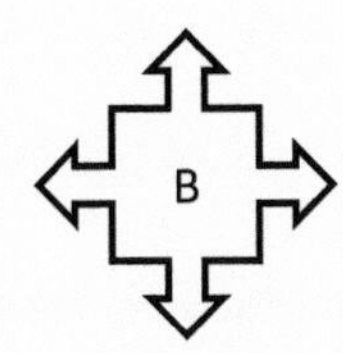

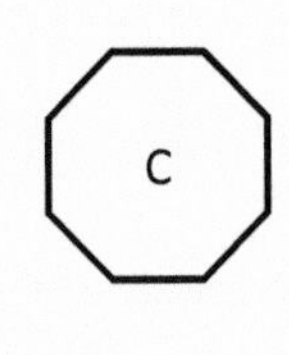

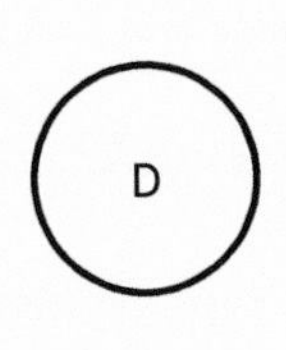

4. What is the ratio between the numbers of lines of symmetry of a regular octagon and a regular decagon?

line segment

Part of a straight line between two points.

e.g.

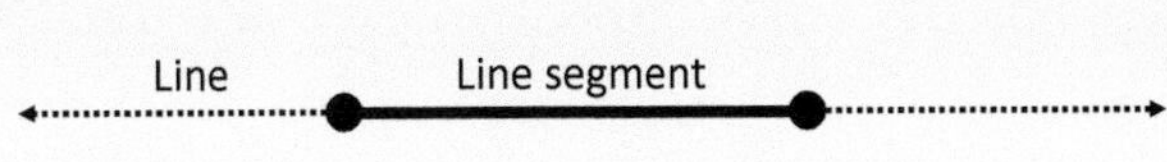

Test yourself

1. Using a straight line, draw the line segment between the two points below.

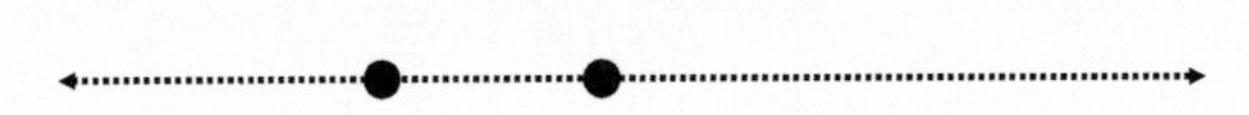

2. Use a ruler to measure the length of the line segment in question 1.

Challenge yourself

1. Line segment A is 50mm and line segment B is 6.5cm in length. What is the ratio of the length of line segment A to line segment B?

2. A line of length 120cm is divided in a ratio of 4:1. What is the length of the longer line segment in cm?

3. On the line AB, there is a point C. C lies on the line where AC is twice as long as CB. If the length of AB is 99cm, calculate the length of the line segment AC in cm.

litre (l)

A *metric unit* of *volume equivalent* to 1,000 *millilitres*.

e.g. 2000ml is equivalent to 2l.

Test yourself

1. What is 3000ml expressed in litres?

2. How many millilitres are there in 5l?

Challenge yourself

1. Convert 45,870ml to litres.

2. Convert 2.3l to millilitres.

3. There are eight buckets that can each hold 5 litres of liquid. What is the total amount of liquid that can be contained within all the buckets? Give your answer in litres.

A B C D E F G H I J K L M N O P Q R S T U V W X Y Z

locus (plural: loci)

A set of points that lie at a fixed *distance* from a point or line.

e.g.

Locus from a fixed point of distance r; i.e. a circle of radius r

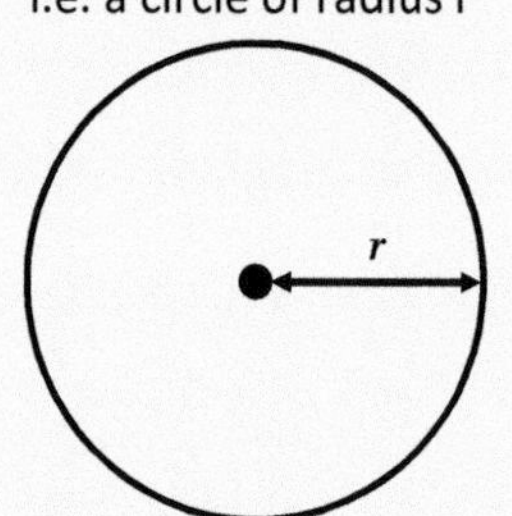

Locus from a line of distance x

Test yourself

1. Draw a locus that is 1cm from point A.

A

Challenge yourself

1. Assume π = 3.14, what is the area enclosed by the locus 4cm from a point? Give your answer in cm^2.

2. What is the area enclosed by the locus 5cm from a line of 5cm? Assume π = 3.14 and give your answer in cm^2.

lowest common denominator

The *lowest common multiple* of all the *denominators* in a *sum* of *fractions*.

e.g. In the sum $^{4}/_{7} + ^{1}/_{3}$, the denominators are 7 and 3, and lowest common multiple of 7 and 3 is 21; that is the lowest common denominator.

Test yourself

1. Given that the lowest common multiple of 2 and 3 is 6, what is the lowest common denominator in the sum $^{5}/_{2} + ^{4}/_{3}$?

2. Given that the lowest common multiple of 3 and 6 is 6, what is the lowest common denominator in the sum $^{4}/_{3} + ^{9}/_{6}$?

Challenge yourself

1. Find the lowest common denominator of $^{5}/_{8}$ and $^{6}/_{9}$, and hence calculate $^{5}/_{8} + ^{6}/_{9}$.

2. Find the lowest common denominator of $^{11}/_{12}$ and $^{11}/_{15}$, and hence calculate $^{11}/_{12} + ^{11}/_{15}$.

lowest common multiple (LCM)

The smallest number that is a *multiple* of two or more numbers.

e.g. The multiples of 2 are: 2, 4, 6, 8,... and the multiples of 4 are: 4, 8, 12,... therefore, the lowest common multiple of 2 and 4 is 4.

Test yourself

1. Given that the first four multiples of 3 are 3, 6, 9 and 12, and the first four multiples of 4 are 4, 8, 12 and 16, what is the LCM of 3 and 4?

2. Given that the first four multiples of 1 are 1, 2, 3 and 4, and the first four multiples of 2 are 2, 4, 6 and 8, what is the LCM of 1 and 2?

Challenge yourself

1. What is the lowest common multiple of 14 and 20?

2. Paul and Will ate 5 and 15 slices of pizza, respectively. What is the lowest common multiple of pizza slices eaten?

lowest terms

See *simplest form*.

***

major arc

When a *chord* divides a *circle* into *segments*, the larger part of the *circumference* is known as the major *arc*.
e.g.

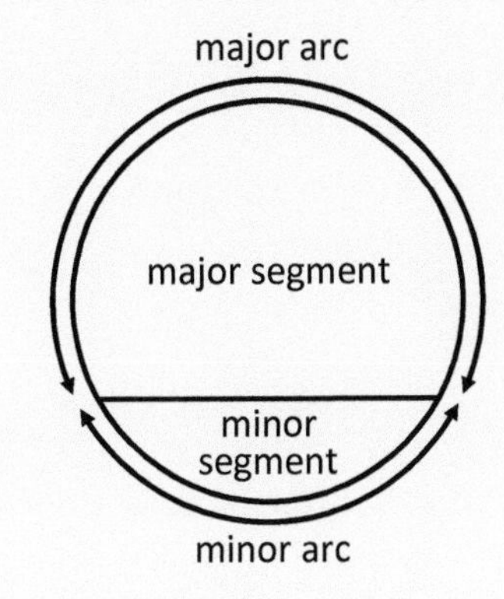

Test yourself

1. Which of the letters A or B represents the major arc?

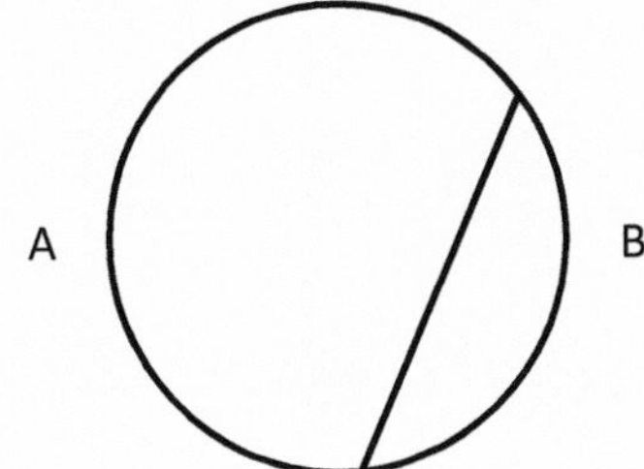

Challenge yourself

1. A circumference of 255cm is divided in a ratio of 6:11. What is the length of the major arc?

2. If the length of the major arc is 15mm when the circumference is divided in a ratio of 2:5, what is the length of the circumference?

major sector

When two *radii* divide the *circle*, the larger section is known as the major *sector*.
Note: Radii is the plural form of *radius*.
e.g.

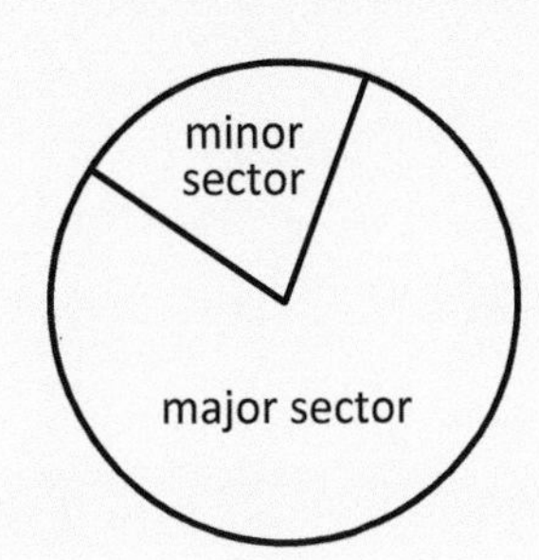

Test yourself

1. Which of the letters A or B represents the major sector?

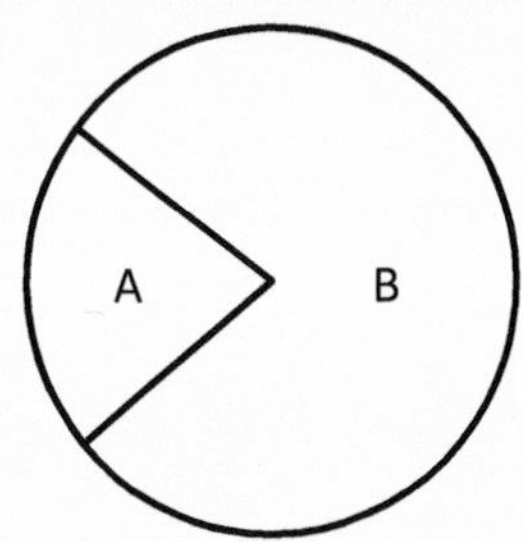

Challenge yourself

1. If the area of a circle is 360mm^2, and 80% of the area is in the major sector, what is the area of the major sector?

2. If the area of a major sector is 25cm^2 and it is 55% of the total area, calculate the total area of the circle.

3. What is the area of the major sector if its area is $^3/_4$ of 250cm^2?

major segment

When a *chord* divides a *circle* into two *segments*, the larger section of the circle is known as major segment.
e.g.

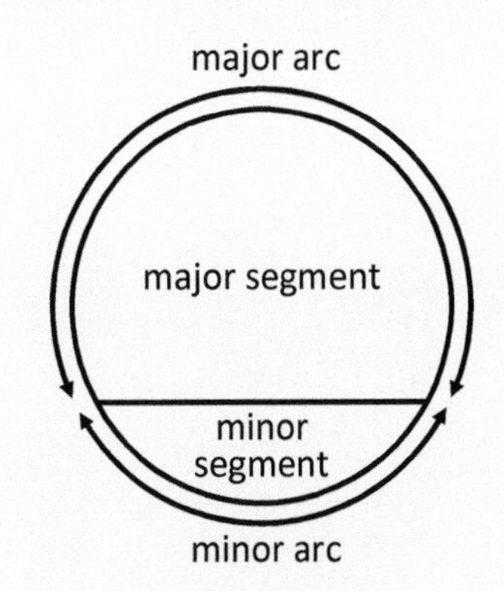

Test yourself

1. Which of the letters A or B represents the major segment?

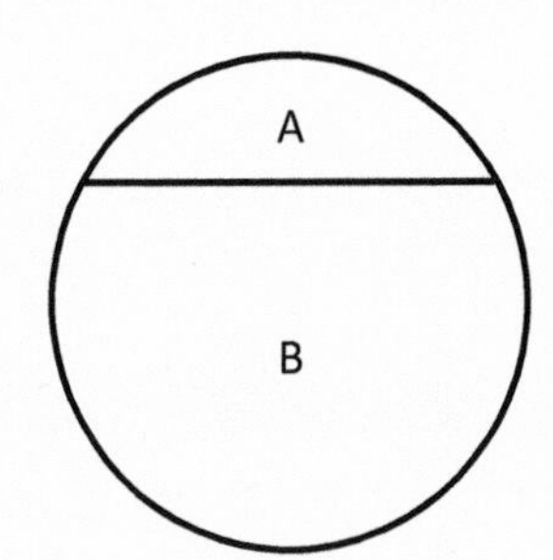

A B C D E F G H I J K L M N O P Q R S T U V W X Y Z

A B C D E F G H I J K L M N O P Q R S T U V W X Y Z

Challenge yourself

1. If the area of a circle is $60mm^2$ and 65% of the area is in the major segment, what is the area of the major segment?

2. If the area of a major segment is $12m^2$ and it is 60% of the total area, calculate the total area of the circle.

3. What is the area of the major segment if its area is $^7/_{10}$ of $584cm^2$?

map

i. A *two-dimensional* drawing representing an *area* of land using a given *scale*.

e.g. The map below is drawn to a scale of 1:100,000. If the side of one small square on the map measures 1cm, the actual distance between point A and point B is 700,000cm; that is, 7km.

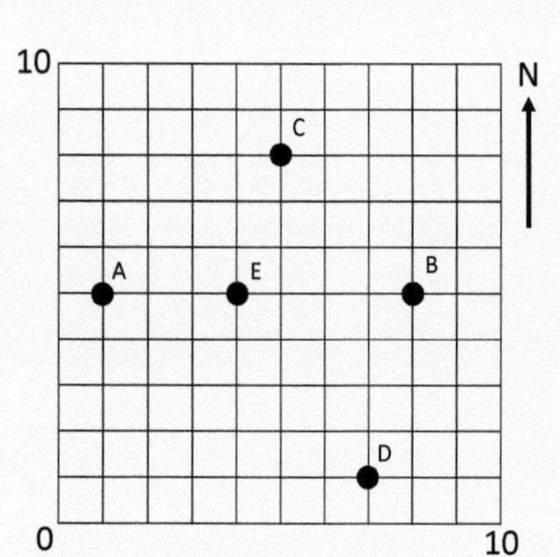

ii. A process in which a given shape undergoes a transformation.

e.g.

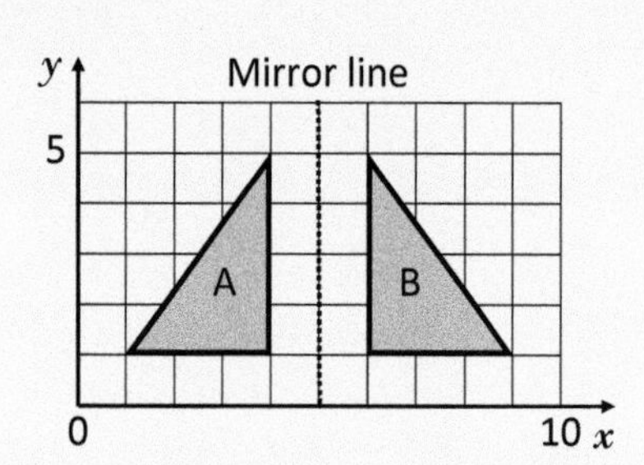

Shape A has been mapped onto shape B via a reflection across the mirror line. Shape B is known as the image of shape A.

iii. See *function*.

***

Test yourself

Answer the following questions using the map in the example above.

1. What is the nearest place to Treasure Island?

2. What is the actual distance between Treasure Island and Radford flat?

Challenge yourself

Answer the following questions using the map in the example.

1. If Jack starts from Wise terrace and drives north for four kilometres, then east for one kilometre. Where is he now?

2. Nav is looking for treasure that is buried on Treasure Island. She starts from Wise terrace and travels west for 6km, north for 4km and east for 2km. Does she find the treasure?

mass

The measure of the amount of matter an object contains. It is measured in *grams*, *kilograms*, *tonnes*, *pounds*, *stone* etc.

e.g. The mass of a book approximately measures 300 grams; that is 0.3 kilograms.

Test yourself

1. Which of the units below are used when measuring the mass of an object?

m^3 kg cm ml g

Challenge yourself

1. If the mass of a car weighs 200kg, what is its mass in grams?

2. Navina has 10 bags of sugar each weighing 1kg. She spills three bags, losing exactly half the sugar in each bag. What is the total mass of the remaining sugar?

matrix

Numbers or *expressions* in rows and columns enclosed by brackets. See also *column vector*.

e.g. The translation of a point 2 units right and 3 units down is expressed as $\begin{pmatrix} 2 \\ -3 \end{pmatrix}$.

Challenge yourself

1. Express, using a matrix, the translation of a point 5 units up and 9 units left.

2. Express, using a matrix, the translation of a point 8 units right and 4 units down.

maximum point

The highest point on a curve, i.e. the peak.

e.g.

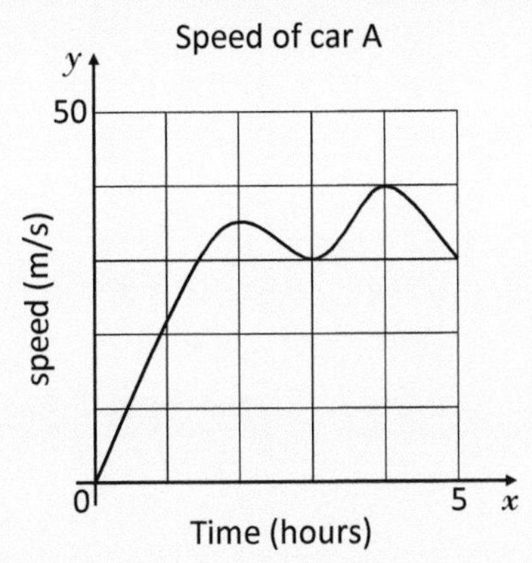

The greatest speed achieved by car A is 40 m/s.

Test yourself

1. On the graph in the example above, draw a cross at the maximum point.

Challenge yourself

Answer the following questions using the graph in the example above.

1. If car A travels for 3.5 hours at the greatest speed it has achieved, how far does it travel?

2. What was the maximum speed of car A during the first 3 hours of its journey?

maximum value

See *greatest value*.

***

mean (arithmetic average)

See *average*.

***

median

The middle *value* in an ordered set of numbers. See also *average*, *order*.

Note: If there is an *even number* of values in a *dataset*, the median is calculated by finding the *mean* of the two values in the middle.

e.g. In the dataset {1, 2, 3, 4, 5, 6}, the median is $^{(3+4)}/_2 = 3.5$.

Test yourself

1. What is the median of the following set of numbers: 2, 4, 9, 2, 1?

2. What is the median of the following set of numbers: 5, 4, 3, 10?

Challenge yourself

1. What is the median of the following set of numbers: 5, 4, 9, 11, 2, -5, 7?

2. What is the median of the following set of numbers: 4, 5, 99, 1, 3, 0?

3. The table below shows the number of apples eaten by Kate last week. What is the median number of apples eaten last week?

Mon	Tues	Weds	Thurs	Fri	Sat	Sun
3	2	0	1	4	6	5

metre (m)

A *metric unit* of *length equivalent* to 100 *centimetres*.

e.g. 7m is equivalent to 700cm.

Test yourself

1. How many centimetres are in 4m?

2. What is 900cm expressed in metres?

Challenge yourself

1. What is 0.27mm in metres?

2. Convert 87.3m into centimetres.

3. A box is 250cm wide. How many boxes can fit side by side in a room that is 10m wide?

4. Given that 1 metre is equal to 1.09 yards, how many yards are there in 25.2 metres?

metres per second (m/s)

A *metric unit* of *speed* expressing the number of *metres* travelled by a body in a *second*.

e.g. A person jogging at a speed of 2m/s will have covered a distance of 10m in 5 seconds.

Test yourself

1. If a sprinter finishes a 100m race in 10 seconds, what is his average speed in m/s?

2. Given 1km = 1000m, convert 1km/s to m/s.

Challenge yourself

1. A car is travelling at a speed of 8m/s. How far does it travel in half an hour?

2. A bus is travelling at 30km/h. What is the speed of the bus in m/s?

3. A taxi is travelling at an average speed of 20 metres per second. If the taxi covers a distance of 6000 metres, how long does the journey take?

4. Calculate the mean of the following speeds.
22m/s, 16m/s, 1200cm/s, 0.8km/s

metric units

The system of *units* based on *multiples* of 10.

e.g.

Units of length	Units of mass	Unit of volume
Millimetre (mm)	Milligram (mg)	Millilitre (ml)
Centimetre (cm)	Centigram (cg)	Centilitre (cl)
Metre (m)	Gram (g)	Litre (l)
Kilometre (km)	Kilogram (kg)	Kilolitre (kl)
	Tonne (t)	

Test yourself

1. Which of the following units is not a metric unit?

metre inch tonne litre kilogram

Challenge yourself

1. Express 58.1 metres first in kilometres and then in millimetres.

2. Express 5 kilograms first in grams and then in milligrams.

3. Express 78 litres in kilolitres.

midday (noon)

12 o'clock in the middle of the *day*, i.e. 12.00pm.

e.g.

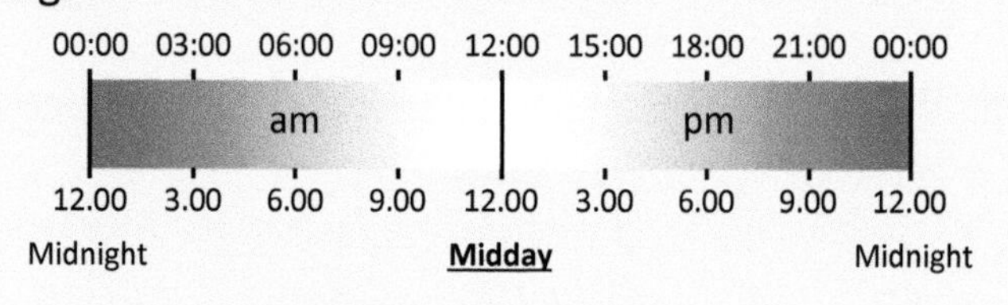

Test yourself

1. Express the time at midday in 24-hour clock format.

2. Express the time at midday in 12-hour clock format.

Challenge yourself

1. The time now is 3 hours and 45 minutes before midday. What is the time 2 hours from now? Express your answer in 12-hour clock format.

2. The time now is 25 minutes past midday. What is the time 4 hours from now? Express your answer in 24-hour clock format.

midnight

12 o'clock in the middle of the night, i.e. 12.00am.

e.g.

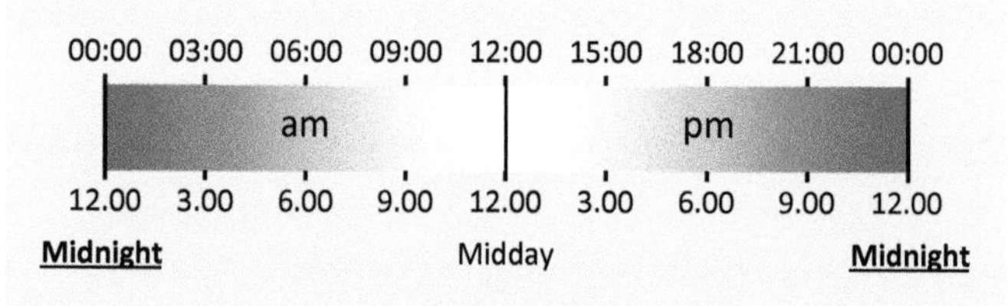

Test yourself

1. Express the time at midnight in 24-hour clock format.

2. Express the time at midnight in 12-hour clock format.

Challenge yourself

1. The time now is 55 minutes past midnight. What is the time 5 hours from now? Express your answer in 12-hour clock format.

2. The time now is 25 minutes to midnight. What is the time 2.3 hours from now? Express your answer in 24-hour clock format.

midpoint

A point *equidistant* from two ends of a line.

e.g.

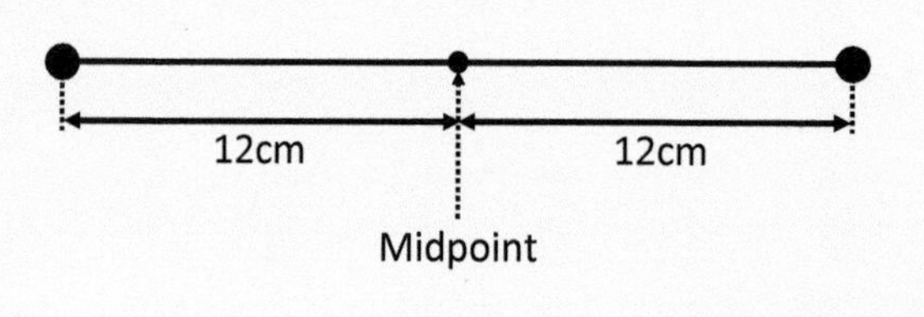

Test yourself

1. Indicate with a cross the midpoint of the straight line shown below.

____

Challenge yourself

1. The coordinates of point A are (5, 22) and the coordinates of point B are (5, 2). What are the coordinates of the midpoint?

2. The coordinates of point A are (31, -5) and the coordinates of point B are (51, -5). What are the coordinates of the midpoint?

mile

An *imperial unit* of *length equivalent* to 1760 *yards*, and approximately 1.6 *kilometres*.
e.g. 8km is approximately equal to 5 miles.

Test yourself

1. Assuming that 8km is approximately equal to 5 miles, approximate 16km in miles.

2. How many yards are there in 3 miles?

Challenge yourself

1. How many yards are there in $^1/_2$ a mile?

2. Given that 1 mile is equal to 1.6 kilometres, approximate 24km in miles.

3. A car travelled 8 miles in 2 hours. Calculate the average speed in miles per hour.

miles per hour (mph)

An *imperial unit* of *speed* which corresponds to the number of *miles* travelled in one *hour*.
e.g. If a car is travelling at a speed of 60mph, in 2 hours the car would have covered a distance of 120 miles.

Test yourself

1. A man is walking 3 miles per hour. How far has he travelled in 3 hours?

2. A bus covered a distance of 46 miles in 2 hours. At what speed was the bus travelling?

Challenge yourself

1. If a car is travelling 30 miles every 1.5 hours, what is its speed expressed in miles per hour?

2. If a car is travelling at 45mph, how far can the car travel in 25 minutes?

3. Express the speed of a car that is travelling 28 miles in 2 hours in miles per hour.

milligram (mg)

A *metric unit* of *mass equivalent* to a *thousandth* of a *gram*.
e.g. 1000mg is equivalent to 1g

Test yourself

1. How many milligrams are in 2 grams?

2. What is 5000 milligrams expressed in grams?

Challenge yourself

1. Convert 0.7 grams to milligrams.

2. Convert 2.55 milligrams to grams.

millilitre (ml)

A *metric unit* of *volume equivalent* to a *thousandth* of a *litre*.
e.g. 1000ml is equivalent to 1l.

Test yourself

1. How many millilitres are in 5 litres?

2. What is 8000 millilitres expressed in litres?

Challenge yourself

1. Convert 2.87 litres to millilitres.

2. Convert 785 millilitres to litres.

millimetre (mm)

A *metric unit* of *length equivalent* to a *thousandth* of a *metre*.
e.g. 4,000mm is equivalent to 4m.

Test yourself

1. How many millimetres are in 9 metres?

2. What is 1000 millimetres expressed in metres?

A
B
C
D
E
F
G
H
I
J
K
L
M
N
O
P
Q
R
S
T
U
V
W
X
Y
Z

Challenge yourself

1. Convert 0.82 kilometres to millimetres.

2. Assuming that $\pi = 3$, calculate the area of a circle with a diameter of 450mm. Give your answer in mm^2.

minimum point

The lowest point on a curve, i.e. the trough.

e.g.

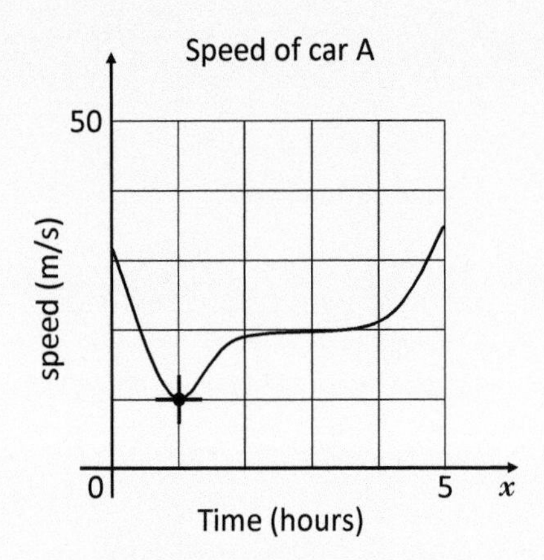

The lowest speed achieved by car A is 10 m/s. The minimum point is indicated on the graph using a cross.

Test yourself

Answer the following questions using the graph in the example above.

1. Approximately, at what hour did car A achieve its minimum speed?

2. How long would car A take to cover a distance of 120m if it was travelling at its minimum speed? Give your answer in seconds.

Challenge yourself

Answer the following questions using the graph below.

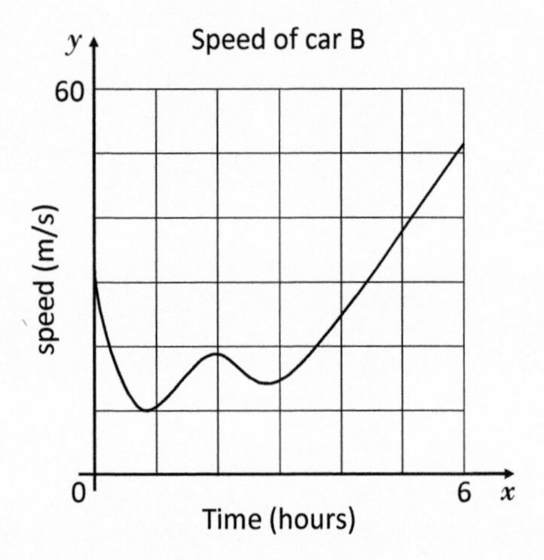

The lowest speed achieved by car B is 10 m/s.

1. What is the minimum speed achieved by car B between the second and the fourth hour?

2. How far can car B travel in 125 minutes if it is travelling at the minimum speed calculated in part 1?

3. Car B is travelling at its lowest speed. Car C travels at 20m/s and is 500m behind car B. How long does it take for car C to catch up with car B?

minimum value (least value)

The smallest *possible value*.

e.g.

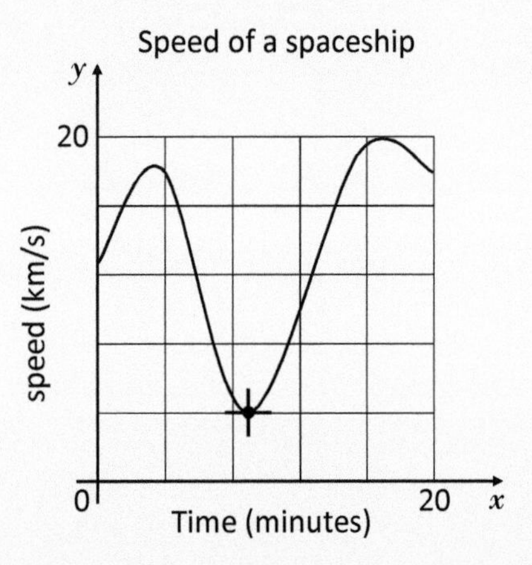

The minimum speed achieved by the spaceship in the first 20 minutes is 4 km/s. The minimum speed is indicated on the graph using a cross.

Test yourself

Answer the following questions using the bar chart below.

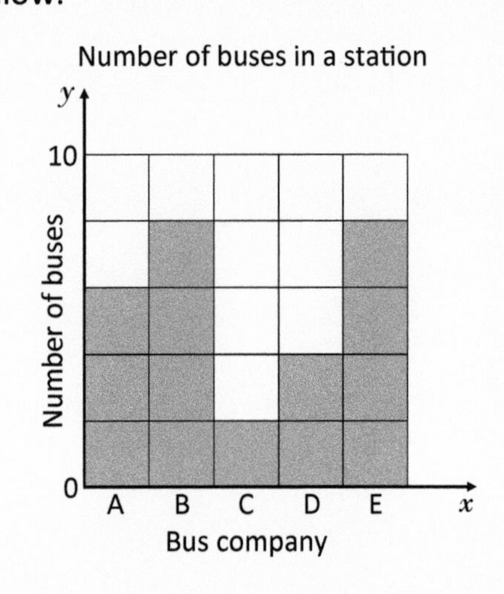

1. Which bus company has the least number of buses at the station?

2. Which bus company has the second least number of buses at the station?

Challenge yourself

Answer the following questions using the bar chart below.

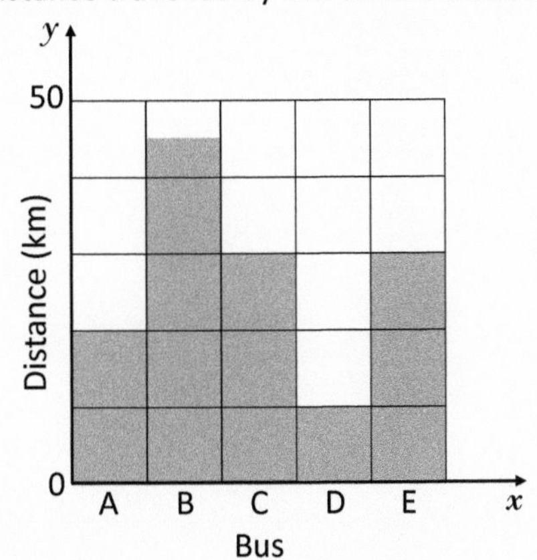

1. Which bus travelled the least distance?

2. What was the average distance travelled by the two buses which travelled the least?

3. What is the range of the distances travelled by the buses?

minor arc

When a *chord* divides a *circle* into two *segments*, the smaller part of the *circumference* is known as the minor *arc*.

e.g.

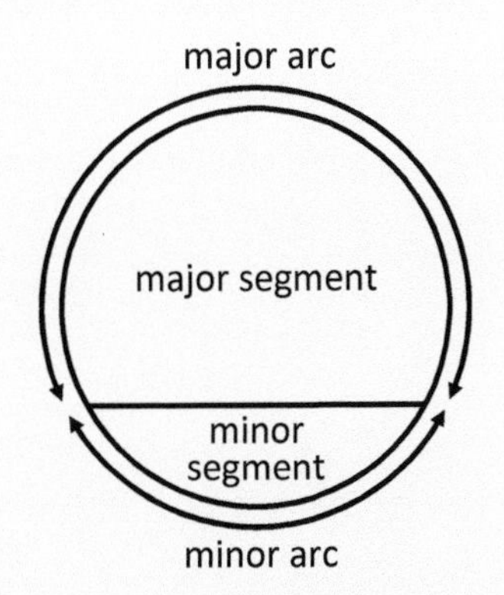

Test yourself

1. Which of the letters A or B represents the minor arc?

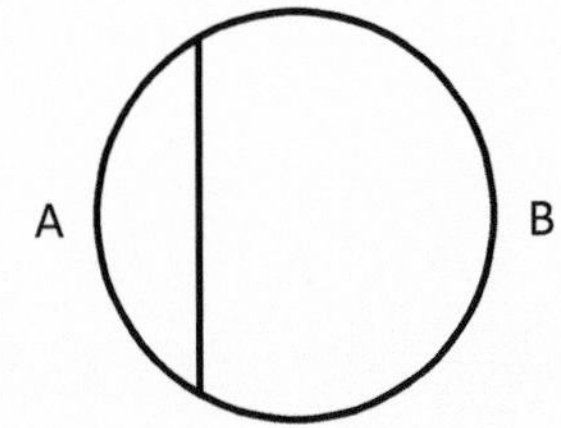

2. Is the minor arc longer than the major arc?

Challenge yourself

1. A circumference of 156cm is divided in a ratio of 5:7. What is the length of the minor arc?

2. If the length of the minor arc is 9mm, and the circumference was divided in a ratio of 2:7, what is the length of the circumference?

3. If the length of the minor arc is 16mm, and the circumference was divided in a ratio of 3:1, what is the length of the major arc?

minor sector

When two *radii* divide a *circle*, the smaller section is known as the minor *sector*.

Note: Radii is the plural form of *radius*.

e.g.

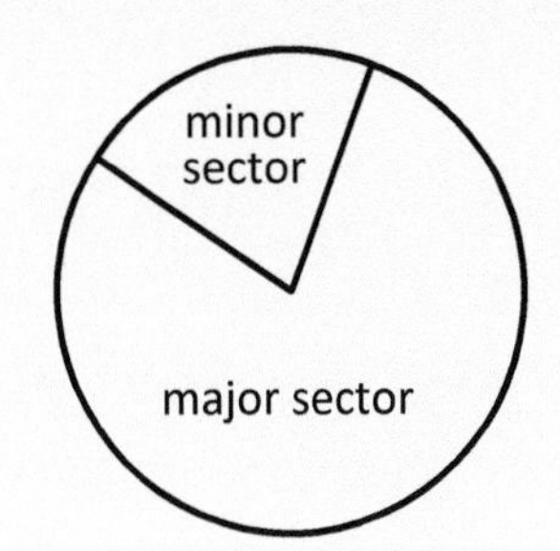

Test yourself

1. Which letter represents the minor sector?

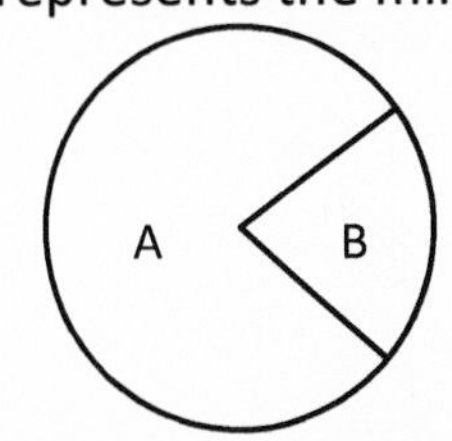

Challenge yourself

1. If the area of a circle is $720mm^2$, and 40% of its area is in the minor sector. What is the area of the minor sector?

2. If the area of a minor sector is $18cm^2$ and makes up 30% of the total area, calculate the total area of the circle.

3. What is the area of the minor sector if its area is $^1/_4$ of $348cm^2$?

minor segment

When a *chord* divides a *circle* into two *segments*, the smaller section of the circle is known as the minor segment.

e.g.

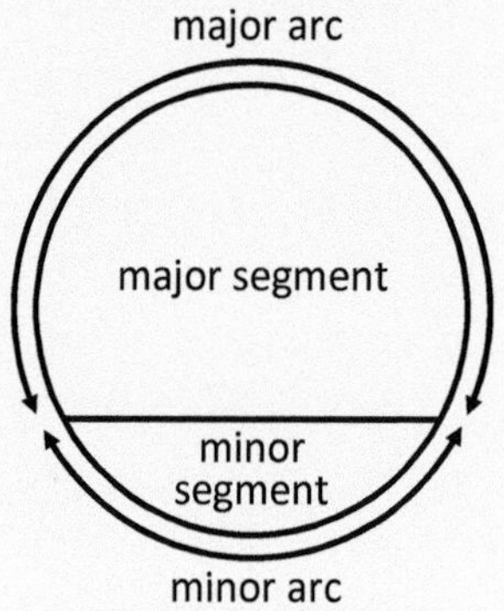

major arc

major segment

minor segment

minor arc

Test yourself

1. Which of the letters A or B represents the minor segment?

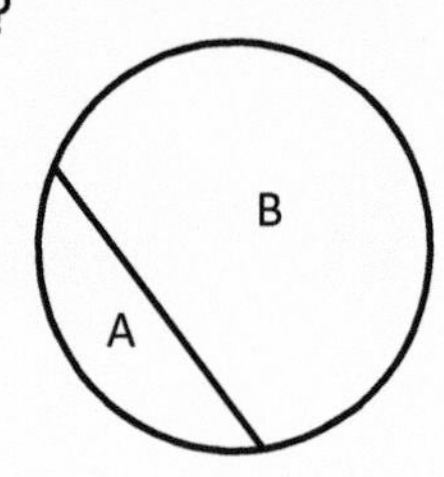

Challenge yourself

1. If the area of a circle is $120mm^2$, and 15% of the area is in the minor segment. What is the area of the major segment?

2. If the area of a minor segment is $15m^2$ and it is 10% of the total area, calculate the total area of the circle.

3. What is the area of the minor segment if its area is $^3/_{10}$ of $1470cm^2$?

minus

See synonym *subtraction*.

***

minute (min)

A *unit* of time *equivalent* to 60 *seconds*; that is, $^1/_{60}{}^{th}$ of an *hour*.

e.g. There are 60 minutes in 1 hour.

Test yourself

1. How many seconds are there in 2 minutes?

2. How many minutes are there in 2 hours?

Challenge yourself

1. How many minutes are there in 2.45 hours?

2. What is 2430 minutes expressed in hours?

mirror line

i. A line across which a given shape is reflected to produce a mirror *image*.

Note: A given shape and its image are *equidistant* from the *mirror line*.

e.g.

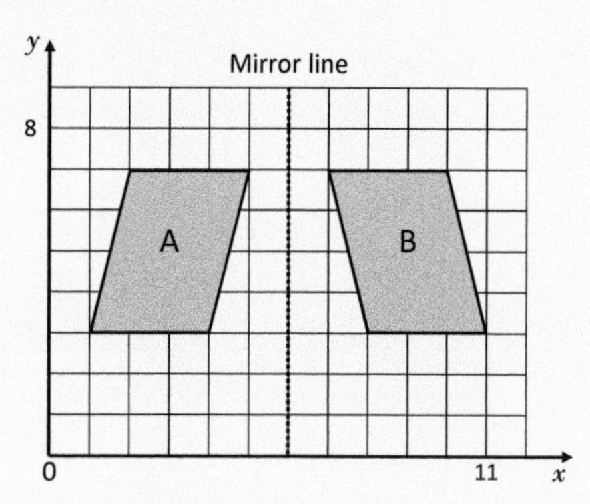

Shape A has been reflected across the mirror line to produce shape B. Shape B is known as the mirror image.

ii. See *line of symmetry*.

***

Test yourself

1. How many mirror lines can be drawn on the shape shown below?

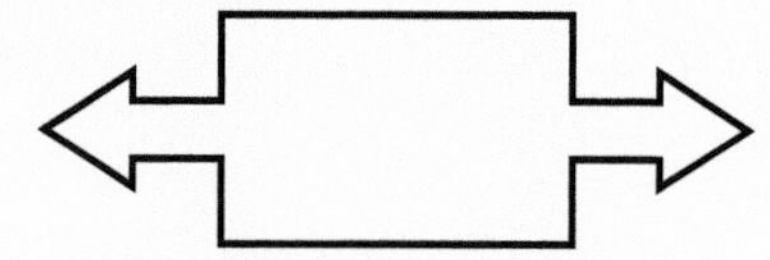

Challenge yourself

1. What is the sum of the mirror lines of the three shapes shown below?

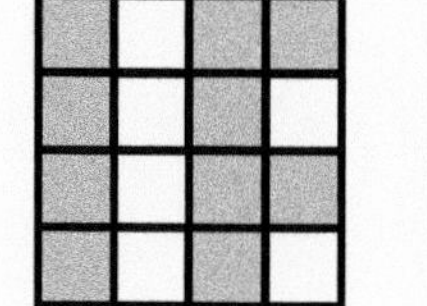
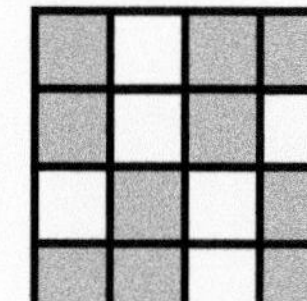
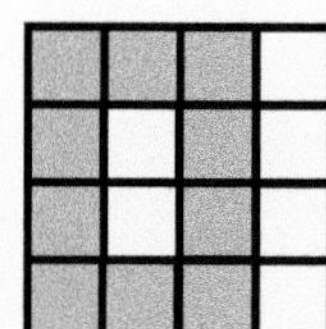

mixed number (mixed fraction)

A number comprised of a *whole number* and a *fraction*.

e.g. $2\ ^1/_3$ and $3\ ^1/_2$ are mixed numbers.

Test yourself

1. Which of the following options, A to E, are mixed numbers?

A	B	C	D	E
$^1/_5$	$^2/_4$	$^5/_8$	$5\ ^3/_2$	$7\ ^2/_7$

Challenge yourself

1. What is $^{11}/_5 + ^9/_7$ expressed as a mixed number?

2. What is $3\ {}^{1}/_{5} + 7\ {}^{2}/_{7}$ expressed as a mixed number?

3. What is ${}^{13}/_{2} - {}^{3}/_{8}$ expressed as a mixed number?

mixed operation

Mathematical calculations which involve more than one type of *operation*.

Note: It must obey *BIDMAS*.

e.g.

(7 - 2) × 3 + 3
= (5) × 3 + 3 — First, solve the bracket.
= 15 + 3 — Second, multiply 5 and 3.
= 18 — Finally, add 15 and 3.

Test yourself

1. Using BIDMAS, calculate 5 + 7 + 6 × 2.

2. Using BIDMAS, calculate 3 + 6 ÷ 2 - 1.

Challenge yourself

1. Using BIDMAS, calculate $(5 + 3^2) + (8 \div 2^2)$.

2. Calculate $2 \times (5 - 2)^3 - 6 \div 2$.

3. What is $1^9 \times 2 \div 3 \times 4 + 5 - 6 + 7 - 8$?

modal group

In a grouped *frequency distribution table*, the modal group is the group with the largest *frequency*.

e.g.

No. of goals	0 - 5	6 - 10	11 - 15	16 +
No. of players	17	12	11	2

The modal group of the number of goals scored is 0 - 5.

Test yourself

1. According to the table in the example above, how many players scored the modal number of goals?

Challenge yourself

Answer the following questions using the table below.

Classes	A - B	C - D	E - F
No. of students	5	11	19

1. Identify the classes with the modal number of students.

2. How many students are in the modal group?

mode

The most frequently occurring *datum* in a *dataset*. See also *average*, *bimodal*.

Note: A dataset may have no mode.

e.g. In the dataset {1, 1, 2, 2, 1}, the mode is 1.

Test yourself

1. What is the mode of the following set of numbers: 1, 1, 2, 2, 3, 3, 3?

2. What is the mode of the following set of numbers: 2, 5, 6, 5, 2, 4, 5?

Challenge yourself

1. What is the mode of the following set of numbers?

5, 8, 7, 5, 5, 7, 7, 9, 5

2. What is the mode of the following set of numbers?

87, 89, 86, 83, 82, 81, 80, 86

month

A *unit* of time which employs the lunar concept; the approximate amount of time taken for the moon to orbit the Earth.

e.g. One month is one of the twelve divisions of the calendar year.

Test yourself

1. How many months are there in a year?

2. How many months are there in 2 years?

3. What is the name given to the 5th month of the year?

Challenge yourself

1. How many months are in $4\ {}^{8}/_{12}$ years?

2. What is 114 months expressed in years?

3. Which month is 6 months before October?

A B C D E F G H I J K L M N O P Q R S T U V W X Y Z

A B C D E F G H I J K L M N O P Q R S T U V W X Y Z

multiple

When a number is added to itself a number of times. See also *lowest common multiple*.
e.g. The first four multiples of 9 are: 9, 18, 27 and 36.

Test yourself

1. What are the first four multiples of 3?

2. What is the fifth multiple of 4?

Challenge yourself

1. What is the ninth multiple of 13?

2. What are the first three multiples of 19?

3. How many multiples of 6 are there before 70?

multiplication

The mathematical *operation* in which a number is added to itself a certain number of times. It has the symbol '×'.
e.g. $6 \times 3 = 6 + 6 + 6 = 18$.

Test yourself

1. Calculate 3×4.

2. Calculate 5×6.

Challenge yourself

1. Calculate $8 \times 9 \times 11$.

2. What is 91×123?

3. Calculate the seventh prime number multiplied by the fourth square number.

4. What is 154×0.3?

multiply out

Expanding the brackets of a mathematical *expression* through *multiplication*. See antonym *factorise*.
e.g. $7(a + b) = 7a + 7b$.

Test yourself

1. Multiply out $2(a + b)$.

2. What is $3(2a + 2)$?

3. Multiply out $5(2a + 7b)$.

4. Multiply out $10(-7a - b)$.

Challenge yourself

1. What is $15(7 + 8)$?

2. Multiply out $8(2a + 11b)$.

3. Multiply out $-2(-5a + 2b)$.

4. Multiply out $-8(-10a - 6b)$.

mutually exclusive events

Two or more *events* that cannot occur at the same time. See also *probability, Venn diagram*.
e.g. An outcome of a single coin toss can result in either heads or tails, but not both as these are mutually exclusive events.

Test yourself

Do the following statements describe mutually exclusive events?

1. Obtaining a positive number and a two when a die is rolled once.

2. Obtaining an even number and a six when a die is rolled once.

3. Obtaining a square number and a three when a die is rolled once.

4. Obtaining a prime number and a five when a die is rolled once.

Challenge yourself

1. What is the probability of picking a King from a deck of cards? Express your answer as a fraction.

2. When two dice are rolled, is obtaining a number less than four on each die and a total of more than nine mutually exclusive?

3. What is the probability of picking a King or a Jack from a deck of cards? Express your answer as a fraction.

4. What is the probability of two mutually exclusive events occurring at the same time?

natural number

A positive *integer*.

e.g. 1, 2, 3, 4,... are natural numbers.

Test yourself

1. Write the first ten natural numbers.
2. What is the twentieth natural number?
3. Is -50 a natural number?

Challenge yourself

1. Which of the following are natural numbers?

-3 2.5 π 5 -4.2 7 6.5

2. Which of the following are natural numbers?

$^5/_2$ 3π 7^2 $^{15}/_3$ $^{-10}/_2$

negative number

A *value* which is less than *zero*.

e.g. -1, $-^1/_2$, -0.7, -π,... are negative numbers.

Test yourself

1. Write the first five negative whole numbers.
2. What is the seventh negative whole number?
3. Is zero a negative number?

Challenge yourself

1. Which of the following are negative numbers?

-(3.1) $^5/_{-3}$ $-(^{-7}/_3)$ $^{-3}/_{-2}$ -0.57

2. Calculate $-3 \times {}^{-18}/_3$.
3. What is -8 + 7 - (-5)?
4. What is -6 × -7 + 5?

net

A *plane* (flat) *figure* that can be folded to form a *three-dimensional* shape.

e.g.

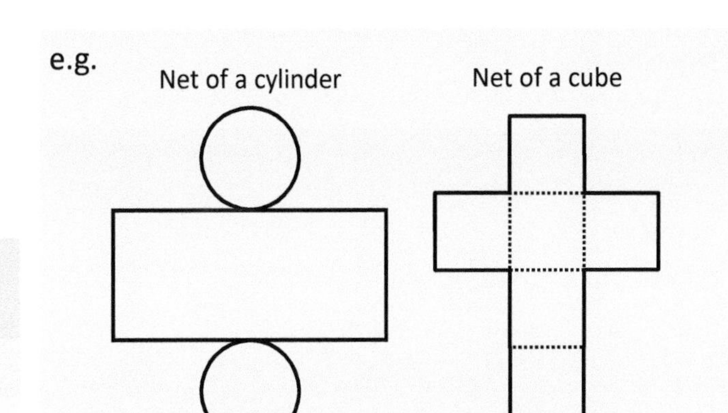

Test yourself

1. Look at the net of a 3D shape below. What is the name of the 3D shape?

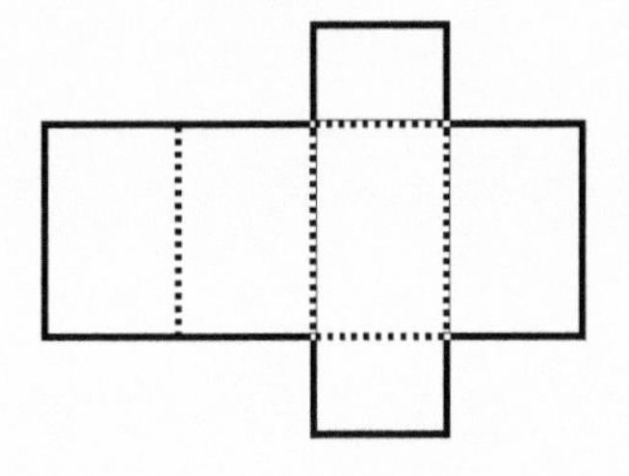

2. What shape does this net correspond to?

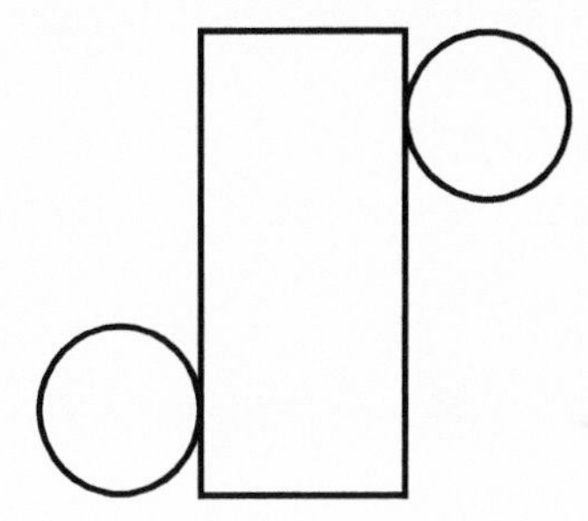

Challenge yourself

1. Add 3 straight lines to the shape below to form a net of a square-based pyramid.

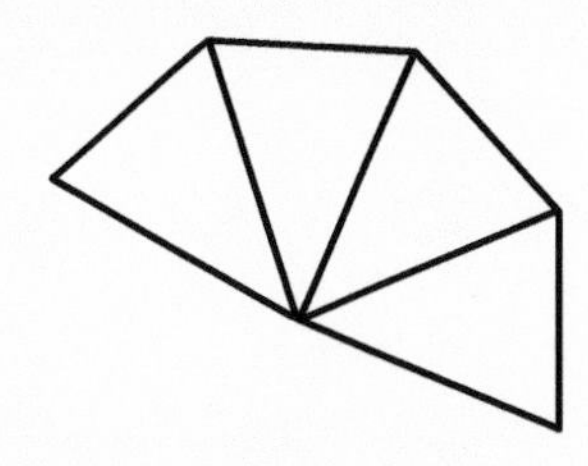

2. Draw the net of a tetrahedron.
3. Add 5 lines to the shape below to form a net of a hexagonal prism.

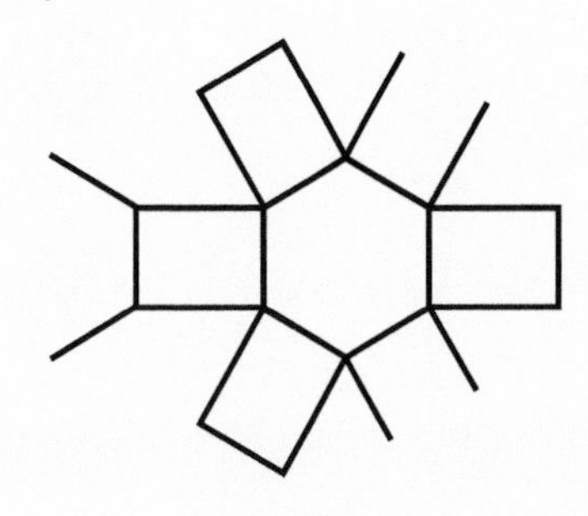

A B C D E F G H I J K L M N O P Q R S T U V W X Y Z

A B C D E F G H I J K L M N O P Q R S T U V W X Y Z

no chance

See *impossible*.

***

nonagon

A nine-sided *polygon*.

e.g.

Regular nonagon:
All 9 interior angles are 140°.
All 9 sides are of equal length.
The sum of the interior angles is 1260°.

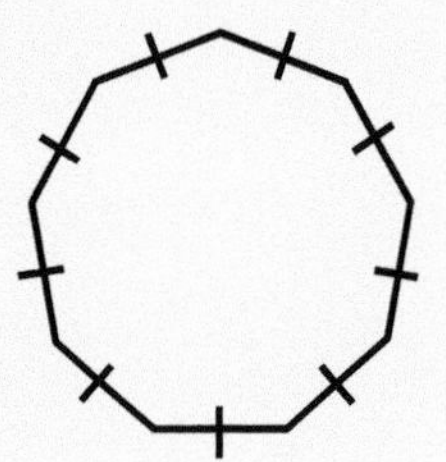

Test yourself

1. How many pairs of parallel sides does a regular nonagon have?

2. Is this a regular or an irregular nonagon?

Challenge yourself

1. How many slices of pizza could be made from the shape below given that the slices are triangular and each cut is made from one of the vertices to the centre?

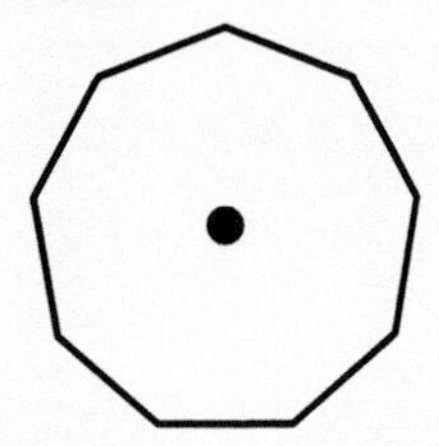

2. What is the perimeter of a nonagon with each side measuring 6.5cm?

3. What is the area of a regular nonagon with an apothem of 5mm and a side of 3.5mm?

4. What is the sum of the number of lines of symmetry and the order of rotational symmetry of a regular nonagon?

noon

See *midday*.

***

north

The *direction* corresponding to a compass point which is 90° *anticlockwise* of *east* or 180° anticlockwise (or *clockwise*) of *south*.

Note: The *bearing* is always measured from a north-pointing line in the clockwise direction.

e.g.

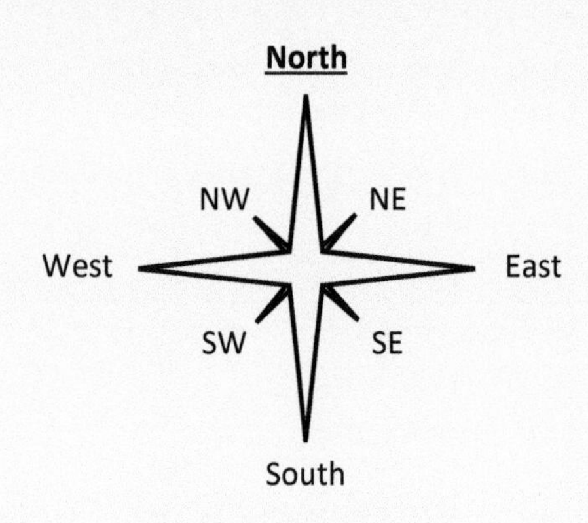

Test yourself

1. Which direction corresponds to a compass point which is 90° clockwise of west?

Challenge yourself

1. Niki is facing north, and she turns 585° clockwise. Which direction is she facing now?

2. How many right angles are there in a turn from north to west in the clockwise direction?

3. If Jeet is 550 metres south of Jane and Jane is 200 metres north of Sam, how far north of Jeet is Sam?

*n*th term

The general form of a number *sequence* expressed in terms of n.

Note: The first *term* is calculated by substituting n = 1 into the general form, the second by substituting n = 2 and so on.

e.g. The *n*th term of the sequence 5, 7, 9, 11, 13,... is 2n + 3.

Test yourself

1. Find the *n*th term of the following sequence.
1, 3, 5, 7, 9,...

2. Find the *n*th term of the following sequence.
0.5, 1, 1.5, 2,...

3. Find the *n*th term of the following sequence.
2, 4, 6, 8, 10,...

Challenge yourself

1. Is the *n*th term of the sequence 11, 15, 19, 23,... $4n + 7$?

2. Find the *n*th term of the following sequence.
3, 6, 9, 12, 15, 18,...

3. What is the *n*th term of the following sequence.
17, 13, 9, 5, 1, -3, -7,...

number line

A line with numbers marked at *intervals* in *order*.

e.g. The probability line.

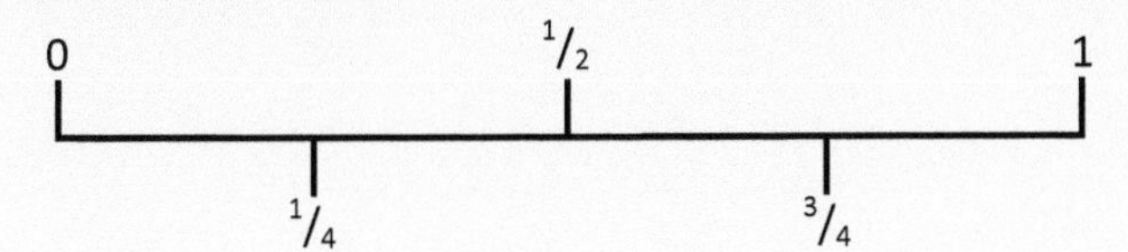

Test yourself

1. Identify the two numbers that are missing from the number line below.

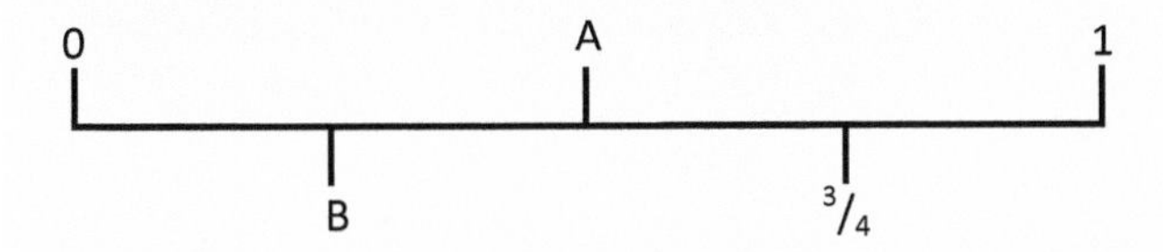

2. Identify the two numbers that are missing from the number line below.

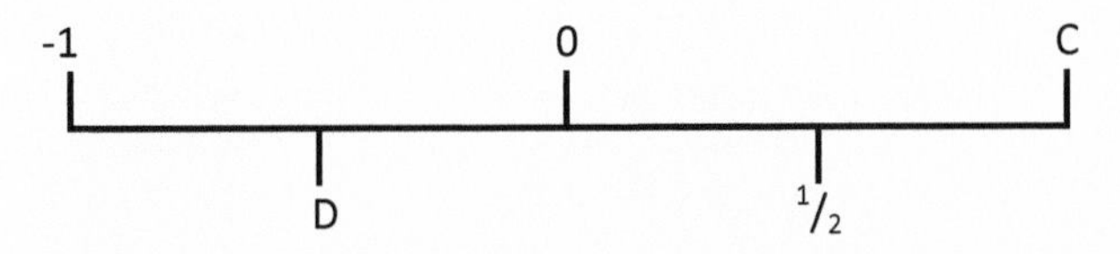

Challenge yourself

Answer the following questions using the number line below.

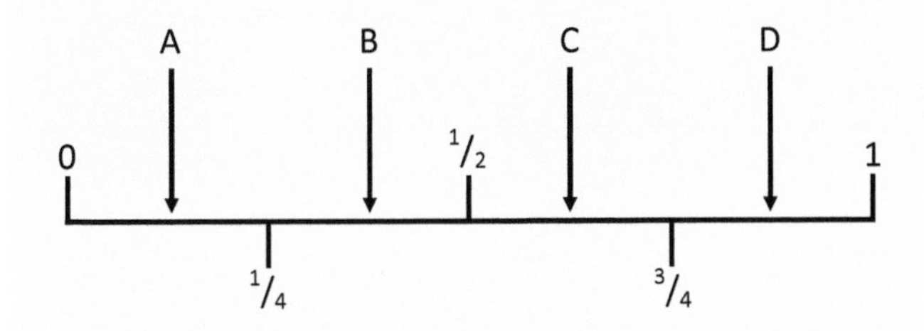

1. Which of the arrows A, B, C or D shows the best position for the probability of choosing the letter A from the word AUSCULTATION?

2. Which of the arrows A, B, C or D shows the best position for the probability of choosing the letter O from the word OBNOXIOUS?

number machine

A mathematical calculation involving diagrams which takes an *input* (number) and applies sets of *operations* to create an *output* (number).

e.g.

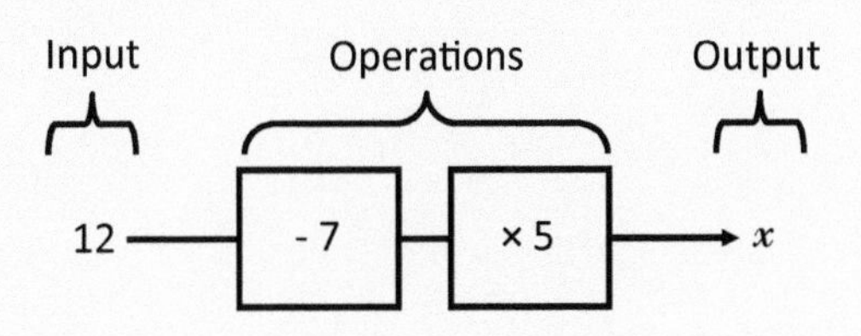

Test yourself

1. Calculate the value of x in the number machine above.

2. A number machine multiplies a given number by 6 then subtracts 15. What is the input if the output is 27?

Challenge yourself

1. What is the missing operation required for the number machine below to work?

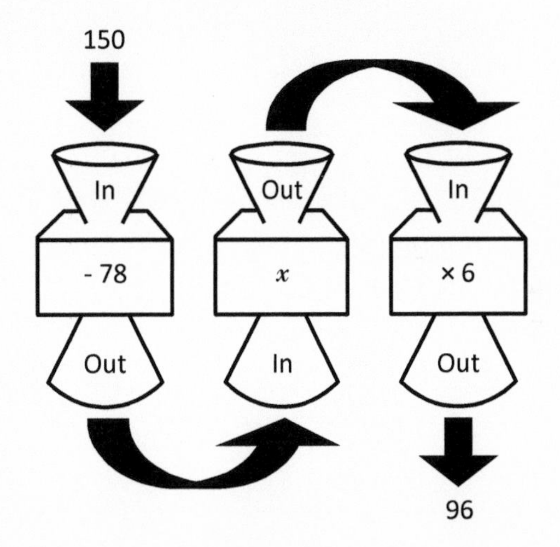

2. Calculate the input of the number machine below if the final output y is 31.

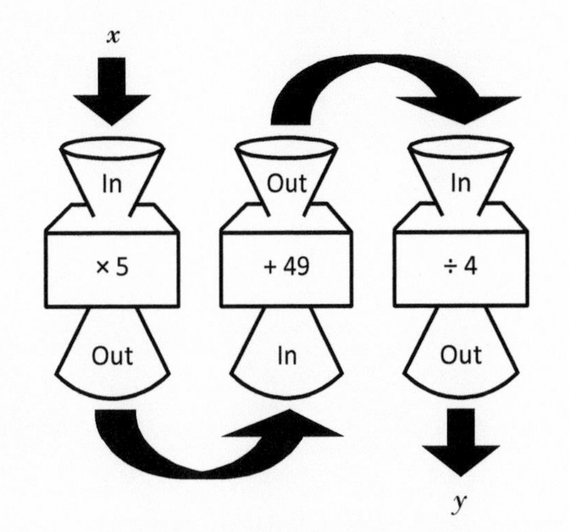

A B C D E F G H I J K L M N O P Q R S T U V W X Y Z

numerator

The number that is found on the top half of a *fraction*.
e.g. The numerator of the fraction $^5/_9$ is 5.

Test yourself

1. What is the numerator of $^2/_{11}$?

2. What is the numerator of $^5/_{91}$?

3. Look at the equation below. Calculate the missing numerator of the fraction on the right-hand side.

$$^5/_{15} = {}^x/_3$$

4. Look at the equation below. Calculate the missing numerator of the fraction on the right-hand side.

$$^{10}/_{40} = {}^x/_4$$

Challenge yourself

1. Look at the equation below. Calculate the missing numerator of the fraction on the right-hand side.

$$^{552}/_{400} = {}^x/_{50}$$

2. Look at the equation below. Calculate the missing numerator of the fraction on the right-hand side.

$$^{488}/_{888} = {}^x/_{111}$$

3. Simplify and state the numerator of the fraction $^{78}/_{14}$.

4. Look at the sum below. Simplify and state the numerator of the sum $^{12}/_{13} + {}^7/_{15}$.

O

oblong

See *rectangle*.

***

obtuse angle

An *angle* between 90° and 180°.
e.g.

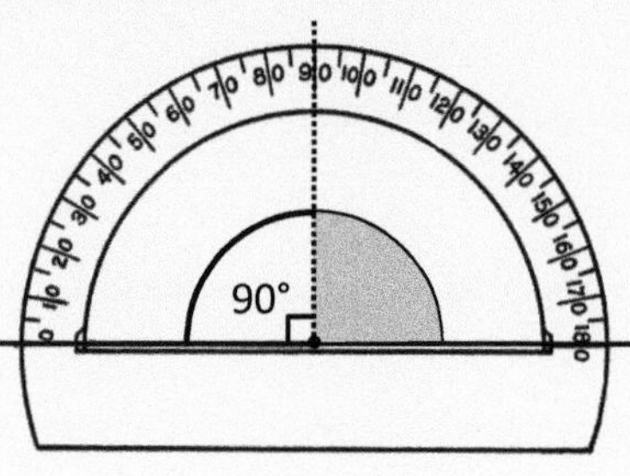

Angles that lie within the shaded region are obtuse angles.
A right angle (90°) and 180° are not obtuse angles.

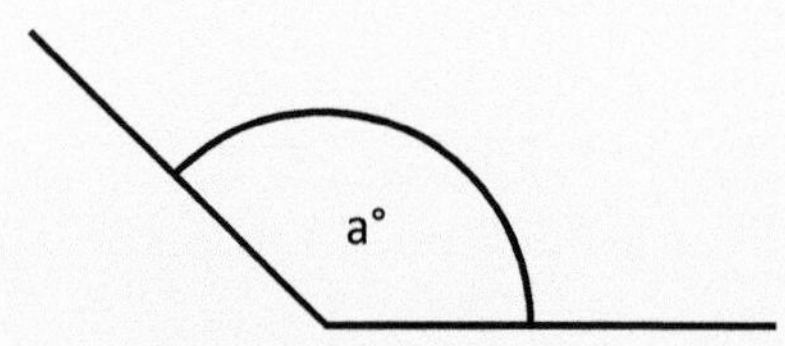

Angle a° is greater than 90° and less than 180°.
Therefore, a° is an obtuse angle.

Test yourself

1. Which of these angles is an obtuse angle?

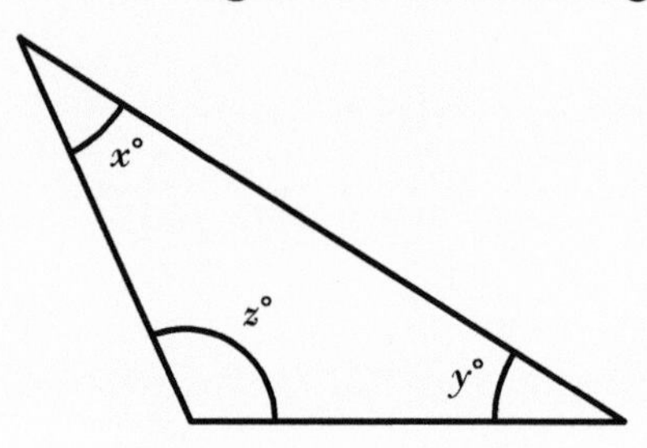

2. Which of these angles are obtuse?

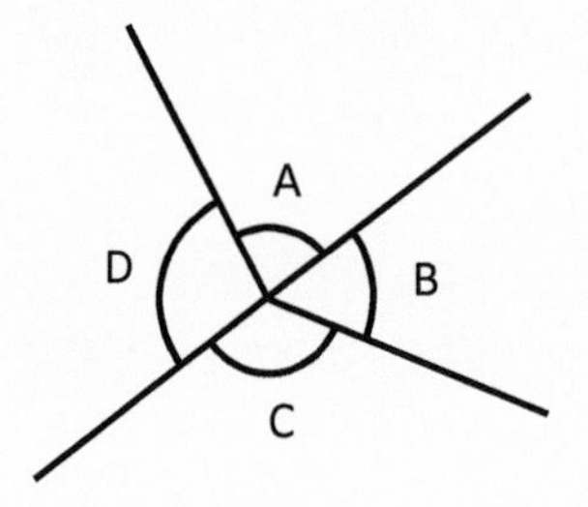

3. Which of the following is an obtuse angle?

a. 5° + 7° - 9° b. 23° × 3 c. 180° - 73°

Challenge yourself

1. Which of these is an obtuse angle?

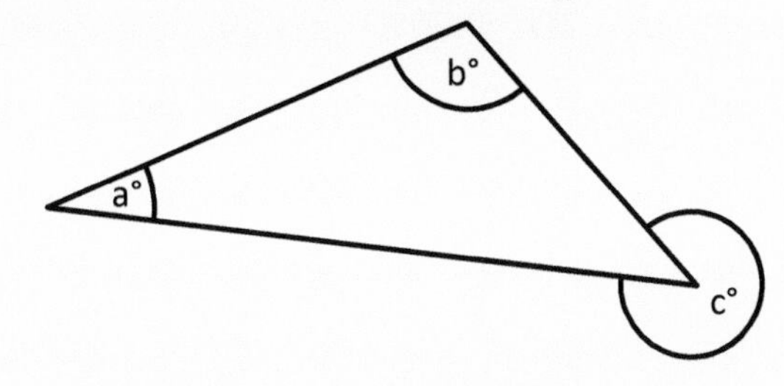

2. If the sum of angles a° and b° in the triangle above is 128°, what is the size of angle c°?

3. Angle x° is equal to the sum of 8.8°, 151.2° and 7.2°. Is x° an obtuse angle?

4. There is a boat at sea. The bearing of the boat from a lighthouse is initially 165° and the bearing increases by 8° every hour. Is the bearing of the boat from the lighthouse obtuse after $2\,^{1}/_{4}$ hours?

obtuse-angled triangle

A *triangle* with one *interior angle* that is between 90° and 180°. See also *obtuse angle*.
Note: Both *isosceles* and *scalene triangles* can be obtuse-angled triangles.

e.g.

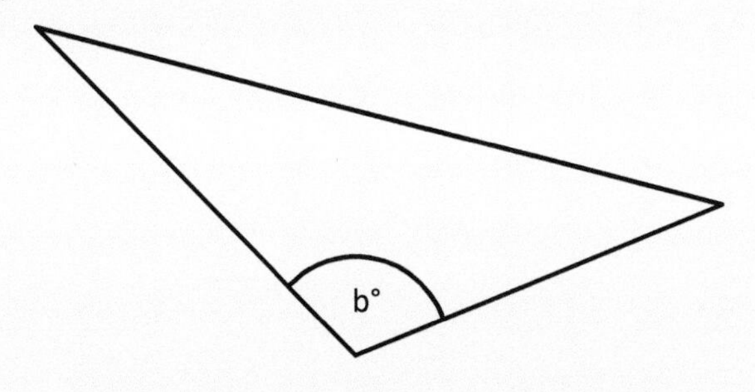

Angle b° is greater than 90° but less than 180°. Therefore, angle b° is an obtuse angle, making this an obtuse-angled triangle.

Test yourself

1. Which of these is an obtuse-angled triangle?

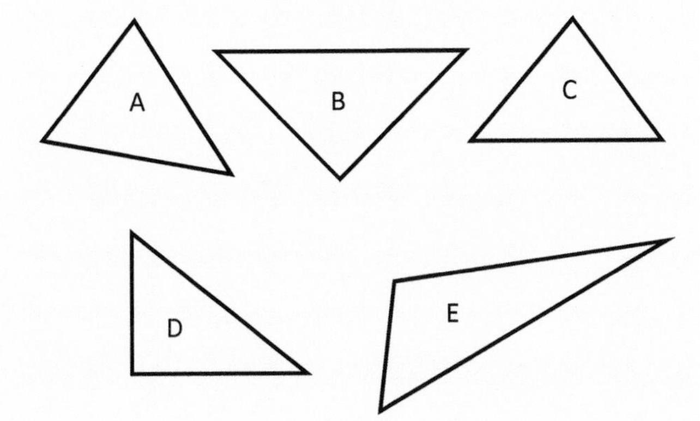

Challenge yourself

1. Which of the following statements is true?

a. There will always be an obtuse angle in a triangle that has two acute angles.
b. The maximum size of an obtuse angle is 270°.
c. If two angles in a triangle are less than 45°, the remaining angle is an obtuse angle.
d. The minimum size of an obtuse angle is 90°.

2. If two interior angles of a triangle are 34° and 55°, is this an obtuse-angled triangle?

3. Can an isosceles triangle also be an obtuse-angled triangle?

octagon

An eight-sided *polygon*.

e.g.

Regular Octagon:
All 8 angles are equal.
All 8 sides are of equal length.
The sum of the interior angles is 1080°.

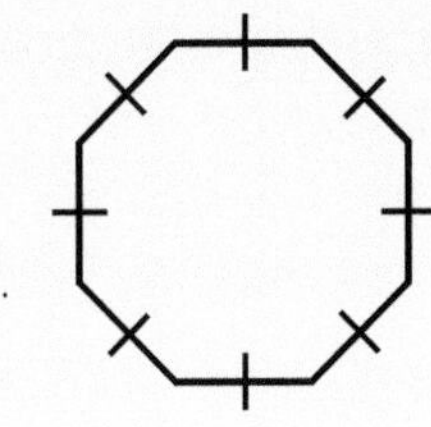

Test yourself

1. How many pairs of parallel sides does a regular octagon have?

2. Is the shape below an octagon?

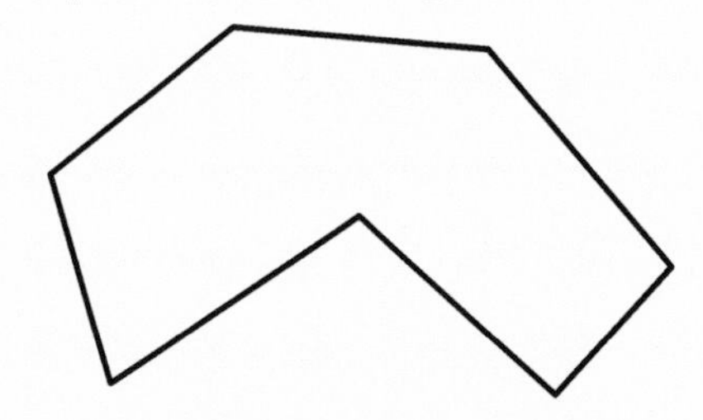

Challenge yourself

1. What is the perimeter of a regular octagon with a side length of 5.5cm?

2. What is the area of a regular octagon with a side of 7mm and an apothem of 8mm?

3. By only connecting lines from the vertices, what is the maximum number of triangles that can be made from drawing 4 lines inside a regular octagon?

A
B
C
D
E
F
G
H
I
J
K
L
M
N
O
P
Q
R
S
T
U
V
W
X
Y
Z

octahedron

A *three-dimensional* shape that is made up of eight triangular *faces*.

e.g.

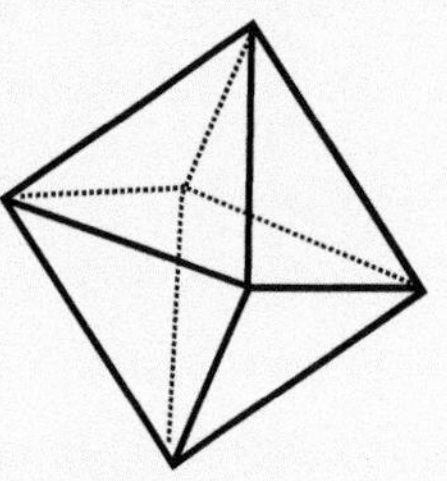

Test yourself

1. What is the name given to the faces of an octahedron?

2. What is the sum of the number of faces, edges and vertices of an octahedron?

Challenge yourself

1. Two identical square pyramids are used to make an octahedron. If the volume of the octahedron is $592mm^3$, what is the volume of one of the square pyramids?

2. If the surface area of a regular octahedron is $48m^2$, what is the area of one of the triangular faces?

odd number

Any *integer* that is not perfectly *divisible* by 2, i.e. numbers that are not *even numbers*.

e.g. 1, 3, 5, 7,...

Test yourself

1. Which of the following numbers is an odd number?

8, 72, 99, 64, 14

2. What is the sum of the seventh and eleventh odd numbers?

Challenge yourself

1. How many of the following numbers are odd?

34, 143, 435, 25, 5, 6, 876

2. Which odd number immediately follows after the number 199?

3. Are all odd numbers prime numbers?

4. There is an even number of cars in a car park at 9.00am. Every two hours the number of cars in the car park increases by an odd amount. Is there an even or odd amount of cars at 3.00pm?

operation

A mathematical process such as *addition*, *subtraction*, *multiplication* and *division*. See also *BIDMAS*.

e.g. +, -, ×, ÷

Test yourself

1. What is the operation replaced by '?' in the following calculation?
44 ? 15 = 59.

2. What is the inverse operation of subtraction?

3. What is the inverse operation of division?

Challenge yourself

1. A number machine has an output of -140 and an operation of '× -8'. What is the input?

2. Using BIDMAS, calculate (5 + 8) - (5 × -3).

3. (50 + 24) - (21 'a' 7) + (7 × 8) = 127. What is the operation 'a' in this calculation?

order

Arranging numbers in a particular way, depending on their *value*. See also *ascending order*, *descending order*.

e.g. A list of values can be put in an ascending order (from smallest to largest) or a descending order (from largest to smallest).

Test yourself

1. Order the following numbers from largest to smallest.

10, 5, 9, 11, 2, 1

2. Order the following numbers from smallest to largest.

3, 19, 12, 55, 25

3. Order the following numbers from smallest to largest.

0, 10, -11, 3, 5, 0.22

Challenge yourself

1. Put the following numbers in ascending order.
45, 23, -45, -1, 0, 23

2. Put the following numbers in descending order.
2.60, 5.10, 5.09, 6.20, 3.99

3. Put the following fractions in ascending order.
$^{5}/_{7}$, $^{8}/_{9}$, $^{2}/_{45}$, $^{1}/_{2}$

4. Put the following percentages in descending order.
1%, -40%, 50%, 0.22%, -0.2%

order of operations

See *BIDMAS*.

***

order of rotational symmetry

The number of times a shape can fit exactly onto itself when rotated about the *centre of rotational symmetry*.

Note: All shapes have a rotational *symmetry* order of at least one. Also, it is common to refer to a shape with a rotational symmetry order of one as having no rotational symmetry.

e.g.

Note: The black dot on the quad arrow is a reference point and is not part of the shape.

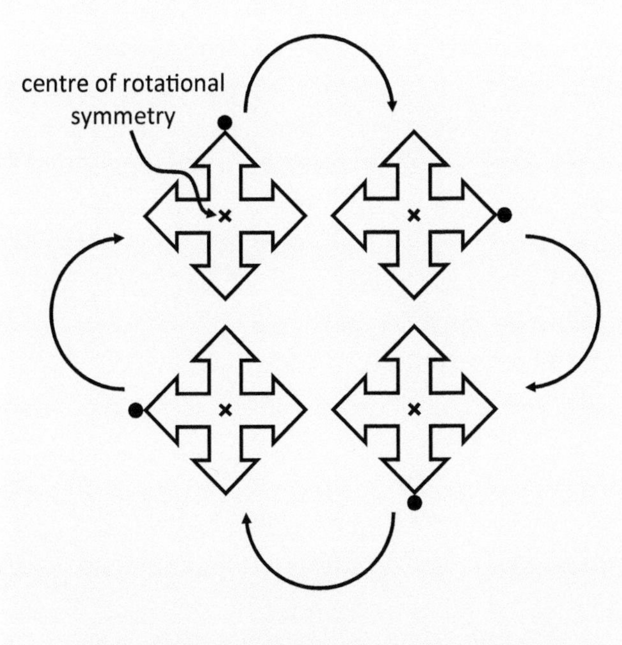

The order of rotational symmetry of the quad arrow is 4. This is because it can be rotated about the centre of rotational symmetry to fit exactly onto itself four times.

Test yourself

1. What is the order of rotational symmetry of the rectangle below?

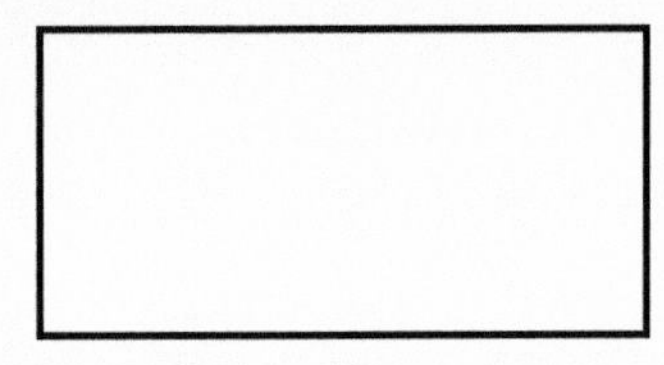

2. What is the order of rotational symmetry of the shape below?

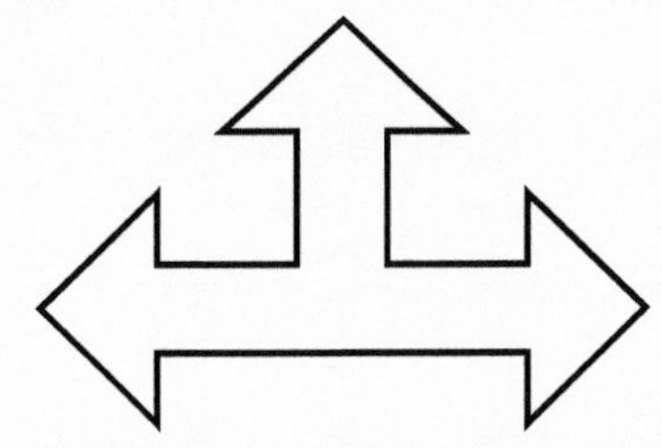

Challenge yourself

1. What is the order of rotational symmetry of a regular hexagon?

2. What is the order of rotational symmetry of the shape below?

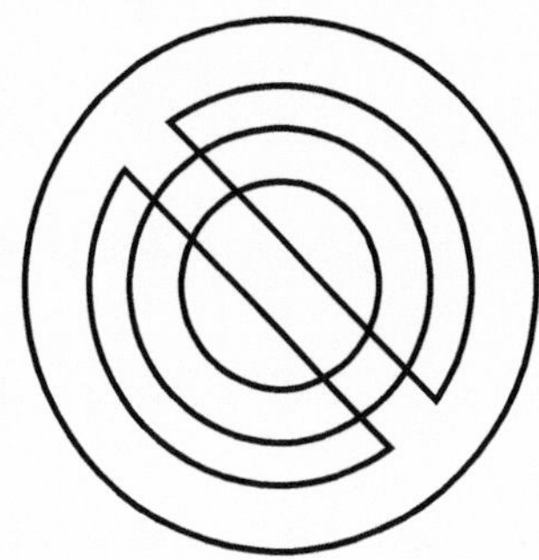

3. Which of the shapes below has the highest order of rotational symmetry?

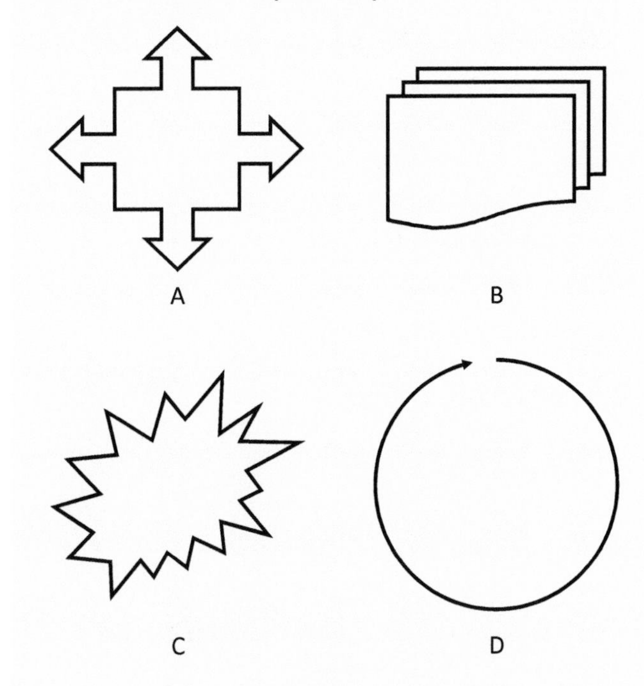

A B C D E F G H I J K L M N O P Q R S T U V W X Y Z

A B C D E F G H I J K L M N O P Q R S T U V W X Y Z

ordinal number

A number which refers to a position.
e.g. 1st, 2nd, 3rd, and 4th are ordinal numbers.

Test yourself

1. What is the fourth multiple of 3?

2. What is the sixth multiple of 2?

3. What is the ninth multiple of 9?

Challenge yourself

1. What is the fifth triangular number?

2. What is the twentieth square number?

3. What is the seventh cube number?

4. What is the seventh prime number?

origin

The point on a graph where the *x-axis* and the *y-axis* intersect (cross). It is always represented by the coordinates (0, 0). See also *intersection*.
e.g.

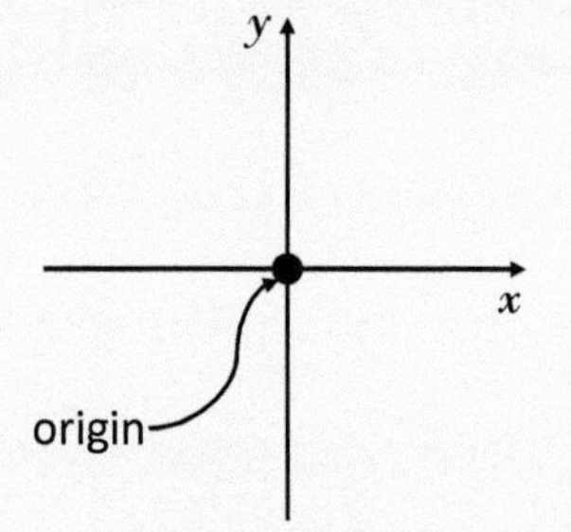

Test yourself

1. What are the coordinates of the origin?

2. Jenar is standing at the origin and moves 5 units to the left and 3 units down. What are the coordinates of his new position?

Challenge yourself

1. One of the vertices of a triangle lies at the point (5, 4). The triangle is rotated 180° about the origin. What are the new coordinates of the vertex?

2. The centre of a rectangle lies on the origin. The rectangle is translated 6 units left and 9 units up. What are the new coordinates of the centre of the rectangle?

ounce (oz)

An *imperial unit* of *mass equivalent* to $^{1}/_{16}{}^{th}$ of a *pound* (lb).
e.g. 16oz is equivalent to 1lb.

Test yourself

1. How many ounces are there in 2 pounds?

2. How many pounds are there in 8 ounces?

Challenge yourself

1. Convert 72oz into pounds.

2. Convert 7.5lbs into ounces.

3. Assuming that 1 ounce is equal to 28 grams, how many grams are there in 153 ounces?

outcome

The result of an *event*.
e.g. An outcome of a tossed coin is tails.

Test yourself

1. List all the possible outcomes of tossing a coin.

2. List all the possible outcomes of rolling a six-sided die once.

Challenge yourself

1. What is the probability of the outcome being two heads when a fair coin is tossed twice?

2. Prasha rolls two four-sided dice and adds the results. What is the probability of the outcome being 3?

3. What is the probability of the sum of the outcomes being greater than 9 when two six-sided dice are rolled?

output

The final result after *operations* have been applied to an *input* (number).
e.g.

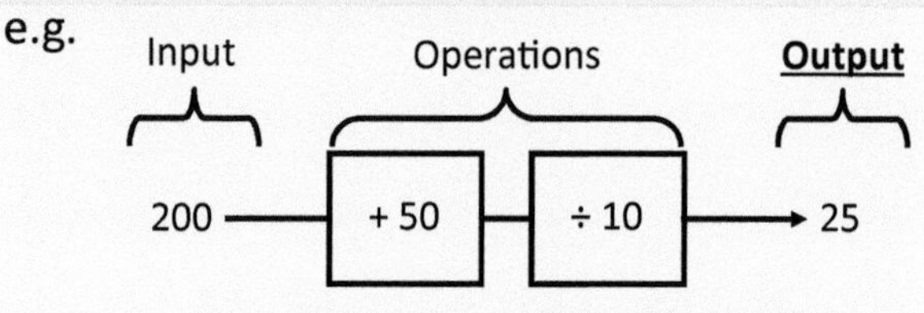

The output of the number machine is 25.

Test yourself

1. Identify the output of the following number machine.

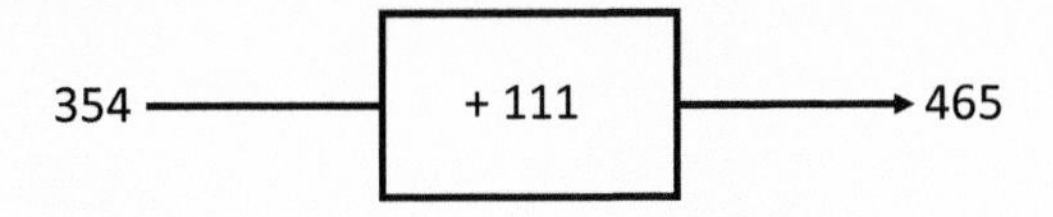

2. What is the output of the following number machine?

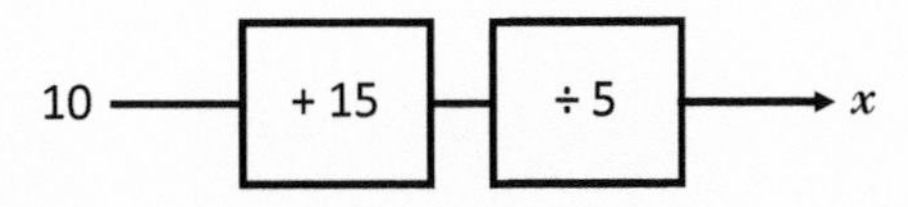

Challenge yourself

1. A number machine has an input of 43 and an operation of '× 1.5'. What is the output?

2. What is the output of the following number machine?

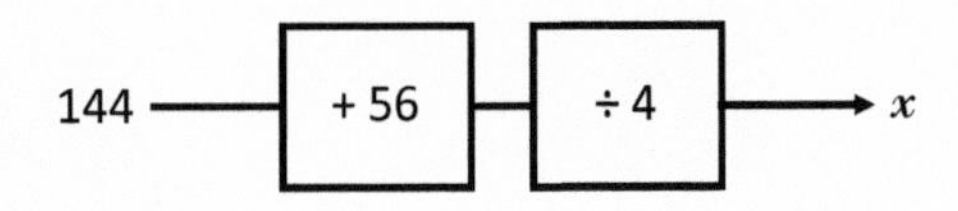

oval (ellipse)

A *plane* (flat) *figure* shaped like an elongated or 'stretched' *circle*.

e.g.

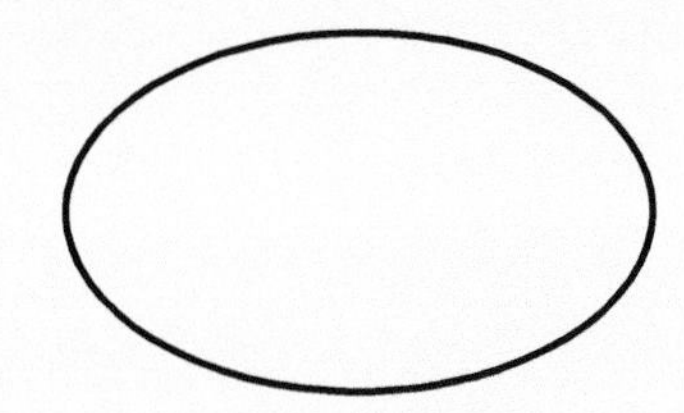

Test yourself

1. Which of the following shapes is an oval?

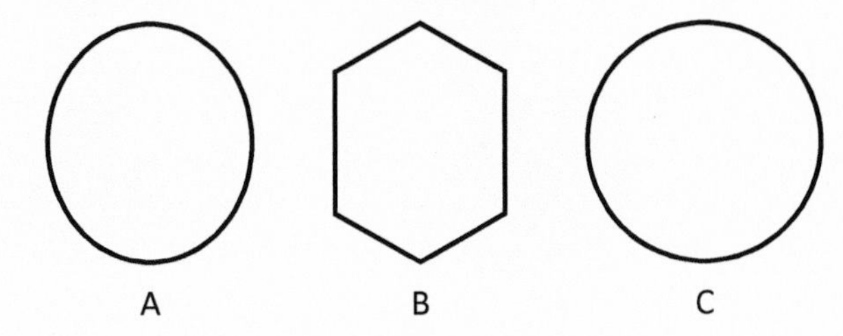

Challenge yourself

1. How many lines of symmetry does an oval have?

2. What is the order of rotational symmetry of an oval?

palindrome

A word or number that reads the same backwards and forwards.

e.g. 2112.

Test yourself

1. Which of these numbers is a palindrome?

10, 65, 102, 55, 42

2. In order to form a palindromic number, what digit is missing from the following number?

12565_1

Challenge yourself

1. In order to form a palindromic number, what digits are missing from the following number?

375_4648_7_

2. What is the product of the palindromes 2442 and 22?

parallel

Describing lines, curves or *surfaces* that are always *equidistant* and will never cross (intersect). See also *perpendicular*.

Note: Lines that are parallel to each other are marked with '>' or '>>'.

e.g.

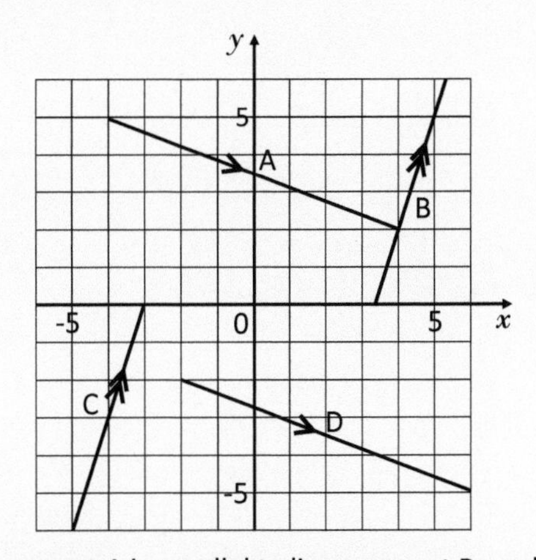

Line segment A is parallel to line segment D, and line segment C is parallel to line segment B.

Test yourself

1. On the graph above, draw a line that is parallel to line segment B and goes through the origin.

A B C D E F G H I J K L M N O P Q R S T U V W X Y Z

A B C D E F G H I J K L M N O P Q R S T U V W X Y Z

2. How many pairs of parallel sides does the parallelogram below have?

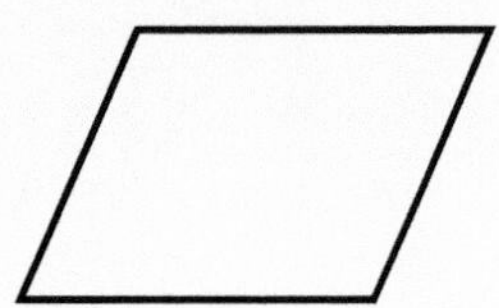

3. How many pairs of parallel sides does the hexagon below have?

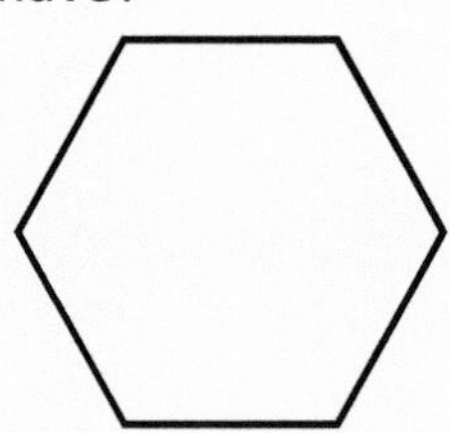

Challenge yourself

1. Line x is parallel to line y, line z is perpendicular to line s and line s is perpendicular to line y. Which two lines are parallel to line x.

2. Which of the following statements are true?
a. The gradients of two parallel lines are equal.
b. Parallel lines must be equal in length.
c. Two parallel lines never intersect each other.

3. Specify the direction and the amount of turn about point C line BC has to make in order to become parallel to line AE.

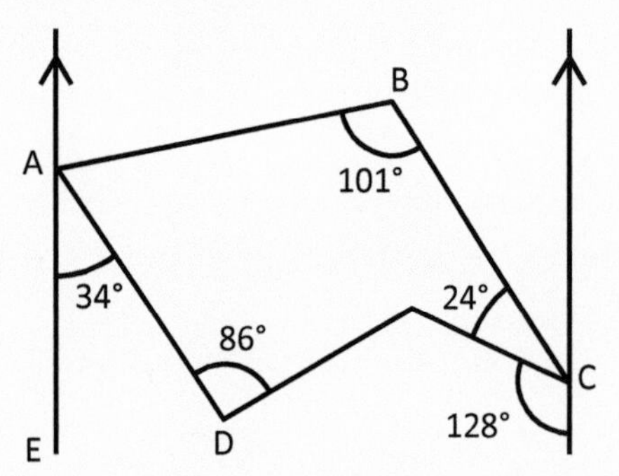

parallelogram

A four-sided shape (*quadrilateral*) with two pairs of *equal* and *parallel sides*, and with equal opposite *angles*. A standard parallelogram has no *lines of symmetry*; however, *squares*, *rectangles* and *rhombuses* are special types of parallelogram.
e.g.

Parallelogram:
Opposite interior angles are equal.
Opposite sides are parallel.
The diagonals bisect each other.
Opposite sides are of equal lengths.

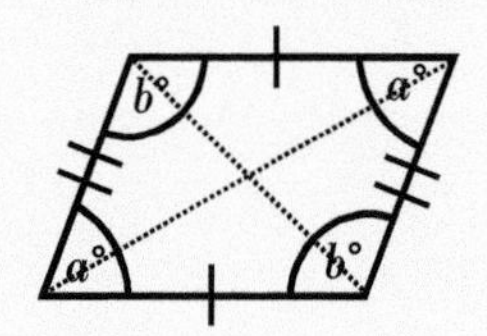

Test yourself

1. Which one of these shapes is not a parallelogram?

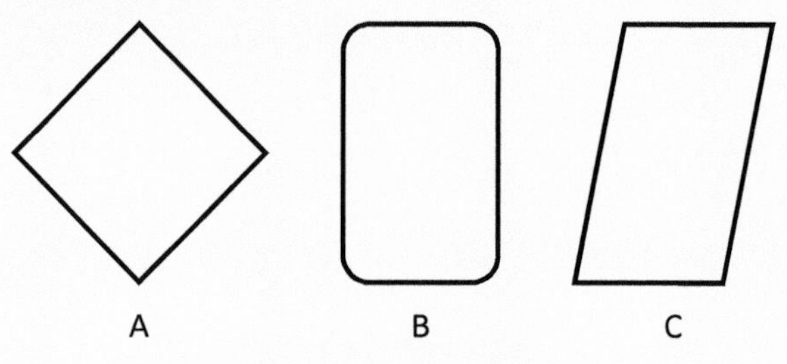

Challenge yourself

1. If one of the interior angles in a parallelogram is 54°, how many lines of symmetry does it have?

2. If the top and bottom sides of a parallelogram each measure 4.5cm, and they are 60mm apart, what is its area? Give your answer in cm^2.

3. What is the size of angle x°?

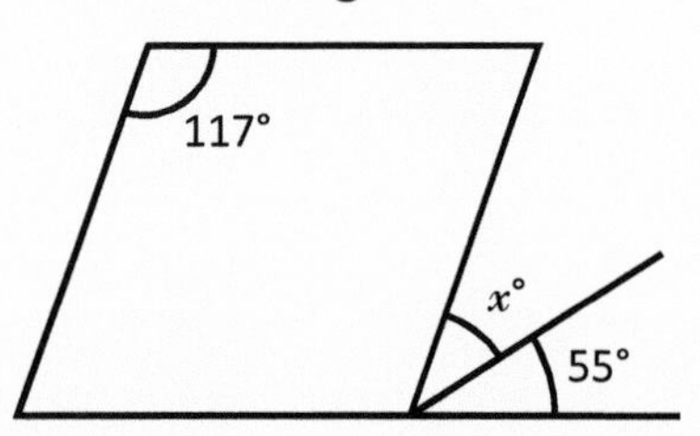

Pascal's triangle

Numbers that are arranged in a triangular formation and follow a specific rule.
Rule: Each number is calculated by adding together the two numbers that are just above it.
e.g.

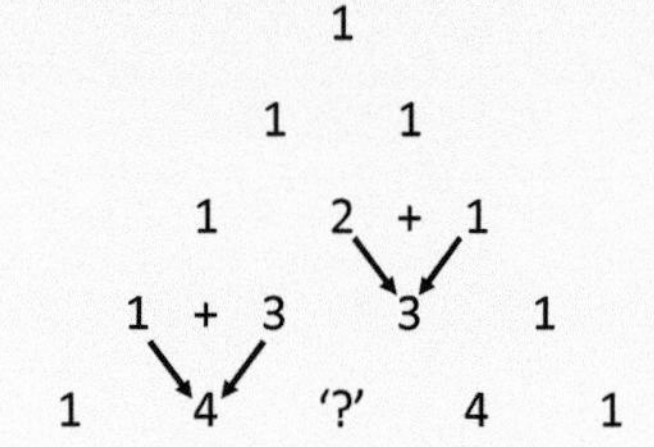

Test yourself

1. Calculate the missing number, '?', in Pascal's triangle shown in the example above.

Challenge yourself

1. Using the rule of Pascal's triangle, calculate the missing numbers in the diagram below.

55 55
55 A 55
55 B C 55

pentagon

A five-sided *polygon*.

e.g.

Regular Pentagon:
All 5 angles are equal.
All 5 sides are of equal length.
The sum of the interior angles is 540°.

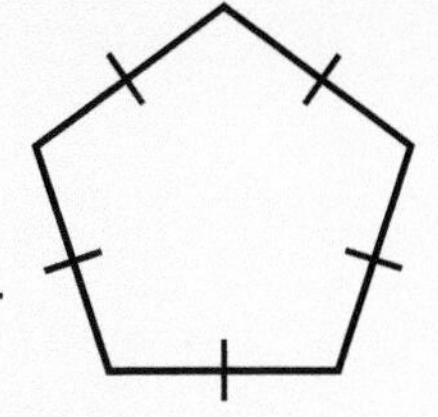

Test yourself

1. How many sides does a pentagon have?

2. Can the following shape be described as a pentagon?

Challenge yourself

1. What is the sum of the interior angles of a pentagon?

2. What is the sum of the exterior angles of a pentagon?

3. The perpendicular height from the base to the centre of a regular pentagon is 7cm. If the perimeter is 35cm, what is its area?

per cent

A single part of a quantity that has been divided into one hundred *equal* parts, i.e. one part in every hundred. It is denoted using the symbol '%'.

Note: 1 per cent can always be calculated by dividing a given number by 100.

e.g. 10 per cent of 120 is $^{10}/_{100} \times 120 = 12$.

Test yourself

1. What is 10 per cent of 100?

2. What is 5 per cent of 20?

Challenge yourself

1. What is 80 per cent of 250?

2. What is 2.5% of 50?

3. What is 19% of 160?

percentage (%)

A way of expressing a *fraction*, *decimal* or proportion in relation to a *whole*.

Note: A percentage can be expressed as a decimal or a fraction. It is denoted using the symbol '%'.

e.g. $^{1}/_{2}$ as a percentage is $^{1}/_{2} \times 100 = 50\%$.

Test yourself

1. Express $^{9}/_{10}$ as a percentage.

2. Express $^{1}/_{25}$ as a percentage.

Challenge yourself

1. Express $5\ ^{8}/_{11}$ as a percentage correct to one decimal place.

2. There are 45 black balls in a bag along with 15 blue balls. What is the percentage of black balls in the bag?

3. Songyo and Seung go on a holiday to Eastbourne from London. The cost of the rail ticket for the return journey is £32 but they get a student discount of 22%. How much money do they save because of the discount?

percentage change

The amount by which a *value* has either been increased or decreased, expressed as a *percentage* of the original value.

Note: A negative result indicates a percentage *decrease*, while a positive result indicates a percentage *increase*.

Percentage change = $^{\text{new value - old value}}/_{\text{old value}} \times 100$

e.g. If the population of pigeons in South Harrow was 100 in 2014, and the population increased by a further 20 in 2015, the percentage increase is $^{(120 - 100)}/_{100} \times 100 = 20\%$.

Test yourself

1. There is 250ml of tea in a mug and Nita drinks 50ml of it. What is the percentage change of tea in the mug?

2. It took Neha 10 minutes to eat a sandwich for lunch on Monday. If she takes 12 minutes to eat the same sandwich for lunch on Tuesday, what is the percentage change in the time it takes her to eat the sandwich?

Challenge yourself

1. The adult bus fare in 2000 was £0.80. In 2013, it had increased to £2.20. Calculate the percentage change in the bus fare.

2. On a particular day in Harrow the temperature at 9.00am was 10.0°C. The temperature had increased by 6.0°C by 2.00pm. What is the percentage change in temperature?

perimeter

The total *distance* around the *edge* of a *two-dimensional* shape.

e.g.

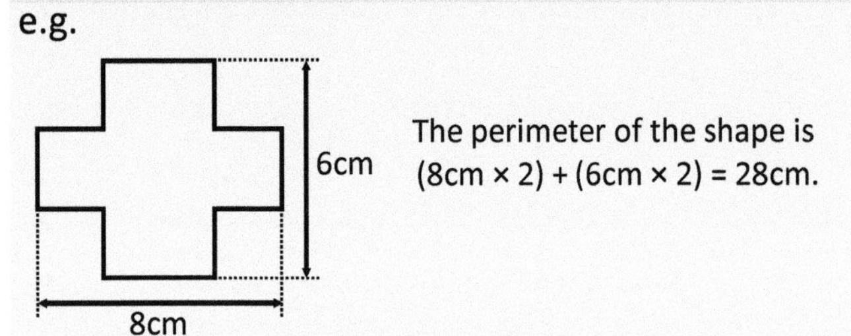

The perimeter of the shape is (8cm × 2) + (6cm × 2) = 28cm.

Test yourself

1. What is the perimeter of the shape below?

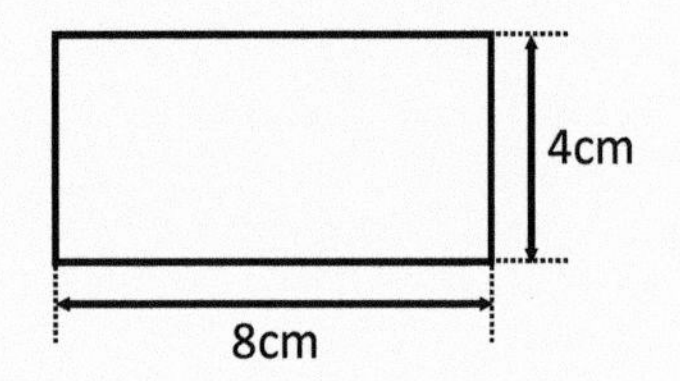

2. What is the perimeter of the shape below?

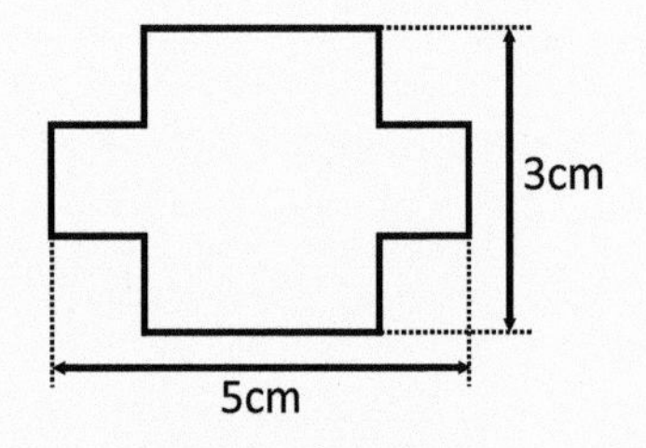

Challenge yourself

1. A circle fits inside a square with a common centre such that the circumference touches the edges of the square. The radius of the circle is 15cm. What is the perimeter of the square?

2. What is the perimeter of the shape below?

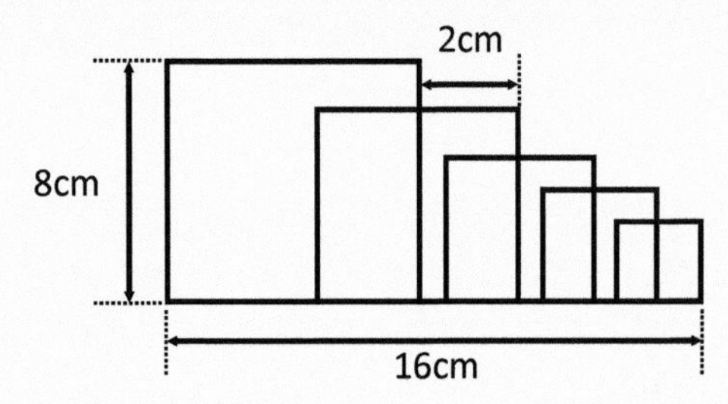

3. If a cuboid has a volume of 300cm^3 and a length of 12cm, what is the combined perimeter of the two squares at the ends of the cuboid?

perpendicular

Describing lines or *surfaces* that are at *right angles* (90°) to one another. See also *parallel*.

e.g.

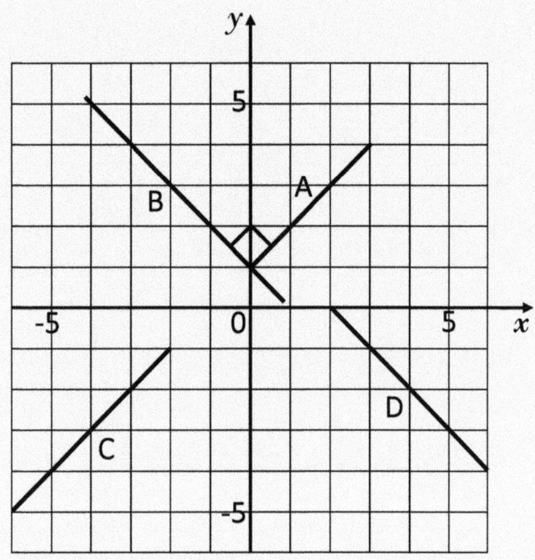

Line segment A is perpendicular to line segment B, and line segment C is perpendicular to line segment D.

Test yourself

1. If two lines are perpendicular to each other, what is the angle between them?

2. Draw a line that is perpendicular to the line shown below.

Challenge yourself

1. On the graph in the example above, draw a line segment that is perpendicular to line segment D and passes through the point (3, -2).

2. Which of the following statements is true?

a. The gradients of two perpendicular lines are equal.

b. Perpendicular lines must be equal in length.

c. The angle between two perpendicular lines is always 90°.

3. Line E is perpendicular to line G, line F is perpendicular to line H, and line H is perpendicular to line G. Which two lines are perpendicular to line E?

perpendicular bisector

A line *segment* that is both *perpendicular* to another line and passes through its *midpoint*.

e.g.

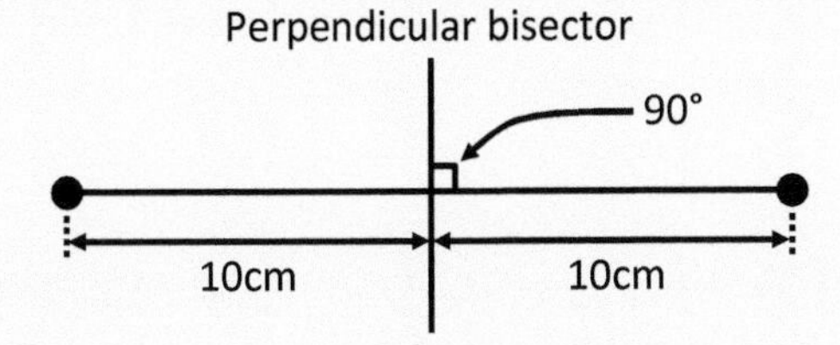

Test yourself

1. Mark the midpoint and draw the perpendicular bisector of each of the lines below.

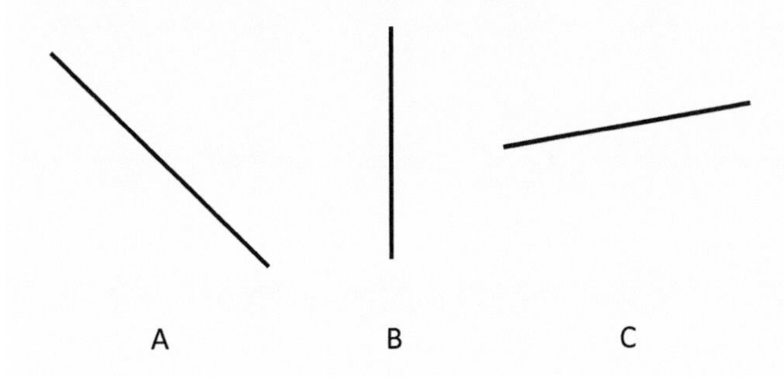

Challenge yourself

1. A 99cm line is divided by a perpendicular bisector. What is the ratio between the lengths that lie to the left and right of the bisector?

pi

An *irrational number* that is *equal* to the *ratio* between the *circumference* of a *circle* and its *diameter*. It has the symbol 'π'.

e.g. Pi is approximately equal to 3.14 or $^{22}/_{7}$.

Test yourself

1. What does pi represent?

2. What is pi correct to 2 decimal places?

Challenge yourself

1. Using the definition of pi and denoting the circumference and radius of a circle as C and R respectively, write an expression for pi.

2. Calculate the circumference of a circle with a radius of 0.5cm. Give your answer in terms of π.

3. Calculate the area of a circle with a radius of 12mm. Give your answer in terms of π.

pictogram

A chart that uses pictures or symbols to represent *frequency*.

e.g. The pictogram below shows the number of footballs in three different gardens.

Garden	No. of footballs
A	
B	
C	

represents 4 footballs

There are 4 + 4 + 1 = 9 footballs in garden A.

Test yourself

Answer the following questions using the pictogram in the example above.

1. How many footballs are in garden B?

2. How many footballs are in garden C?

3. What is the sum of all the footballs in all three gardens?

4. What is the mean number of footballs in each garden?

Challenge yourself

Answer the following questions using the pictogram below.

A pictogram showing the favourite foods of children in a school

Fruit	Frequency
Apple	
Orange	
Banana	

represents 12 children

1. How many students favour oranges?

2. How many more students favour apples and bananas to oranges?

3. What is the total number of children in the school?

pie chart

This is a circular chart that is divided into *sectors* where the relative sizes of the sectors represent numerical *values*.

e.g.

Pie chart illustrating the proportion of bananas to apples in a large container.

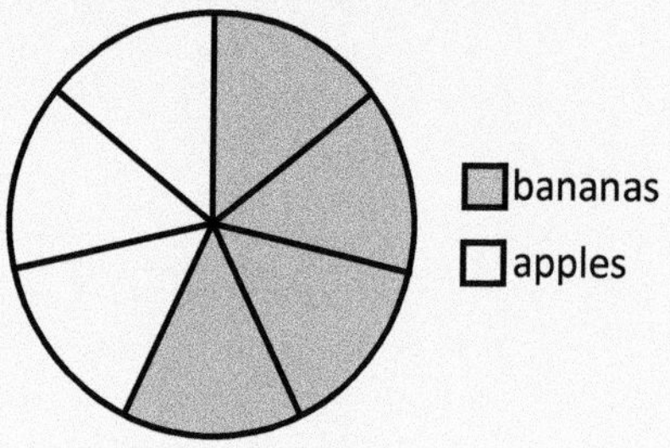

<u>Test yourself</u>

1. According to the pie chart in the example above, are there more bananas than apples?

<u>Challenge yourself</u>

Answer the following questions using the pie chart in the example above.

1. What is the ratio of the number of bananas to apples?

2. Express the amount of apples as a fraction of the total number of fruits.

3. If there were 133 fruits in total, how many apples are there?

pint (pt)

An *imperial unit* of *volume* equal to 20 ounces.

e.g. 8 pints is equivalent to a gallon (160 ounces).

<u>Test yourself</u>

1. How many gallons are there in 16 pints?

2. How many pints are there in 3 gallons?

<u>Challenge yourself</u>

1. How many pints are there in 6.5 gallons?

2. How many gallons are there in 76 pints?

placeholder

See *zero*.

***

place value

The numerical *value* that a *digit* has due to its position within a number. See also *zero*.

e.g. In the number 5431.9, the place value of 5 is 5000.

<u>Test yourself</u>

1. What is the digit in the tens column in the number 52?

2. What is the value of the digit in the hundreds column in the number 805?

<u>Challenge yourself</u>

1. What is the digit in the thousands column in the number 559,623?

2. What is the value of the digit in the hundredths column in the number 541.596?

3. What is the value of the digit in the tens column in the product of 52 and 67?

plan

A *two-dimensional* drawing of an object as viewed from above.

e.g.

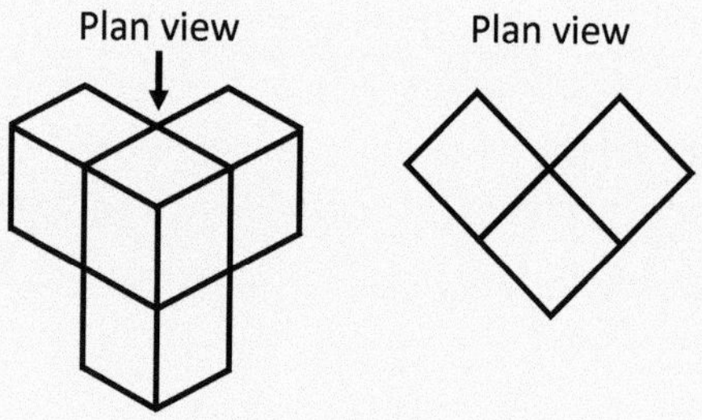

<u>Test yourself</u>

1. Draw a plan of a cube.

2. Draw the plan of the shape below.

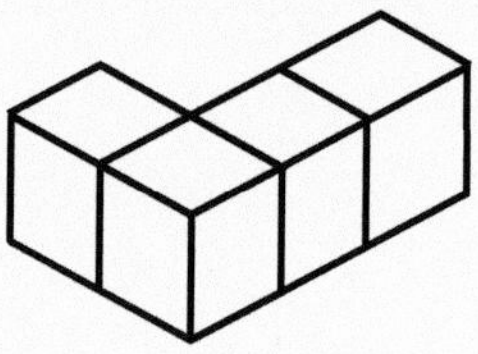

<u>Challenge yourself</u>

1. Draw the plans of the shapes below.

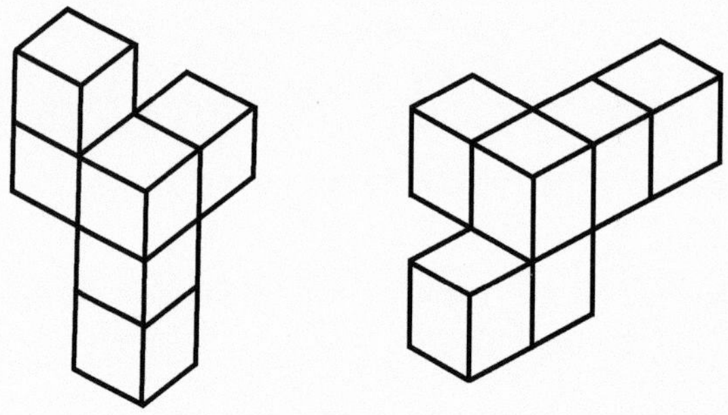

A B

plane figure

A *two-dimensional* shape with a *length* and a *width*, but no depth.

e.g.

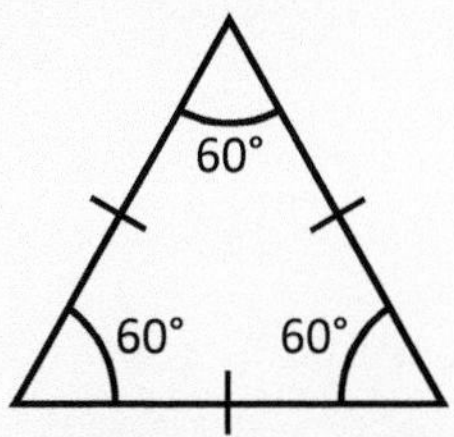

Equilateral Triangle:
All 3 angles are equal (60°).
All 3 sides are of equal length.

Isosceles Triangle:
2 angles are equal.
2 sides are of equal length.

Test yourself

1. Draw a plane figure that has four equal sides.

2. What is the name given to the plane figure below?

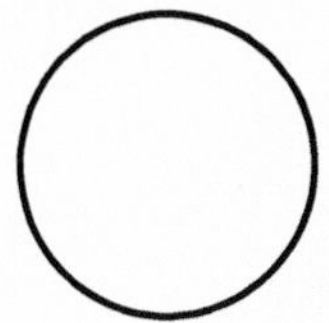

Challenge yourself

1. Draw a plane figure with two pairs of equal sides and a pair of opposite angles that are equal in size.

2. Name the plane figure that has one pair of parallel sides which are different in length.

plus

See synonym *addition*.

***

PM (p.m.)

The abbreviation for 'post meridiem' meaning 'after *midday*', and it refers to the period from midday until just before *midnight*.

e.g. 15:20 is equivalent to 3.20pm.

Test yourself

1. Express 3.00pm in 24-hour clock format.

2. Express 16:00 in 12-hour clock format.

Challenge yourself

1. Express 19:59 in 12-hour clock format.

2. Express 6.35pm in 24-hour clock format.

3. Nikhil left his house for work at 11.23am and travelled for an hour and forty-seven minutes. At what time did he get to his workplace? Give your answer in 12-hour clock format.

polygon

A *two-dimensional* shape that has three or more straight *sides*.

Note: All sides of any *regular* polygon are of *equal length*. See also *regular*.

e.g.

Regular Octagon:
All 8 angles are equal.
All 8 sides are of equal length.
The sum of the interior angles is 1080°.

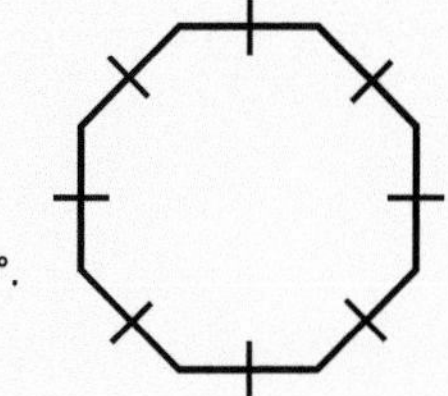

Test yourself

1. What is the name of a polygon with 5 sides?

2. Can the following shape be described as a regular polygon?

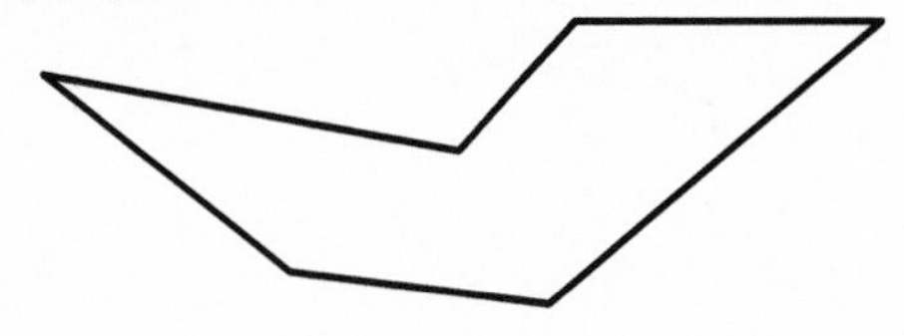

3. What is the general name given to a four-sided polygon?

Challenge yourself

1. How many sides does a hexagon have?

2. What is the name of a polygon with 9 sides?

3. Write a formula for the area of a regular polygon using AP and P to denote its apothem and perimeter respectively.

polyhedron (plural: polyhedra)

A *three-dimensional* shape with polygonal *faces*. See also *Euler's polyhedral formula*, *regular*.

e.g.

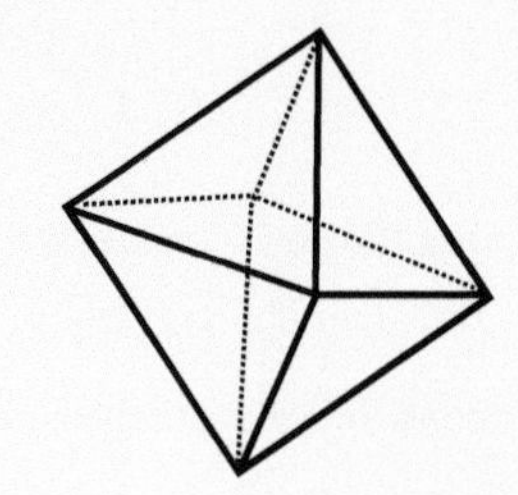

Octahedron:
It has 8 faces.
It has 6 vertices.
It has 12 edges.

A B C D E F G H I J K L M N O P Q R S T U V W X Y Z

Test yourself

1. What is the name of a polyhedron which has 4 triangular faces?

2. How many faces does an octahedron have?

3. How many edges does a tetrahedron have?

Challenge yourself

1. What is the sum of the numbers of vertices, edges and faces of an octahedron?

2. What is the name of the polyhedron with 6 faces, 8 vertices and 12 edges of equal length?

population

The number of inhabitants of a particular *area*.

Note: A population is usually defined at a certain time.

e.g. The population of South Korea in 2014 was approximately 50 million.

Test yourself

1. The population of foxes in Northolt in 2010 was 250, and by the end of 2013 the population had decreased by 73. What was the population of foxes at the end of 2013?

2. The population of snakes in Pinner in 2013 was 40, and by the end of 2014 the population had increased by 6. What was the population of snakes at the end of 2014?

Challenge yourself

1. Harrow's population had increased by 0.5% between 2013 and 2014. If the population in 2014 was 201,000, what was the population at the end of 2013?

2. In 2014, residents that were of working age in Harrow made up 65% of the total population. If the total population of Harrow was 243,000, how many people were at working age in 2014?

positive number

A number that is *greater than zero*.

Note: The *plus* symbol, '+', is usually omitted when writing positive numbers.

e.g. $^1/_8$, 0.2, 3, π,... are positive numbers.

Test yourself

1. Is '6' a positive number?

2. Which of the following numbers are positive?

A	B	C	D
2	-0.7	$^1/_5$	-10

Challenge yourself

1. Which of the following numbers are positive?

A	B	C	D	E	F
5	0.7	0	$^{21}/_{11}$	-0.2	-(-7)

2. Using the fact that the product of two negative numbers is a positive number, calculate

$$(-18 \div 2) - 5 \times -15 + 7.$$

possible

An *event* that is capable of occurring.

e.g. Picking a King from a deck of cards is possible.

Test yourself

1. Which of the following events are possible?

a. A fair die landing on an odd number.

b. The temperature in London reaching 800°C.

c. Picking a Queen from a deck of cards.

d. Rolling a 7 on a six-sided die numbered 1 to 6.

Challenge yourself

1. Which of the following statements are false?

a. Possible events have a probability of greater than 0.5.

b. Possible events have a probability of zero.

c. Possible events must have a probability that is greater than zero.

d. Possible events have a negative probability.

pound (£ or lb)

i. The *unit* of money *equivalent* to 100 pence, used in Great Britain and Northern Ireland. It has the symbol '£'.

e.g. 450p is equivalent to £4.50.

ii. A unit of *mass equivalent* to 16 *ounces* and approximately *equal* to 450 *grams*. It has the symbol 'lb'.

e.g. 7lbs is approximately 3kg.

Test yourself

1. What is 600 pence expressed in pounds?

2. How many pence are in £8.50?

3. What is 32 ounces expressed in pounds?

4. How many ounces are in 5 pounds?

Challenge yourself

1. Kate has forty 50p coins. She buys four chocolate bars that cost £0.80 each. How much change does she have in total after the purchase?

2. In a box there are twenty 5p coins, seventeen 2p coins and nine 20p coins. What is the value of the coins in the box to the nearest pound?

3. A keyboard weighs 98 pounds. Assuming that 7 pounds is approximately equal to 3kg, how much does the piano weigh in kilograms?

4. In a warehouse there are 4450 bottles of lotion. If each bottle weighs 4 ounces, how much do all the bottles in the warehouse weigh in pounds?

power (index/exponent)

A mathematical notation indicating how many times a number is used in a *multiplication*.

e.g. $5^2 = 5 \times 5 = 25$.

Test yourself

1. Evaluate 2^4.

2. Evaluate 5^3.

3. What is $5^3 + 6^3$?

Challenge yourself

1. Calculate $1^1 + 2^2 + 3^3 + 4^4$.

2. Calculate $0^1 + 5^2 + 10^3$.

3. What is the square root of 4^4?

prime factor

A *factor* that is also a *prime number*.

e.g. 8 expressed as a product of its prime factors is $2 \times 2 \times 2 = 2^3$.

Test yourself

1. List the prime factors of 10.

2. Express 12 as a product of its prime factors.

Challenge yourself

1. Express 52 as a product of its prime factors.

2. What is the median of the prime factors of 30?

3. What is the mean of the prime factors of 64?

prime number

A number whose only *factors* are 1 and itself.

Note: 1 is not a prime number.

e.g. 2, 3, 5, 7, 11,...

Test yourself

1. What is the sixth prime number?

2. Which of the following are prime numbers?

A	B	C	D	E
2	67	9	27	47

Challenge yourself

1. How many prime numbers are there between 1 and 20?

2. Which two prime numbers between 1 and 20 have a product of 143?

prism

A *three-dimensional figure* with two *parallel*, *identical* polygonal *faces* that are joined by *rectangles*, i.e. a *solid* with a *uniform cross-section*.

e.g.

Triangular Prism:
It has 5 faces.
It has 6 vertices.
It has 9 edges.

Test yourself

1. How many vertices does a cuboid have?

2. How many edges does a cylinder have?

A B C D E F G H I J K L M N O P Q R S T U V W X Y Z

3. What is the sum of the numbers of vertices and faces of a triangular prism?

4. What is the name given to the cross-section of a triangular prism?

Challenge yourself

1. What is name given to the cross-section of a hexagonal prism?

2. In addition to two parallel hexagonal bases, how many rectangles are needed to construct a hexagonal prism?

probability (chance/likelihood)

A measure of how *likely* it is for an *event* to occur. The probability of *event* 'A' happening is given by:

P(A) = number of ways it can happen / total number of outcomes

Note: The probability of an event is always between 0 and 1, and it can be expressed as a *fraction*, *percentage* or *decimal*.

e.g. The probability of a die landing on an even number is $^1/_2$.

Test yourself

1. When tossing a coin, there are two possible outcomes: heads or tails. Using the formula given in the definition above, calculate the probability of getting a head when a fair coin is tossed.

2. If the probability of randomly finding a £5 note on the pavement is 0.1, what is the probability of not finding a £5 note?

Challenge yourself

1. If a fair coin is tossed three consecutive times, what is the probability of the coin landing on tails three times?

2. If a fair coin is tossed three times consecutively, what is the probability that the coin does not land on tails three times?

3. Two fair dice are thrown and the values are added together. What is the probability of rolling a total of 5?

4. Two fair dice are thrown. What is the probability of throwing a total of 5 or 6?

probability scale

A *scale* that goes from *zero* to one, measuring the *likelihood* of an *outcome*.

e.g.

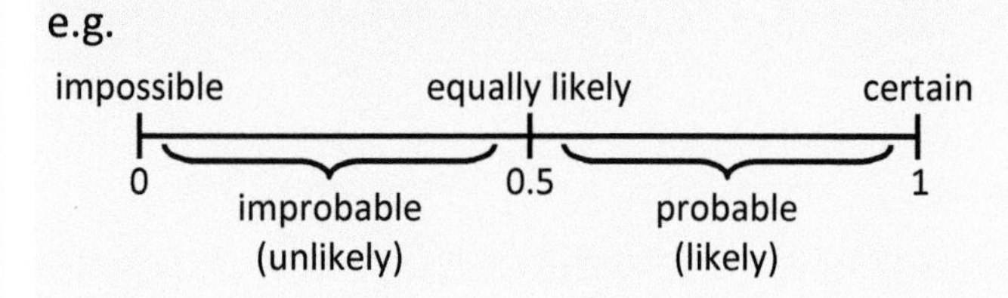

Test yourself

Answer the following questions using the probability scale below.

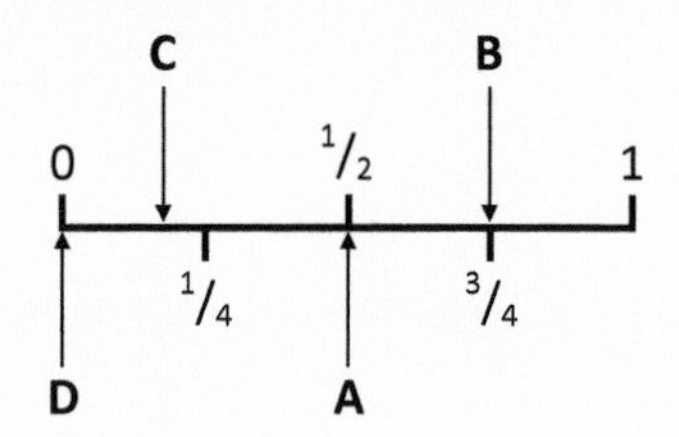

1. Which of the arrows represents the probability of 0.75?

2. Which of the arrows indicates the best position on the probability line for an event that is impossible.

Challenge yourself

Answer the following questions using the probability scale below.

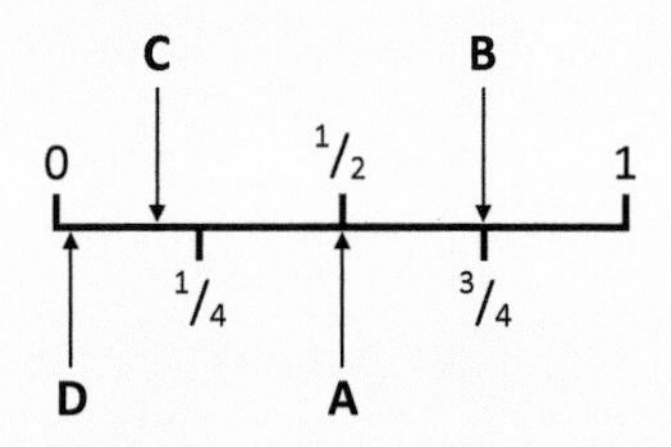

1. Which of the arrows indicates the best position on the probability line for selecting a royal card (King, Queen or Jack) from a pack of 52 playing cards?

2. Which of the arrows indicates the best position on the probability line for the event of a fair coin landing on tails 20 consecutive times?

probable

When an *event* is probable, it has a high *chance* of occurring.

Note: It is common to say that a probable event has a *probability greater than* 0.5 but *less than* 1.

e.g. It is probable that it will be sunny in London in July.

Test yourself

1. Which of the events below is most probable?
a. Snowing in July in London
b. The temperature reaching 40°C in December in London.
c. Running into traffic during rush hour.

Challenge yourself

1. Which of the events below is most probable?
a. Picking a diamond from a pack of playing cards.
b. Five being greater than twenty.
c. Picking a red marble from a bag of six blue marbles.
d. Not winning a lottery.

2. Which of the arrows below indicates the best position on the probability line for an event that is described to be probable?

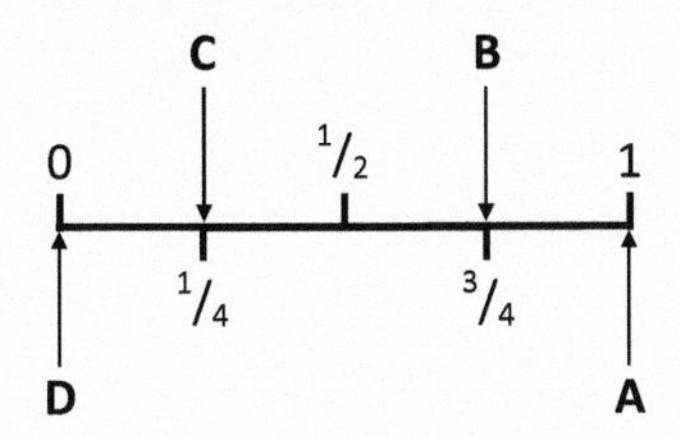

product

The result obtained when two or more numbers are multiplied together.
e.g. The product of 5 and 7 is 35.

Test yourself

1. Evaluate the product of five and ten.

2. Evaluate the product of seven and twelve.

Challenge yourself

1. What is the product of 3^3 and 15?

2. What is the product of the first four multiples of 5?

3. What is the product of 1.2, 13.5 and 10?

4. What is the product of $^{12}/_3$ and $^{16}/_9$?

proper fraction

A *fraction* in which the *numerator* is smaller than the *denominator*.
e.g. $^1/_8$, $^8/_{11}$ and $^9/_{10}$ are proper fractions.

Test yourself

1. Which of the following fractions are proper fractions?

$^5/_2$ $^3/_4$ $^1/_{13}$ $^{11}/_6$ $^{21}/_2$

2. If $^x/_{17}$ is a proper fraction, what is the greatest possible value of x?

Challenge yourself

1. Which of the following fractions are proper fractions?

$^5/_2$ $^{3\pi}/_4$ $^{12}/_{13}$ $^{15}/_3$ $^{-1}/_2$

2. What is $(^5/_8 \times {}^2/_{15}) + {}^7/_{12}$?

3. Is the answer to question 2 a proper fraction?

proportional

When two *variables* have a *constant ratio*.
e.g. The size of a bag is proportional to the number of marbles it can hold. If a bag of size x holds 4 marbles, then a bag of size $3x$ can hold 12 marbles.

Test yourself

1. The size of a bag is proportional to the number of marbles it can hold. If a bag of size x holds 8 marbles, how many marbles can fit inside a bag of size $5x$?

2. Equilateral triangles A and B are similar, hence the length of a side of A is proportional to the corresponding side of B. If the side of A is proportional by a factor 3, what is the length of a side of triangle B?

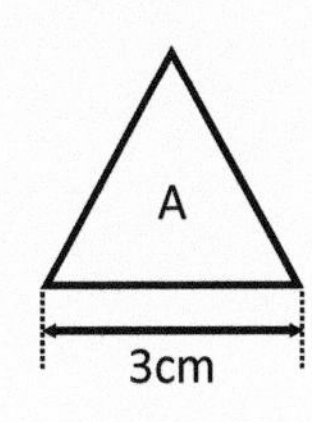

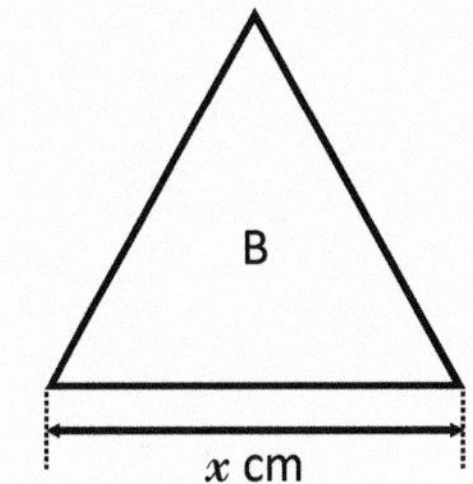

Challenge yourself

1. Variable y is proportional to variable x. When y is 10, x is 15. What is y if x is 40?

2. The number of flowers in a field is proportional to the area of the field. If a field of size $x\text{m}^2$ has 27 flowers, how many flowers are there in a field of size $5x\text{m}^2$?

A
B
C
D
E
F
G
H
I
J
K
L
M
N
O
P
Q
R
S
T
U
V
W
X
Y
Z

pyramid

A *three-dimensional* shape with a polygonal *base* and triangular *faces* that all meet at a single point called the *apex*. See also *polygon*.

e.g.

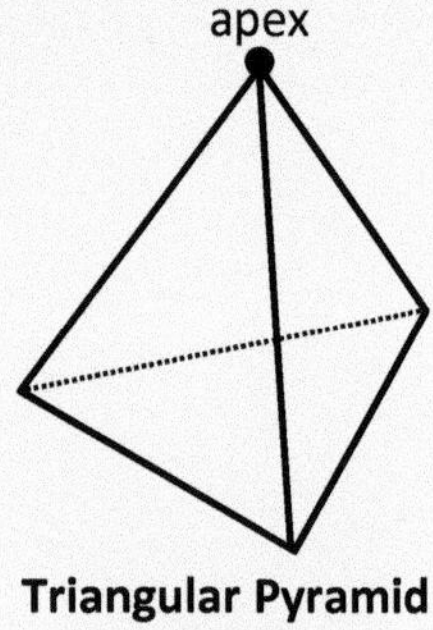

Triangular Pyramid (Tetrahedron):
It has 4 faces.
It has 4 vertices.
It has 6 edges.

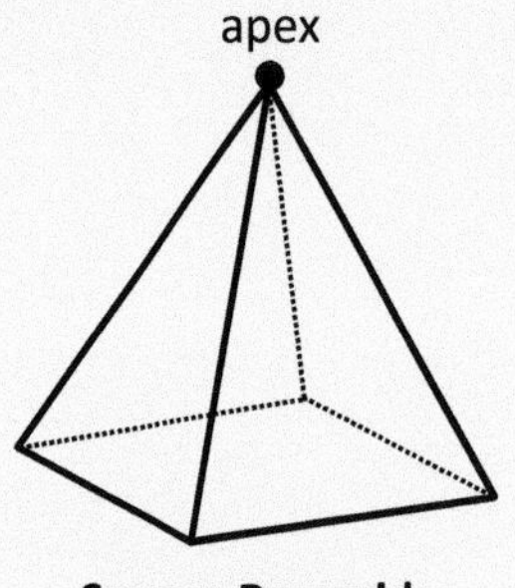

Square Pyramid:
It has 5 faces.
It has 5 vertices.
It has 8 edges.

Test yourself

1. What is the name of a pyramid with a square base?

Challenge yourself

1. How many edges are there in a hexagonal pyramid?

2. According to Euler's formula, if a pyramid has 11 faces and 11 vertices, how many edges should the shape have?

3. What is the name of the shape of the pyramid's base described in question 2?

Pythagoras' theorem

In a *right-angled triangle*, the *sum* of the *squares* of the *lengths* of the two shortest *sides* is *equal* to the square of the length of the longest side, which is also known as the *hypotenuse*.

e.g.

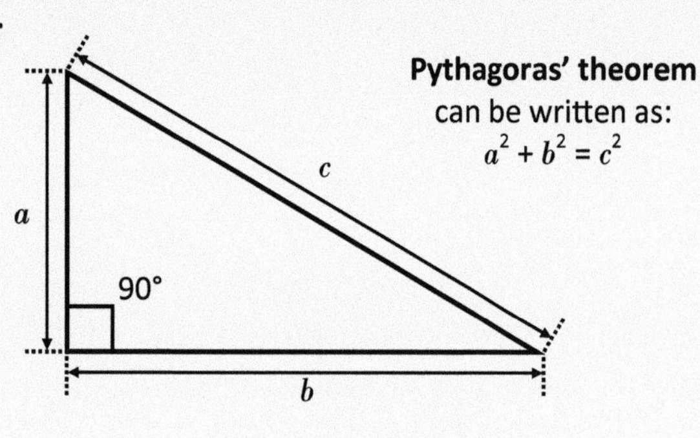

Challenge yourself

1. What is the length of the hypotenuse if the lengths of the other two sides of a right-angled triangle are 8cm and 6cm?

Q

quadrant

i. A quarter of a *circle*.

e.g.

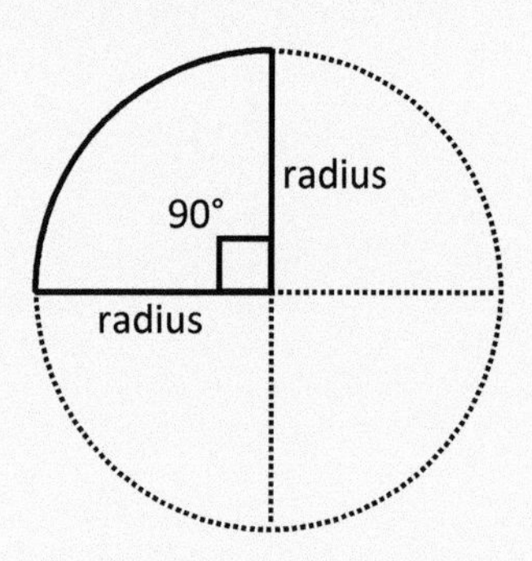

ii. Any of the four regions made when the x and y *axes* divide an *area* to form a *coordinate* system.

e.g.

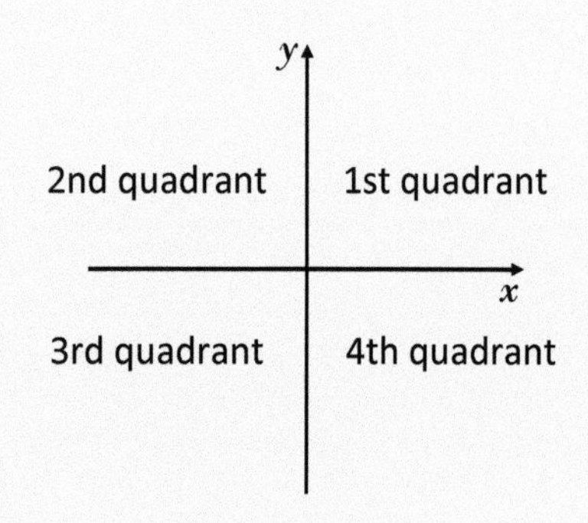

Test yourself

1. If the area of a circle is 180cm^2, what is the area of one of its quadrants?

2. Which letter represents the 4th quadrant on the graph below.

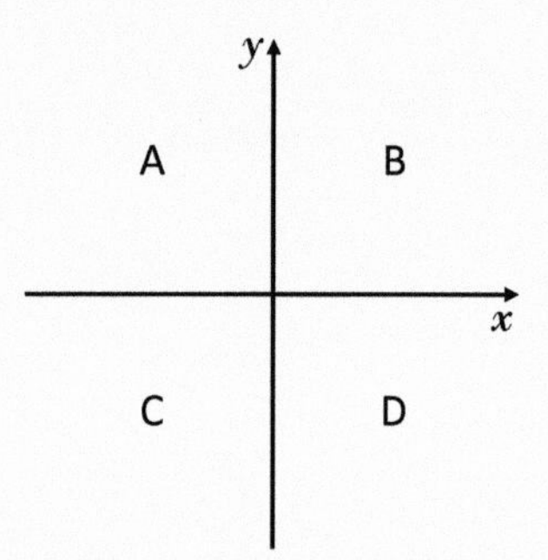

3. If a quadrant of a circle has an area of 45mm^2, what is the area of the entire circle? Give your answer in mm^2.

4. What is the name given to the point at which the four quadrants touch?

Challenge yourself

1. Express the area of a quadrant of a circle with radius r. Give your answer in terms of π and r.

2. Express, in terms of π and r, the perimeter of a quadrant of a circle with radius r.

3. Given that both x and y are positive, identify the quadrant to which each point belongs.

A(x, -y), B(x, y), C(-x, -y), D(-x, y)

quadratic equation

An *equation* containing a *variable* that is raised to the *power* of two.

Note: The general form of a quadratic equation is $ax^2 + bx + c$, where a, b and c are random numbers.

e.g. $y = x^2$.

Test yourself

1. Which of the following can be described as a quadratic equation?

a. $y = 2x - 3$

b. $y = x^2 - 5$

c. $y = x + 2$

d. $y = 3 - 2x^2$

Challenge yourself

1. Which of the following are solutions to the quadratic equation below?
(Hint: substitute in the values to see if both sides of the equation are satisfied.)

$$x^2 - 4x + 3 = 28 - 4x$$

A	B	C	D	E
5	-10	-5	10	3

quadratic sequence

A number *sequence* in which the *second difference* between any two *consecutive terms* is *constant*.

e.g.

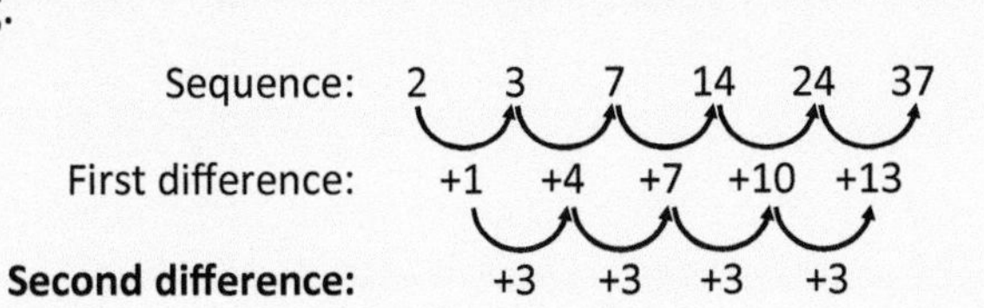

Test yourself

1. What is the second difference of the following quadratic sequence?

1, 3, 6, 10, 15,...

2. What is the second difference of the following quadratic sequence?

1, 3, 7, 13, 21,...

Challenge yourself

1. Complete the quadratic sequence below so that the pattern stays the same.

1	2	4		11	16	

2. Complete the quadratic sequence below so that the pattern stays the same.

	8	18	32		72	

3. Complete the quadratic sequence below so that the pattern stays the same.

6	12	20	30	42		

quadrilateral

A four-sided *polygon*.

e.g.

Square:
All 4 angles are equal (90°).
All 4 sides are of equal length.
The diagonals bisect each other at 90°.

Trapezium:
1 pair of opposite and parallel sides.

Test yourself

1. How many sides does a quadrilateral have?

2. Name the quadrilateral with two pairs of parallel sides that are all of equal lengths?

Challenge yourself

1. How many pairs of parallel sides does a kite have?

2. What is the size of one exterior angle found on a regular quadrilateral?

A
B
C
D
E
F
G
H
I
J
K
L
M
N
O
P
Q
R
S
T
U
V
W
X
Y
Z

quadruple
To *increase* a *value* by a *factor* of four, i.e. multiply a given number by four.
e.g. Quadruple 3 is $3 \times 4 = 12$.

Test yourself
1. What is quadruple 2?

2. What is quadruple 7?

3. Calculate 13×4.

4. Calculate 20×4.

Challenge yourself
1. If I quadruple a number and the answer is 44, what is the original number?

2. What is the sum of quadruple 5 and quadruple 5^3?

3. Given that y is quadruple x, what is the value of x in the equation below?
$$5x + y = 108$$

4. Given that y is quadruple x, what is the value of x in the equation below?
$$3x + 2y = 1331$$

quotient
The answer obtained when a number is divided by another number, i.e. the *ratio* of two numbers.
e.g. The quotient of 6 and 2 is $^6/_2 = 3$.

Test yourself
1. What is the quotient when 9 is divided by 3?

2. What is the quotient when 12 is divided by 4?

Challenge yourself
1. What is the quotient when 165 is divided by 15?

2. The quotient of 208 and x is 16. What is the value of x?

3. Calculate $1272 \div 8$.

4. Calculate the value of x in the equation below.
$$x \div 8 = 175$$

radius (plural: radii)
The radius of a *circle* is the *length* of a line *segment* between a point on the *circumference* and the centre; that is half of the *diameter*.
e.g.

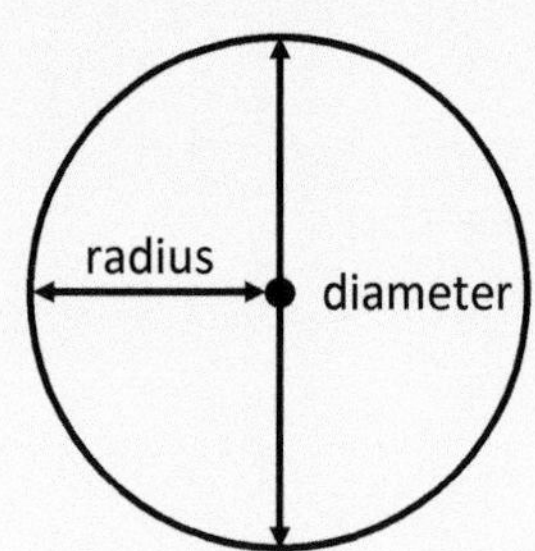

Test yourself
1. What is the radius of a circle with a diameter of 6cm?

2. If the diameter of a circle is 12mm, what is its radius?

Challenge yourself
1. What is the perimeter of the rectangle if the radius of each circle inside the rectangle is 5.5cm?

2. What is the ratio of the radii of circle A to circle B with radii of 4.5mm and 3cm respectively?

random
Something that occurs without *order* or structure, but simply by *chance*.
e.g. The probability of randomly picking a King from a deck of cards is $^1/_{13}$.

Test yourself
1. Which of the following events is random?
a. Picking every fifth card from a deck of cards.
b. Picking a King from a deck of playing cards that are all face down.
c. Going to the gym every Tuesday evening.

Challenge yourself

1. What is the probability of randomly picking a red card from a deck of playing cards?

2. A box is filled with stuffed animals. There are 3 teddies, 7 bunnies, 4 dogs and 6 cats. One animal is removed at random, which animal is it most likely to be?

3. In a jar there are 5 small, 5 medium and 5 large pebbles. A handful of pebbles are taken using a random selection. 3 are small, 2 are medium and 1 is large. Without replacement, what is the new probability of picking a small pebble in the next single pick?

4. When two fair dice are randomly rolled, what is the probability of getting a sum of 12 from the two numbers rolled.

range

A measure of the spread of a *dataset*. It is the *difference* between the highest and lowest *values*.
e.g. In the dataset {1, 5, 7}, the range is 7 - 1 = 6.

Test yourself

1. What is the range of the following set of numbers: 5, 10, 9, 6, 2?

2. What is the range of the following set of numbers: 0, 1, 9, 15, 22?

Challenge yourself

1. The heights of five students are 143cm, 1.5m, 1.48m, 139cm and 1.7m. What is the range of their heights in cm?

2. What is the range of the following set of numbers: 99, 150, -200, 64, 0?

3. The weights of 5 zoo animals are recorded. The results are as follows: 64kg, 44 pounds, 78kg, 24kg and 68.2 pounds. Assuming 1kg = 2.2lbs, what is the range of animal weights in kg?

ratio

The relative sizes of two or more *values*.
Note: The ratio of n to m is written in the form $n{:}m$. It is also valid to write the *quotient* $^{n}/_{m}$.
e.g. If there are 15 red hats and 3 blue hats, the ratio of red hats to blue hats is 15:3, or 5:1.

Test yourself

1. What is the ratio 5:10 in its simplest form?

2. There are 7 red books and 21 blue books. What is the ratio of blue to red books? Give your answer in its simplest form.

Challenge yourself

1. What is the ratio 24:28 in its simplest form?

2. What is the ratio of the number of lines of symmetry of a regular octagon to that of a square?

3. Tony and Nicky share a bag of sweets in the ratio 7:4 respectively. How many sweets does Tony get if there are 77 sweets in total?

rational number

Any number that can be expressed as a *fraction*, where both the *numerator* and *denominator* are positive or negative *integers*.
e.g. Since 0.75 can be expressed as $^{3}/_{4}$, 0.75 is a rational number.

Test yourself

1. Which of the following numbers are rational?

a. 0.8 b. $\sqrt{2}$ c. 0.1

Challenge yourself

1. Which of the following numbers are rational?

a. 0.45 b. 2π c. -0.2 d. π^0 e. $2\sqrt{2}$

2. Show that the sum of 0.55 and -1.25 is a rational number.

3. Elena and Belinda are each given a set of numbers. Elena's numbers are 2, 7, $\sqrt{4}$, $\sqrt{3}$ and 6. Belinda's numbers are $\sqrt{9}$, 10, $\sqrt{6}$, 2 and 3. Each are told to multiply together the rational numbers within their set. Who has the highest result and what is their value?

real numbers

All *rational* and *irrational numbers*, i.e. all the numbers that can be thought of.

A B C D E F G H I J K L M N O P Q R S T U V W X Y Z

e.g. 0.75, -10 and π are all real numbers.

Test yourself

1. What is the largest real number in the following set of numbers?

0.7   2 $^7/_9$ 0   0.9

Challenge yourself

1. What is the range of the following real numbers: 5, -2, π, √5?

2. What is the smallest value that can be represented by the fraction $^s/_t$ if s and t can be any of the real numbers below?

8, -2, π, √2, 0.99

reciprocal

A reciprocal of a number is one divided by the given number.

Note: To find the reciprocal of a *fraction*, switch the *numerator* and the *denominator*.

e.g. The reciprocal of 3 is $^1/_3$, and the reciprocal of $^2/_7$ is $^7/_2$.

Test yourself

1. What is the reciprocal of 5?

2. What is the reciprocal of $^1/_8$?

Challenge yourself

1. Is the reciprocal of -7 greater than the reciprocal of -8?

2. What is the reciprocal of 3.5 expressed as a proper fraction?

3. What is $^5/_{12} \div {}^3/_4$?

rectangle (oblong)

A four-sided *polygon* with four *right angles* and two pairs of opposite *sides* that are *parallel* and of *equal length*.

e.g.

Rectangle (oblong):
All 4 angles are equal (90°).
There are 2 pairs of parallel sides.

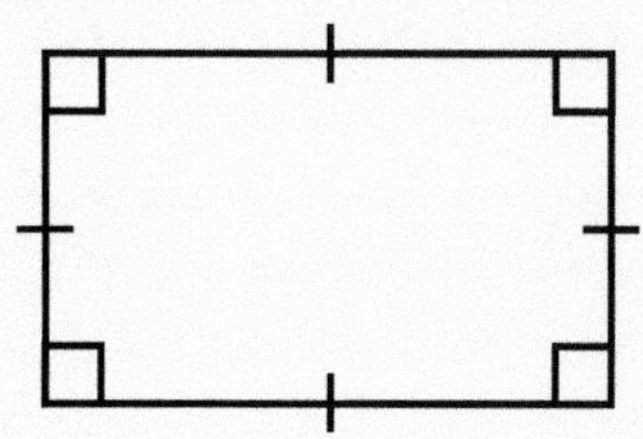

Test yourself

1. How many sides does a rectangle have?

2. What is the sum of all the 4 angles inside a rectangle?

Challenge yourself

1. What is the area of a rectangle with sides of length 4cm and 2.5cm? Give your answer in cm^2.

2. If the perimeter of a rectangle is 22cm and one side measures 9cm, what is its area in cm^2?

3. If the area of a rectangle is $32mm^2$ and the ratio of the two perpendicular sides is 2:1, what is the length of the longest side?

rectangular prism

See *cuboid*.

***

recurring decimal

A special type of *decimal* in which a single *figure* or a group of figures is repeated indefinitely.

Rule: Recurring numbers are indicated by a single dot above the first number and last number of the repeated pattern.

e.g. $^1/_3 = 0.33333... = 0.\dot{3}$; $^2/_{11} = 0.181818... = 0.\dot{1}\dot{8}$

Test yourself

1. Given that $^1/_9 = 0.1111...$, what is the recurring digit when 1 is divided by 9?

2. Given that $^1/_{11} = 0.0909...$, what are the recurring digits when 1 is divided by 11?

3. Is $^{45}/_{50}$ a recurring decimal?

4. Is $^{26}/_{50}$ a recurring decimal?

Challenge yourself

1. Which of the following fractions can be converted to a recurring decimal?

$^7/_9$ $^2/_5$ $^1/_5$ $^2/_1$ $^1/_4$

2. Express the sum $^1/_2 + {}^1/_3 + {}^1/_4$ as a recurring decimal.

3. Express $^{13}/_{555}$ as a recurring decimal.

reduce
See *decrease*.

***

reflection
A *transformation* in which each point of a shape is mapped on to a corresponding point that is an *equal distance* (*equidistant*) from a *mirror line*, in the opposite *direction*.

e.g.

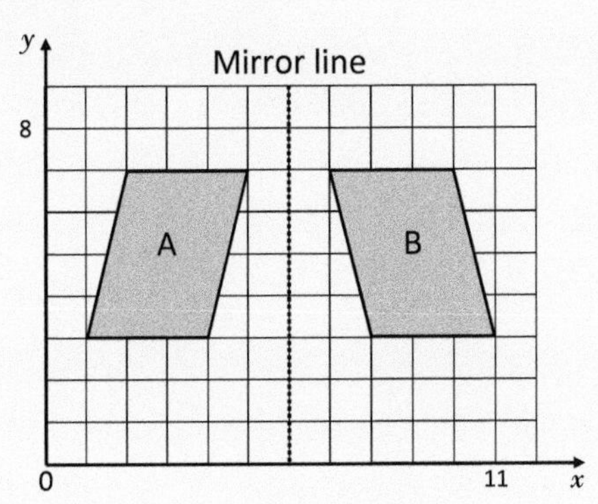

Shape A has been reflected across the mirror line to produce shape B.
Shape B is known as the mirror image of shape A.

Test yourself

1. What is the name given to the shape made when the following lines are reflected across the dotted line?

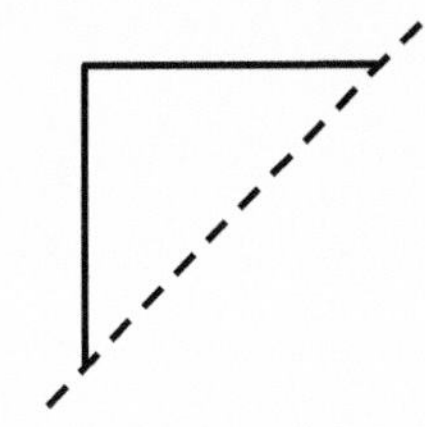

2. Reflect the triangle across the dotted line.

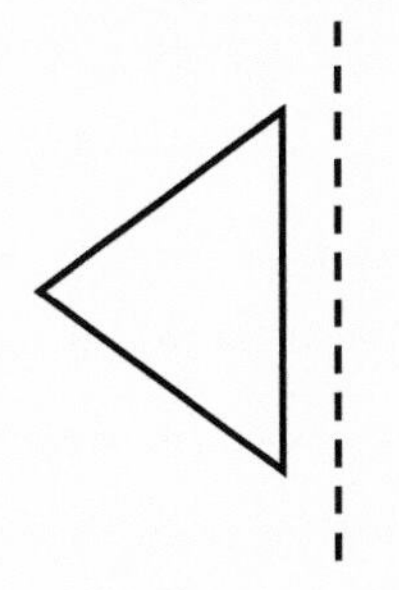

Challenge yourself

1. What are the coordinates of point A (5, -7) after a reflection in the x-axis?

2. What are the coordinates of point B (-2, 4) after a reflection in the y-axis?

3. What are the coordinates of point C (9, 10) after a reflection in the y-axis followed by a translation of seven units to the right?

reflective symmetry
A shape has reflective *symmetry* if it can be divided into two *equal* parts, which are mirror *images* of each other. See also *line of symmetry*, *mirror line*.

e.g.

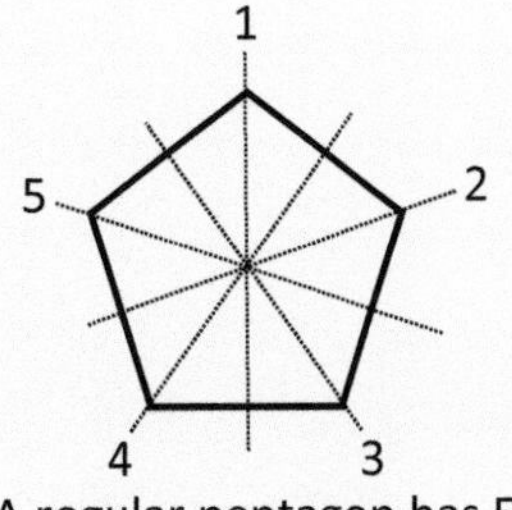

A regular pentagon has 5 lines of symmetry.

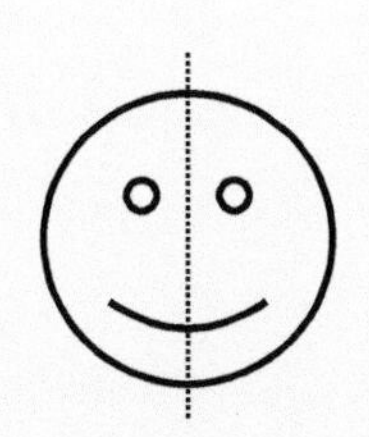

This shape has 1 line of symmetry.

Test yourself

1. Which of the following shapes has reflective symmetry?

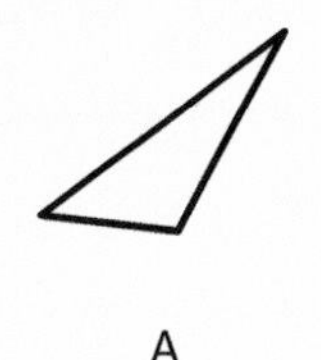

A

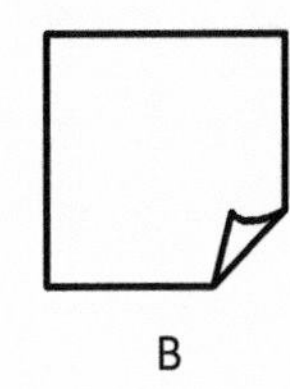

B

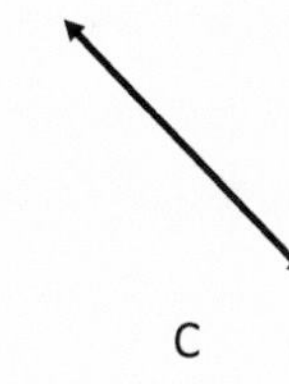

C

Challenge yourself

1. How many lines of symmetry does a regular heptagon have?

2. What is the ratio of the number of lines of symmetry of a rectangle to that of an equilateral triangle?

3. How many lines of symmetry does a circle have?

reflex angle
An *angle* between 180° and 360°.

e.g.

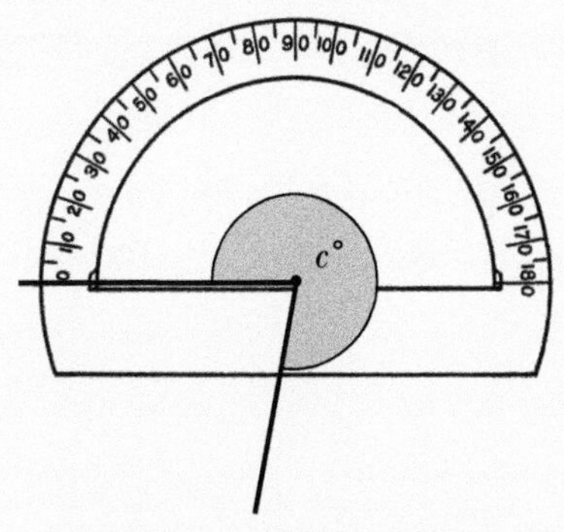

Angle c° is greater than 180° but less than 360°. Therefore, it is a reflex angle.

A B C D E F G H I J K L M N O P Q R S T U V W X Y Z

Test yourself

1. Which of the following angles is not reflex?

A	B	C	D	E
177°	246°	190°	181°	320°

Challenge yourself

Answer the following questions using the diagram below.

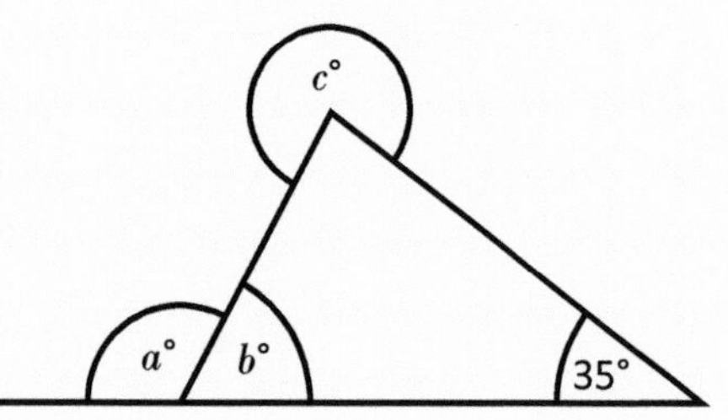

1. Which of the angles can be described as a reflex angle?

2. Given that the reflex angle on the diagram above is 290°, calculate the size of the other two angles.

3. What is the name given to the triangle?

regular

i. A regular *polygon* has *sides* of *equal length* and *angles* of equal size.

e.g.

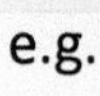

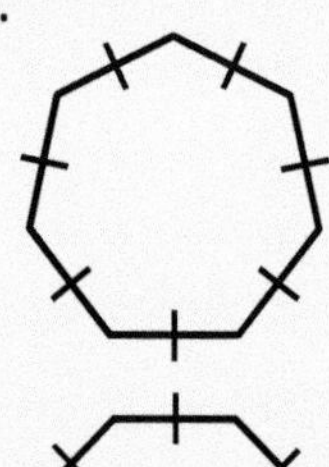

Regular Heptagon:
All 7 angles are equal.
All 7 sides are of equal length.
The sum of the interior angles is 900°.

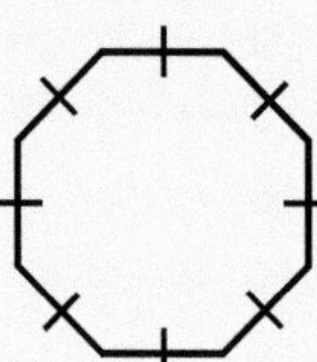

Regular Octagon:
All 8 angles are equal.
All 8 sides are of equal length.
The sum of the interior angles is 1080°.

ii. A regular *polyhedron* has polygonal *faces* that are *identical* and regular.

e.g.

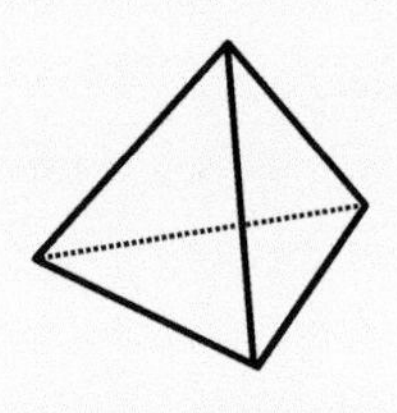

Triangular Pyramid:
It has 4 faces.
It has 4 vertices.
It has 6 edges.

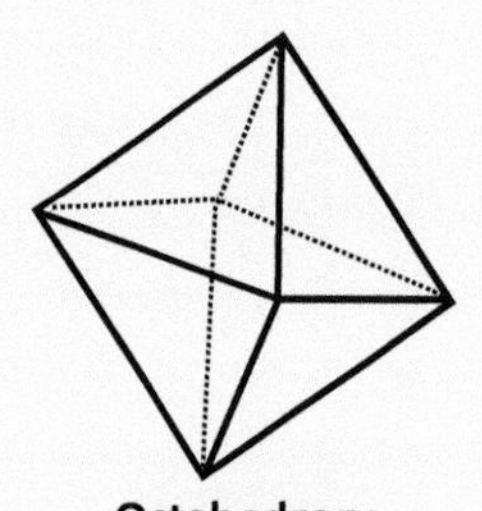

Octahedron:
It has 8 faces.
It has 6 vertices.
It has 12 edges.

Test yourself

1. Draw a regular polygon with 5 sides.

2. Draw a regular polyhedron that has 6 square faces.

Challenge yourself

1. What is the size of the interior angle of a regular polygon with 8 sides?

2. How many sides does a regular polygon with an interior angle of 140° have?

3. What are the names given to regular polyhedra with 6 faces, 8 vertices and 12 edges?

4. What is the name given to a regular polyhedron with 8 faces, 6 vertices and 12 edges?

remainder (rem.)

The *value* left over when a number cannot be divided exactly by the *divisor*.

e.g. 32 ÷ 6 = 5 rem. 2.

Test yourself

1. What is the remainder when 6 is divided by 4?

2. What is the remainder when 15 is divided by 6?

Challenge yourself

1. What is the remainder when 35 is divided by 8?

2. What is the remainder when 59 is divided by 12?

3. What is the remainder when 84 is divided by 11?

revolution

A *rotation* of 360°, i.e. one complete turn.

e.g.

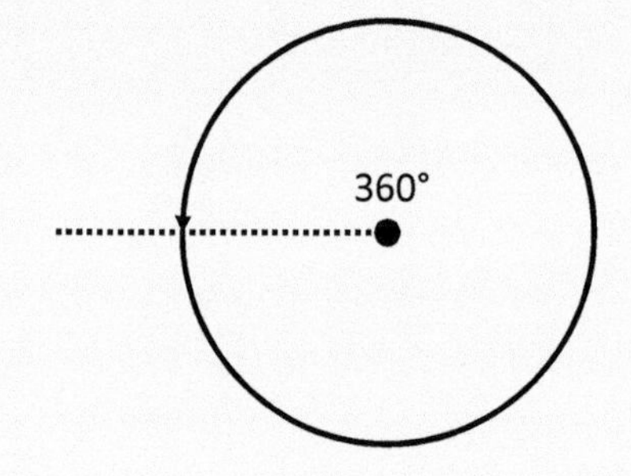

Test yourself

1. How many revolutions are there in 720°?

2. Anna is facing north and makes two full turns. In which direction is she now facing?

3. What is the angle that is equal to three full revolutions?

Challenge yourself

1. How many full turns are required to make an angle of 1620°? Give your answer as a fraction.

2. If I am facing north-west and make three and a half revolutions, in which direction am I now facing?

rhombus

A special type of *parallelogram* in which all four *sides* are of *equal length* and opposite *angles* are equal.

e.g.

Rhombus:
Opposite angles are equal.
Opposite sides are parallel.
All sides are of equal length.
The diagonals bisect each other at 90°.

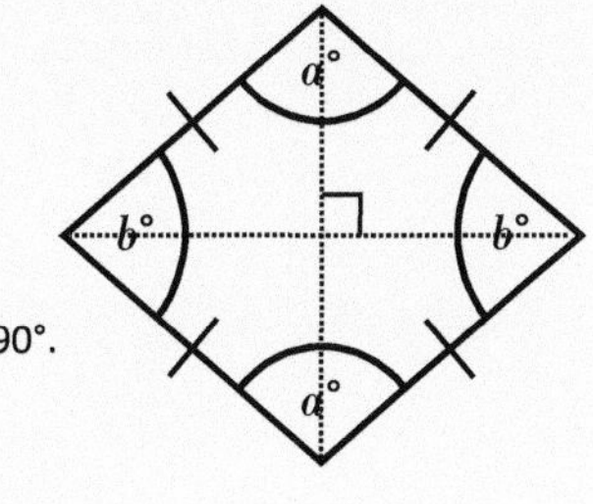

Test yourself

1. What are the properties of a rhombus?

2. On the diagram in the example above, indicate the right angle opposite to the one shown.

Challenge yourself

1. Calculate the area of the rhombus below.

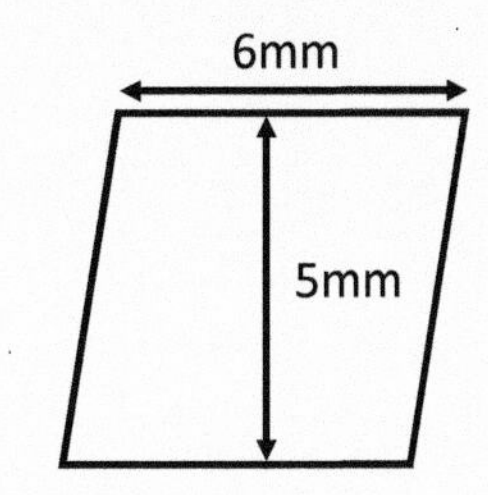

2. How many lines of symmetry does a rhombus have?

3. What is the order of rotational symmetry of a rhombus?

right angle

An *angle* of 90°. It has the symbol '⌐'.

e.g.

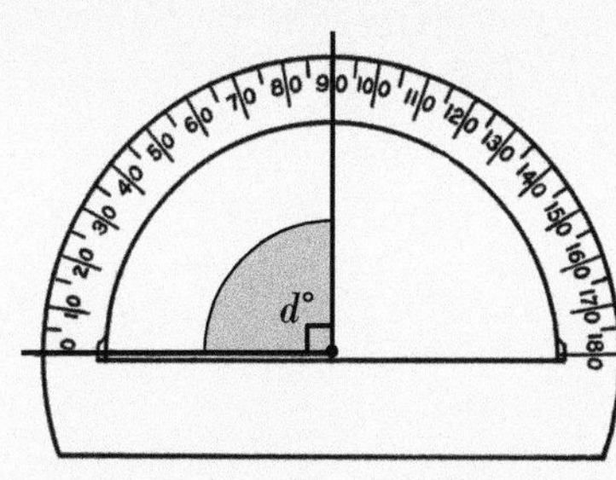

The size of angle d° is exactly 90°.
Therefore, it is a right angle.

Test yourself

1. How many degrees are there in 2 right angles?

2. How many 45° angles are there in a right angle?

Challenge yourself

1. Ilesh is facing south-west and makes 8 right angle turns anticlockwise. In which direction is he now facing?

2. How many right angles are there in 1260°?

right-angled triangle

A *triangle* in which one angle inside (interior *angle*) is a *right angle* (90°).

e.g.

Right-Angled Triangle:
1 angle is a right angle (90°).
1 pair of complementary angles.

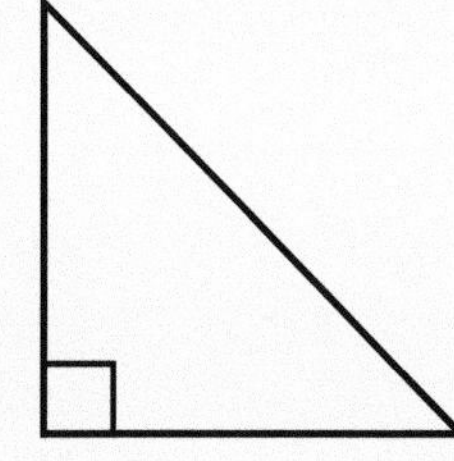

Test yourself

1. On the diagram below, indicate the right angle.

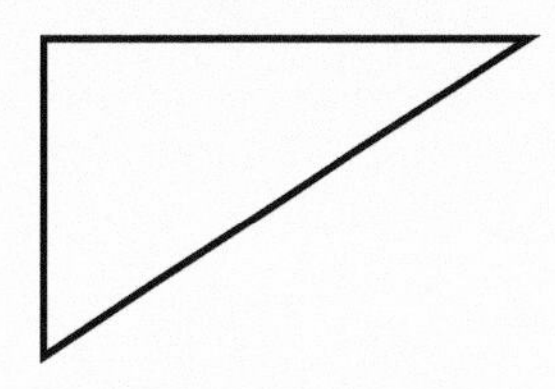

Challenge yourself

1. One of the interior angles of a right-angled triangle is 35°. What is the size of the other two interior angles?

2. If the area of a right-angled triangle is $72mm^2$ and the base is 1.2cm, what is the height of the triangle in cm?

A B C D E F G H I J K L M N O P Q R S T U V W X Y Z

Roman numerals

The Roman numeral system is the numbering system used by the ancient Romans.

Rule: If a symbol appears after another symbol of greater value, the values they represent are added. But if a symbol appears before another symbol of greater value, the values they represent are subtracted. Also, no symbol is used more than three times in a row.

1	**I**
2	II
3	III
4	IV
5	**V**
6	VI
7	VII
8	VIII
9	IX
10	**X**
20	XX
30	XXX

40	XL
50	**L**
60	LX
70	LXX
80	LXXX
90	XC
100	**C**
200	CC
300	CCC
400	CD
500	**D**
1,000	**M**

e.g. IX is 10 - 1 = 9 and XVI is 10 + 5 + 1 = 16.

Test yourself

1. What is 5 in Roman numerals?

2. What is 17 in Roman numerals?

3. What is 23 in Roman numerals?

Challenge yourself

1. What do the Roman numerals XXIV represent?

2. What do the Roman numerals XXXII represent?

3. What do the Roman numerals CM represent?

4. What do the Roman numerals LXV represent?

root

i. See *square root*.

ii. See *cube root*.

***

rotation

A *transformation* in which a given *figure* is turned about a fixed point (*centre of rotation*).

e.g.

The dot marks the centre of rotation.

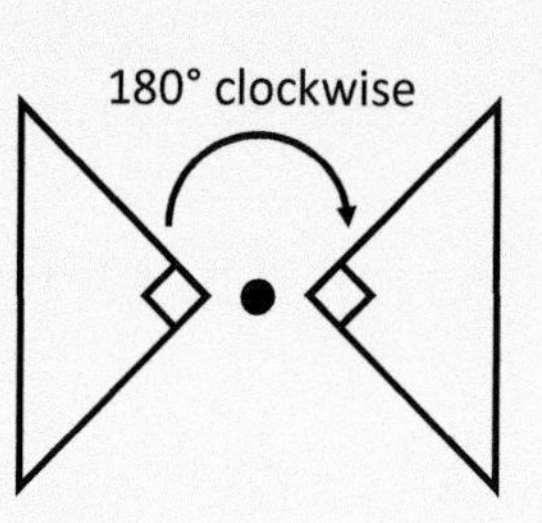

Test yourself

1. Shape A is rotated 90° to give shape B. In which direction is shape A rotated?

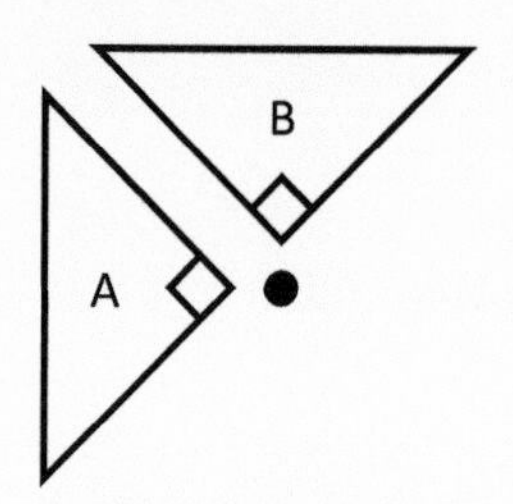

Challenge yourself

1. Point P (5, 7) is rotated 180° about the origin. What are the new coordinates of point P?

2. Shape ABCD shown below is rotated 270° about the origin in an anticlockwise direction to give shape A'B'C'D'. What are the coordinates of A' and D'?

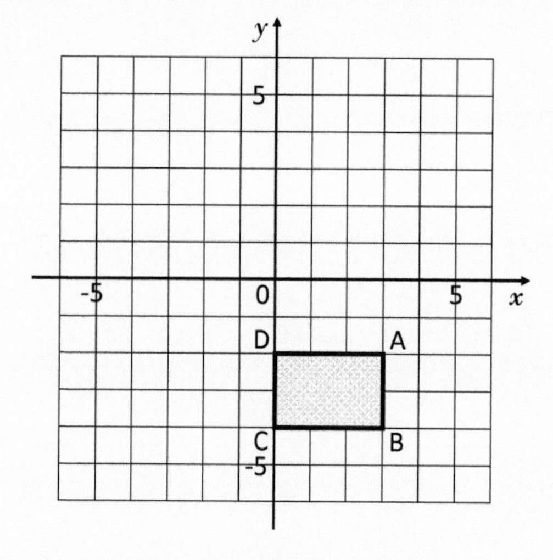

3. If the shape $wxyz$ shown below is rotated 180° in the anticlockwise direction followed by a clockwise rotation of 90° about the origin, what are the new coordinates of y?

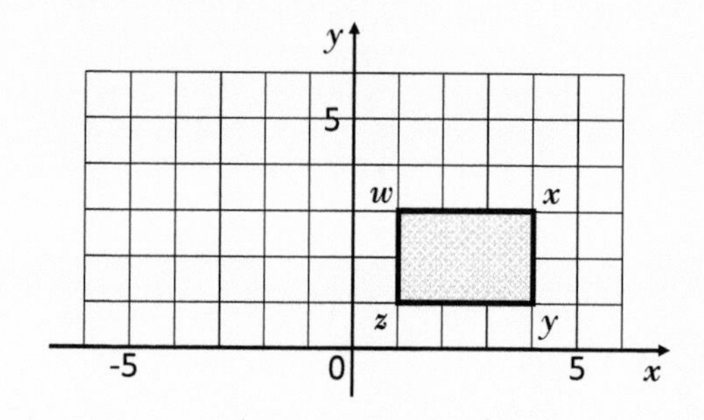

rotational symmetry

A shape has rotational *symmetry* if it can be rotated about its centre to fit exactly onto itself. See also *order of rotational symmetry*.

e.g.

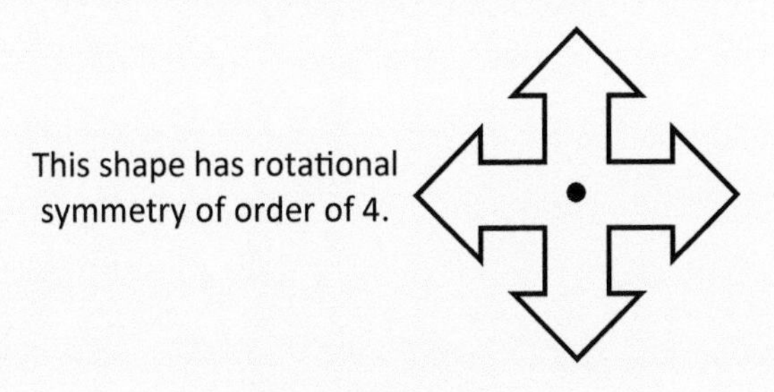

Test yourself

1. What is the order of rotational symmetry of the shape blow.

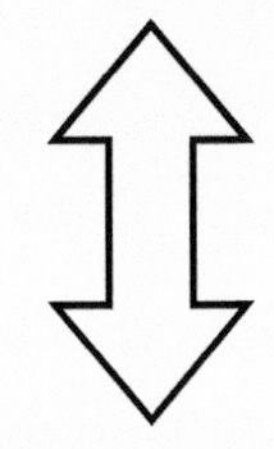

Challenge yourself

1. What is the order of rotational symmetry of the following shapes?

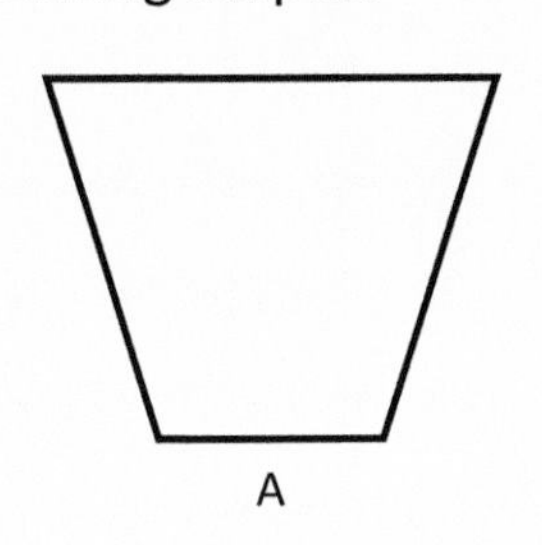

A

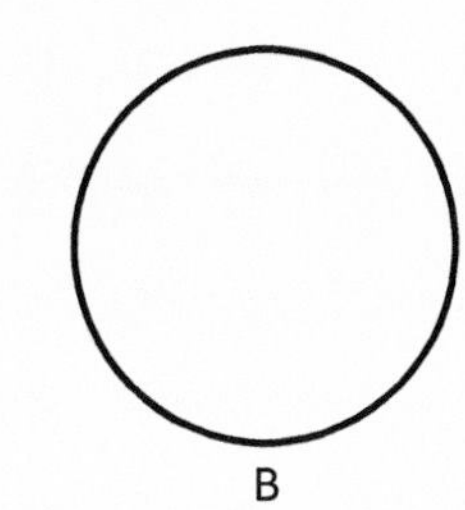

B

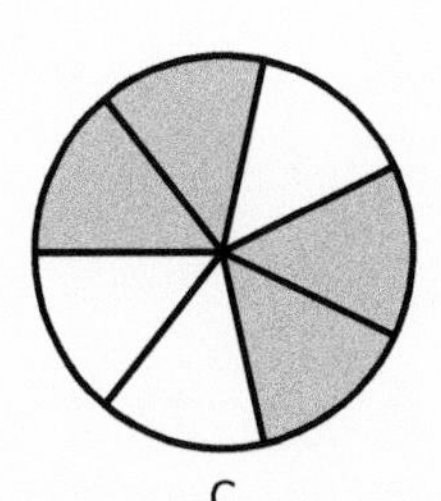

C

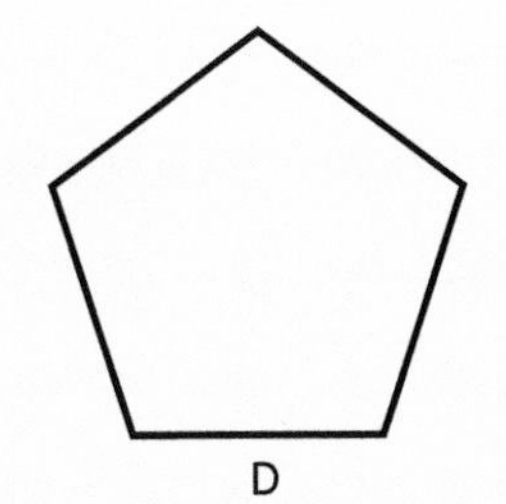

D

2. What is the order of rotational symmetry of the shape below?

3. What is the mean of the orders of rotational symmetry of a regular hexagon and heptagon?

rounding

A method used to *reduce* the *digits* of a number to make it easier to use in calculations. See also *decimal place, significant figures*.

Rule: When rounding to a particular *place value*, if the digit to the right of that place value is 0, 1, 2, 3 or 4, the digit in the given place value does not change. Otherwise, *increase* the digit by one.

e.g. Rounding the number 5.56 to one decimal place is 5.6 because the hundredths column is greater than 5.

Test yourself

1. What is 7.58 correct to 1 decimal place?

2. What is 0.057 correct to 1 decimal place?

3. What is 0.962 + 0.512 correct to 2 decimal places?

4. What is 0.848 - 0.353 correct to 2 decimal places?

Challenge yourself

1. Write -5.245 correct to 2 decimal places.

2. Calculate 15 ÷ 7 correct to 3 decimal places.

3. What is 125.12 - 57.21 correct to 1 decimal place?

4. What is 1524.58 grams to the nearest ten grams?

A B C D E F G H I J K L M N O P Q R S T U V W X Y Z

S

scale

i. A measuring line which is marked at *constant intervals*.

e.g. The scale on the thermometer reads 7°C.

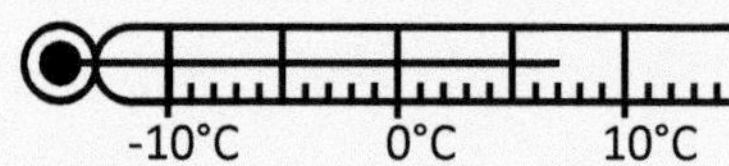

ii. The *ratio* of the size of a drawing to the actual size of the object. This is written in the form $n{:}m$.

Note: The scale of a *map* is conventionally given in *centimetres*.

e.g. The map below is drawn to a scale of 1:100,000, meaning that 1cm on the map represents 100,000cm in reality. If the side of one small square on the map below measures 1cm, the actual distance between point A and point B is 700,000cm, or 7km.

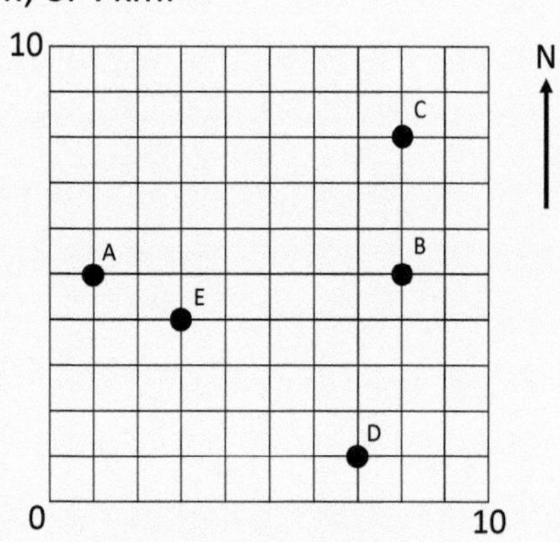

Test yourself

1. What is the temperature according to the thermometer below?

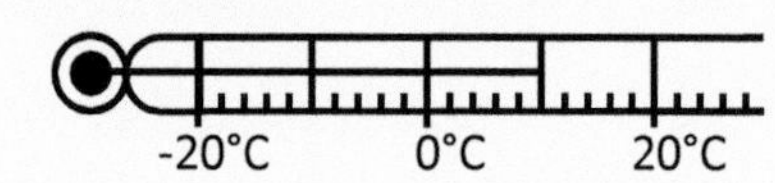

2. If a map is drawn to a scale of 1:5000, what is the distance represented by 2cm on the map?

Challenge yourself

1. What is 13°C above the temperature shown on the thermometer below?

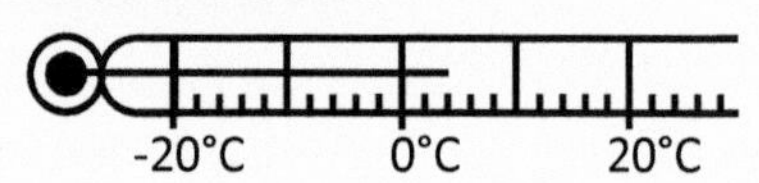

2. If a map is drawn to a scale of 1:100 and the distance between two points on the map is 5.5cm, what is the actual distance between them?

3. The map below is drawn to a scale of 1:20,000. If the side of a small square on the map measures 1cm, what is the actual distance between point C and D? Give your answer in km.

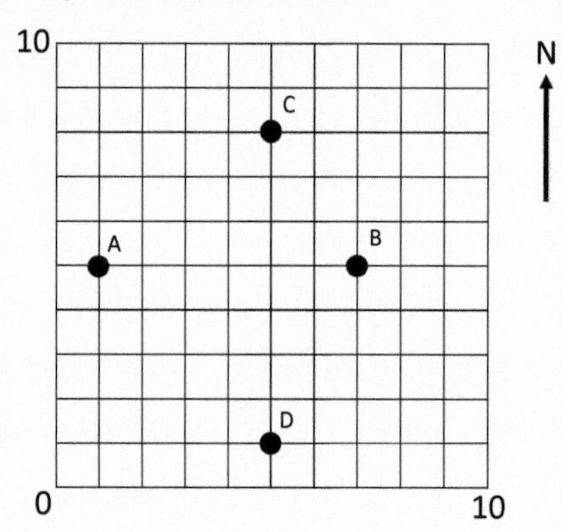

scale drawing

A drawing with its *lengths* increased or decreased by a given *ratio*. See also *enlargement*.

e.g.

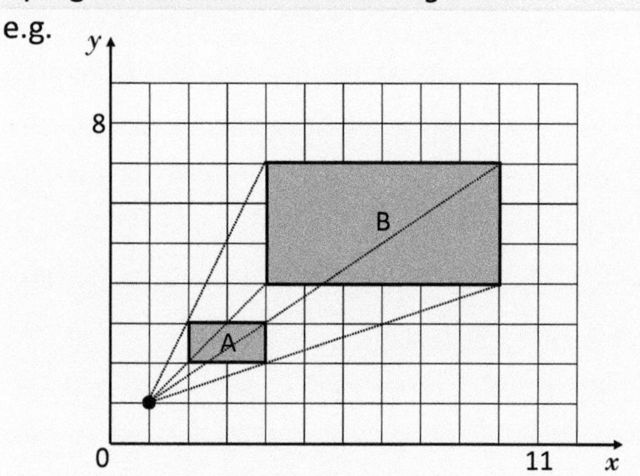

Shape B is a scale drawing of shape A with a scale factor 3.

Test yourself

1. If the shorter side of a rectangle is 3cm and it is scaled up by a factor of 3, what is its new length?

2. A side measures 4cm and when scaled up it measures 16cm. What is the scale factor?

Challenge yourself

1. Given that the area of a square on the graph below is $1cm^2$ and shape C is a scale drawing of shape D with a scale factor 4, what is the area of shape D?

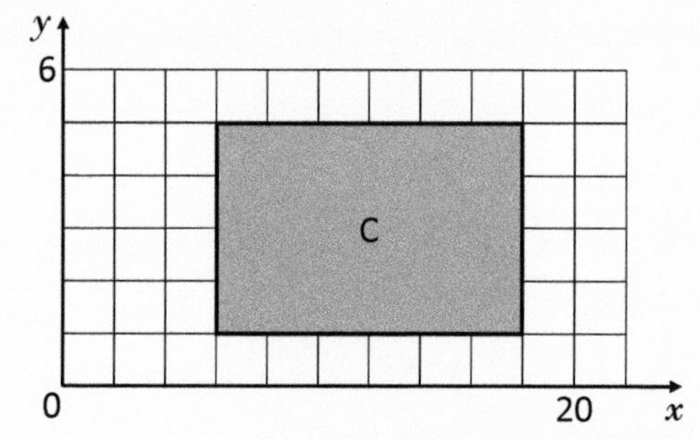

scalene triangle

A *triangle* in which all three *sides* differ in *length*.

e.g.

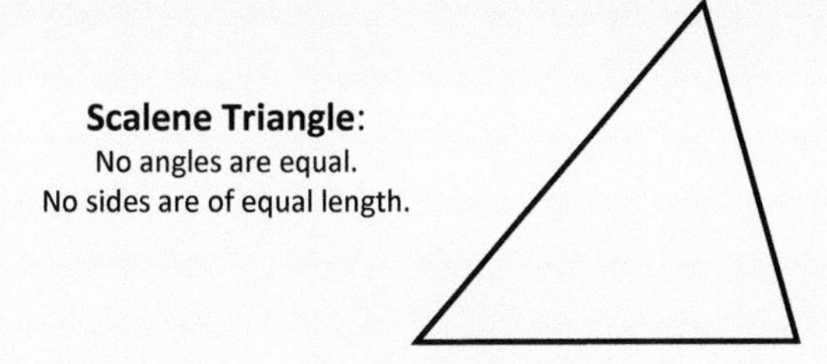

Test yourself

1. How does a scalene triangle differ from an isosceles triangle?

2. Which of the following shapes is both a scalene and right-angled triangle?

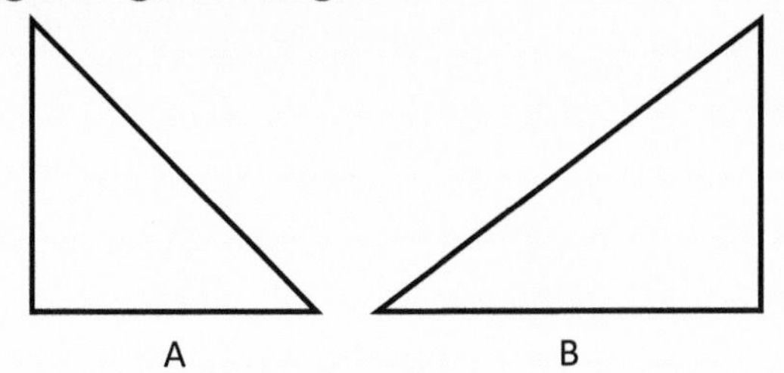

Challenge yourself

1. How many lines of symmetry does a scalene triangle have?

2. What is the order of rotational symmetry of a scalene triangle?

3. What is the sum of all the interior angles of a scalene triangle?

4. What is the sum of all the exterior angles of a scalene triangle?

scatter graph

A graph of plotted points that is used to identify a possible relationship between two *variables*.

e.g.

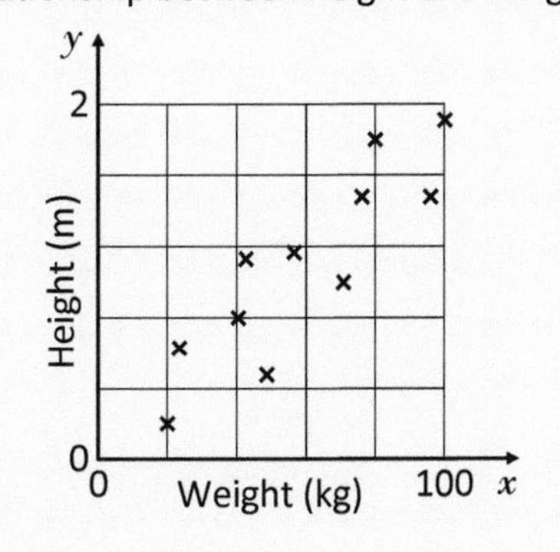

Test yourself

1. According to the scatter graph in the example, how many people were surveyed?

Challenge yourself

1. According to the scatter graph in the example, describe the general relationship between height and weight?

second (sec/s or 2nd)

i. A *unit* of *time equivalent* to $^{1}/_{60}{}^{th}$ of a *minute*, i.e. there are 60 seconds in a minute.

e.g. 120 seconds is equivalent to 2 minutes.

ii. The *ordinal number* after first and before third.

e.g. The second triangular number is 3.

Test yourself

1. How many seconds are there in 5 minutes?

2. What is the second prime number?

Challenge yourself

1. How many seconds are there in 4.5 hours?

2. What is the product of the second cube number and the third square number?

3. It takes me 3 seconds to complete one question and there are 21 questions in the paper but only 40 seconds available to complete it. What fraction of the paper will I have completed in the 40 seconds?

second difference

The *difference* between the first differences of a given number sequence. See also *quadratic sequence*.

e.g.

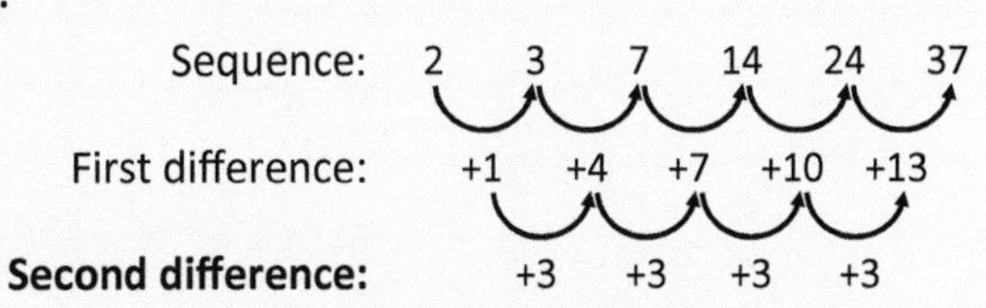

Test yourself

1. Given that the second difference is 3, find the next two terms of the sequence below.

3, 7, 14,...

A B C D E F G H I J K L M N O P Q R S T U V W X Y Z

A B C D E F G H I J K L M N O P Q R S T U V W X Y Z

2. What is the second difference of the sequence below?

1, 2, 4, 7, 11

Challenge yourself

1. What is the second difference of the sequence below?

4, 9, 16, 25, 36

2. Calculate the second difference and complete the sequence below so that the pattern stays the same.

	10	15	30		90	

sector

The *area* contained by two *radii* and the connecting *arc* of a *circle*.

Note: Radii is the plural form of *radius*.

e.g.

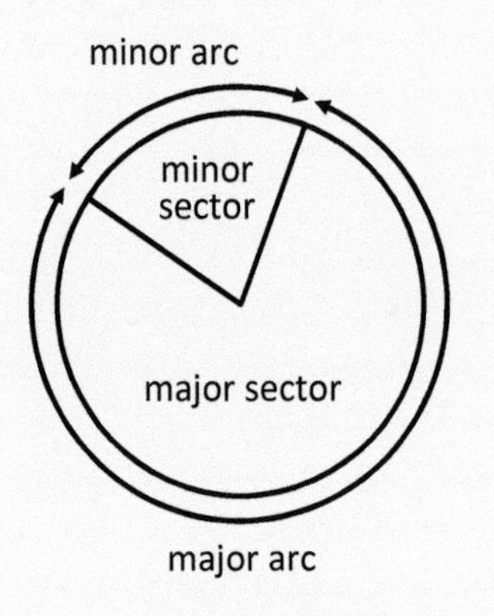

Test yourself

1. Which one of these illustrates a sector?

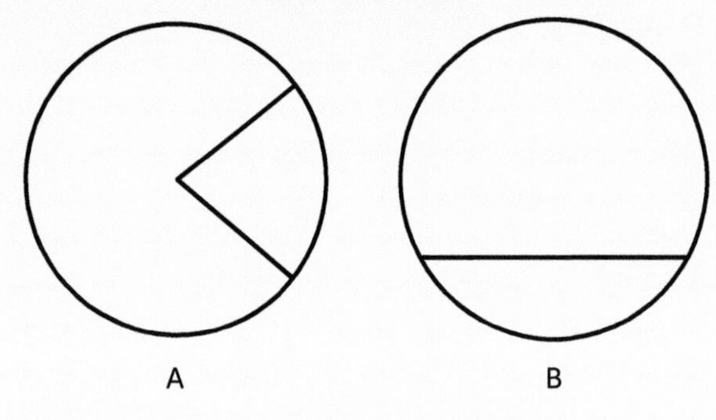

Challenge yourself

1. If the total area of a circle is $720cm^2$, and 60% of the area is in the major sector. What is the area of the major sector?

2. If the area of a major sector is $30cm^2$ and it is $^4/_5$ of the total area, calculate the total area of the circle.

segment

The *area* of a *circle* contained by a *chord* and an *arc*.

e.g.

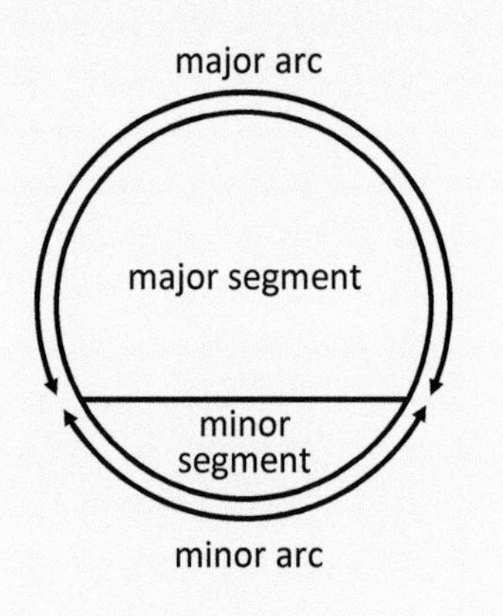

Test yourself

1. Join points A and B with a straight line and shade in the minor segment.

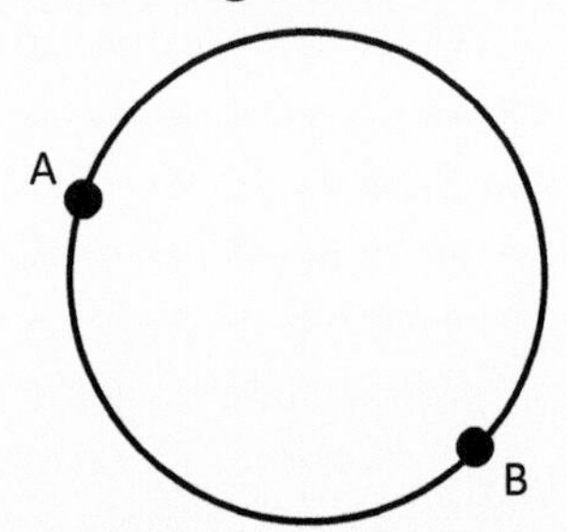

Challenge yourself

1. If the total area of a circle is $80mm^2$, and 70% of the area is in the major segment. What is the area of the major segment?

2. If the area of a major segment is $8m^2$ and it is 80% of the total area, calculate the total area of the circle.

3. What is the area of the major segment if its area is $^6/_7$ of $14cm^2$?

semicircle

Half a *circle*.

e.g.

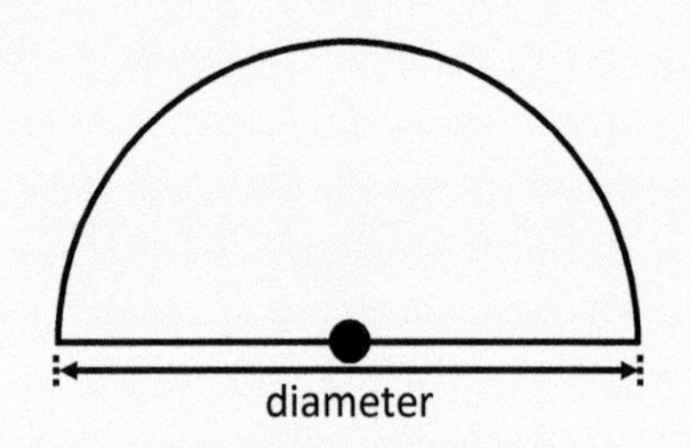

Test yourself

1. If the area of a circle is $10cm^2$, what is the area of a semicircle with the same diameter?

Challenge yourself

1. If the area of a circle with radius x is 752cm^2, what is the area of a semicircle with radius x?

2. Assuming $\pi = 3.14$, what is the area (in cm^2) of a semicircle with radius 4cm?

sequence

An ordered arrangement of numbers governed by a particular rule or set of rules.
Types of sequences include:
i. See *arithmetic sequence*.

ii. See *Fibonacci sequence*.

iii. See *geometric sequence*.

iv. See *quadratic sequence*.

***

set

A collection of numbers that are referred to as *elements*. See also *disjoint sets*, *subset*.
Note: Two curly brackets, {...}, are used to enclose all the elements of a set.
e.g. In the set {1, 2, 3, 4}, there are four elements.

Test yourself

1. How many elements are there in set A below?
Set A = {1, 0, 5, 10}

2. How many elements are there in set B below?
Set B = {-1, 0, 5, 10, 11, $^3/_4$}

Challenge yourself

1. How many even numbers are there in the set below?
{2, 0.003, 1236, 898, 10}

2. How many odd numbers are there in the set below?
{1, 9, 9984, 12, 135, 50}

3. How many prime numbers are there in the set below?
{1, 0, 3, 59, 66, 14}

4. A set is comprised of the first three triangular numbers and the fifth prime number. List all the elements in the set.

side

i. For a *two-dimensional* shape, see *edge*.

ii. For a *three-dimensional* shape, see *face*.

***

significant figures (s.f.)

The number of *digits* required to represent a number to a certain degree of accuracy. See also *rounding*.
Rule: Significant figures are counted from left to right, starting from the first non-zero digit. Any *zeros* between two non-zero *figures*, and after the last non-zero figure are significant.
e.g. The number 8451 correct to 2 significant figures is 8500 because the tens column is equal to 5.

Test yourself

1. Write 1234 correct to 2 significant figures.

2. What is $^1/_3$ correct to 3 significant figures.

3. Write 0.0145 correct to 2 significant figures.

Challenge yourself

1. Write 584,720 correct to 3 significant figures.

2. What is $^3/_{11}$ correct to 2 significant figures?

3. What is 2.008 + 0.984 correct to 1 significant figure?

signs

Symbols that show which mathematical *operations* are being used.
e.g. +, -, ×, ÷

Test yourself

1. Fill in the table below with the correct sign of the operation.

Sign	Operation
	Addition
	Subtraction
	Multiplication
	Division

Challenge yourself

1. Which sign should replace '?' in order to satisfy the number machine below?

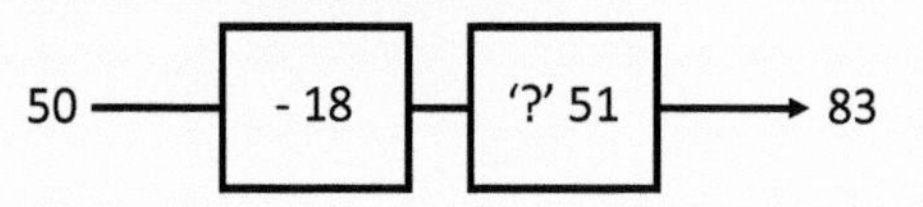

2. Which sign should replace '?' in order to satisfy the number machine below?

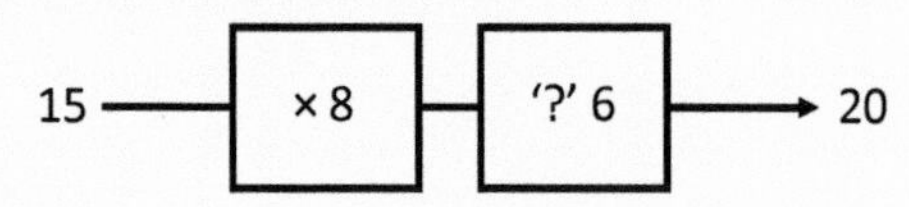

similar figures

Similar *figures* have the same shape with *equal* corresponding *angles*, but the figure can differ in *size* and orientation.

e.g.

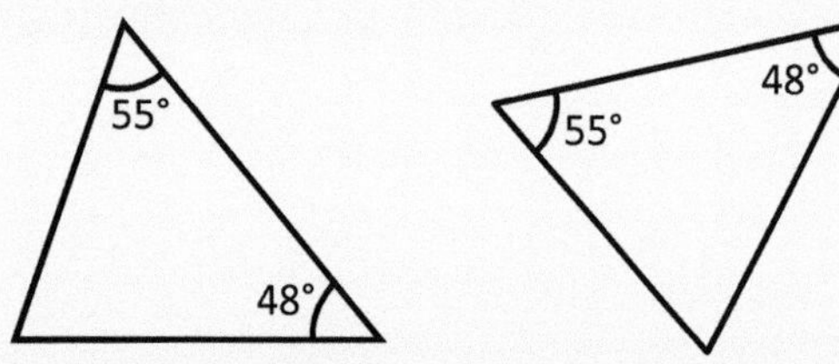

In this example, the interior angles of the two shapes are identical in size. Therefore, the two triangles are similar.

Test yourself

1. Are these triangles below similar?

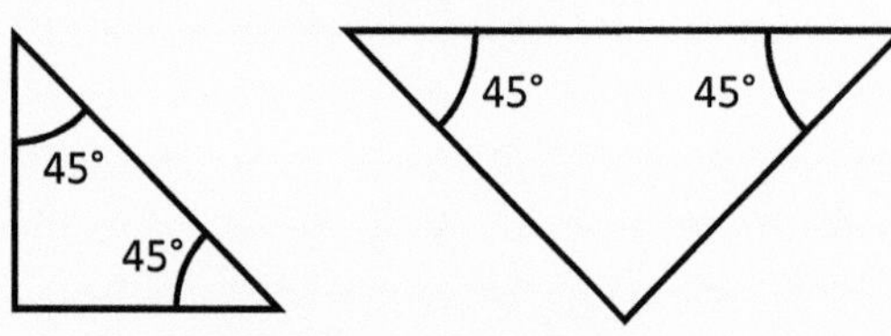

Challenge yourself

1. Are these triangles below similar?

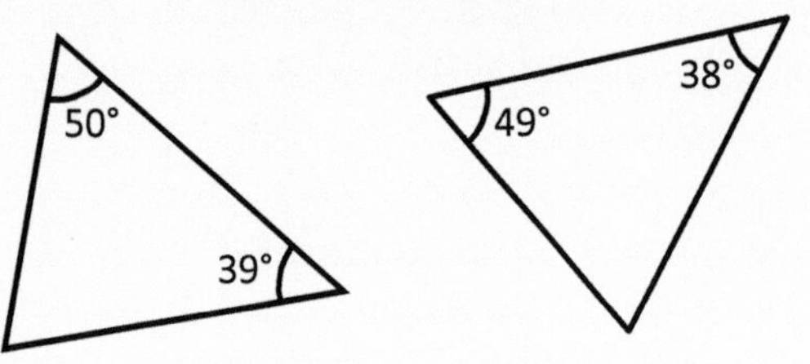

2. Given that the two shapes shown below are similar, what is the size of angle z?

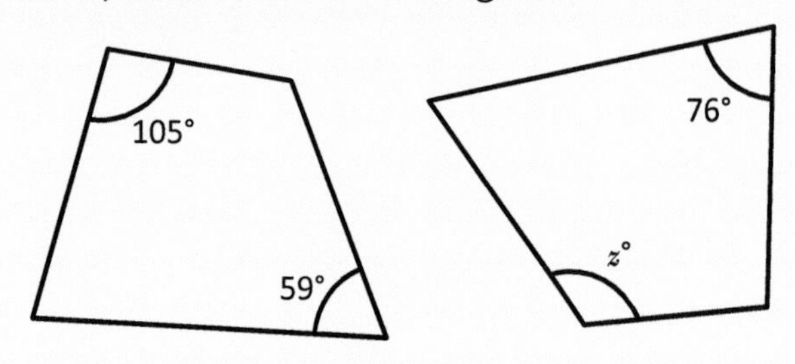

simplest form (lowest terms)

i. A *fraction* is in its simplest form when the *numerator* and *denominator* have no *factor* in common except 1. See also *equivalent fractions*, *simplify*.

e.g. 5 is the highest common factor of 45 and 50, so $^{45}/_{50}$ simplifies to $^{9}/_{10}$.

ii. An algebraic *expression* is in its simplest form when all the *like terms* are combined together. See also *like terms*, *unlike terms*.

e.g. The algebraic expression $3x + 4y + 2x - 5y$, simplifies to $5x - y$.

Test yourself

1. Write $^{5}/_{20}$ in its simplest form.

2. Write $11x + 17x$ in its simplest form.

Challenge yourself

1. Write $3x + 7x^2 + 9x^3 + 5x$ in its simplest form.

2. Write $5x + 7x - 7x^2 + 9x^2$ in its simplest form.

3. Add and simplify $^{15}/_{32}$ and $^{12}/_{15}$.

simplify

To make something easier to work with by collecting *like terms* or factorising.

e.g. The algebraic expression $10x - 2y + x - 3y$, simplifies to $11x - 5y$.

Test yourself

1. Simplify $2y + 18y$.

2. Simplify $19x - 3x$.

3. Simplify $^{18}/_{27}$.

Challenge yourself

1. Simplify $17x - 7y + 52x - 11y$.

2. Simplify $9x \times 4y + 5x - 11y + 8xy$.

3. Express and simplify $4\,^{2}/_{12}$ as an improper fraction.

4. Express and simplify $5\,^{15}/_{20}$ as an improper fraction.

slope
See *gradient*.

***

solid
Figures with *three-dimensions*: *length*, *width* and *height*.
e.g.

Pentagonal Prism:
It has 7 faces.
It has 10 vertices.
It has 15 edges.

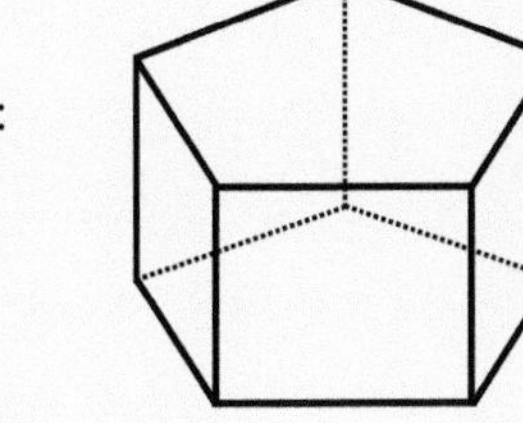

Test yourself
1. Which of the following shapes can be described as a solid?
a. sphere b. pentagon c. semicircle
d. square e. prism f. tetrahedron

Challenge yourself
Look at the shape shown below and answer the following questions.

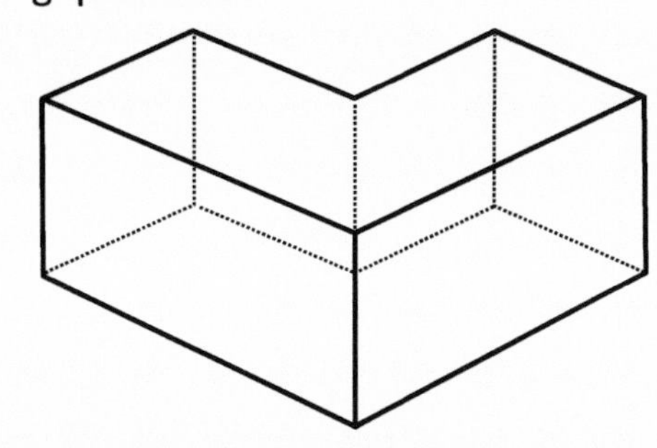

1. How many faces does it have?

2. How many edges does it have?

3. How many vertices does it have?

4. If the given shape is constructed using three cubes with sides of 13mm, what is its volume? Give your answer in mm^3.

solve
To find the *value* of a *variable* that satisfies an *equation*. See also *simplify*.
e.g. Solving the equation $5x - 7 = 13$ gives $x = 4$.

Test yourself
1. Solve $x - 7 = 18$.

2. Solve $x + 3 = 2$.

3. Solve $2x - 4 = 12$.

4. Solve $x = 16 + 3x$.

Challenge yourself
1. Solve $2x - 18 = -12$.

2. Solve $7x - 9 = 17 + 6x$.

3. Solve $3(x + 12) = 2(7 - x)$.

4. Solve $x(8 - 6) = 7(x + 5)$.

south
The *direction* corresponding to the compass point that is 180° *clockwise* of *north* and 90° clockwise of *east*.
e.g.

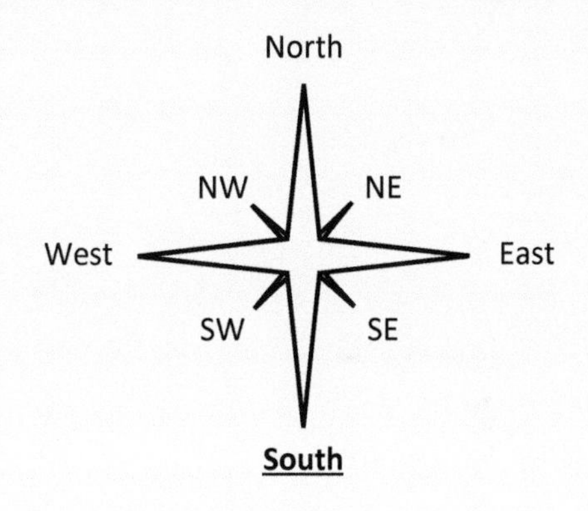

Test yourself
1. What is the direction corresponding to the compass point which is 90° anticlockwise of west?

2. What is the direction corresponding to the compass point which is 180° clockwise of south?

Challenge yourself
1. How many right angles are there in a turn from south to north in the clockwise direction?

2. Shreya is facing south. In which direction will she be facing after turning 315° anticlockwise?

speed
See *average speed*.

***

A B C D E F G H I J K L M N O P Q R S T U V W X Y Z

A B C D E F G H I J K L M N O P Q R S T U V W X Y Z

sphere

A perfectly round *three-dimensional* shape such that every point on the surface is equidistant from the centre.

e.g.

Sphere:
It has no flat faces.
It has 1 curved face.
It has no edges.
It has no vertices.

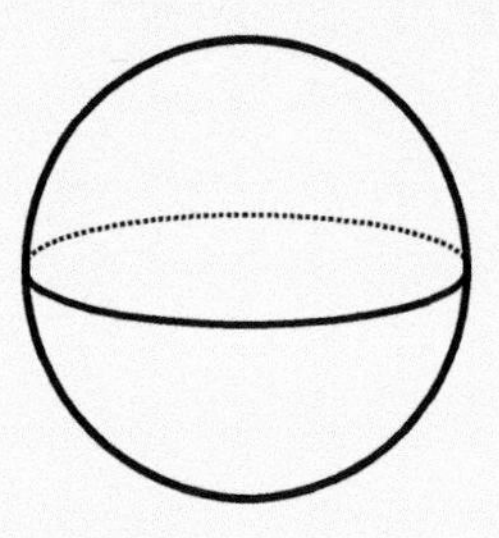

Test yourself

1. How many edges does a sphere have?

2. How many flat faces does a sphere have?

Challenge yourself

1. Given that the surface area of a sphere is $4\pi r^2$, calculate the surface area if $\pi = 3.14$ and $r = 2$cm. Give your answer in cm^2.

square

i. A *regular* four-sided *polygon*.

e.g.

Square:
All 4 angles are equal (90°).
All 4 sides are of equal length.
The diagonals bisect each other at 90°.

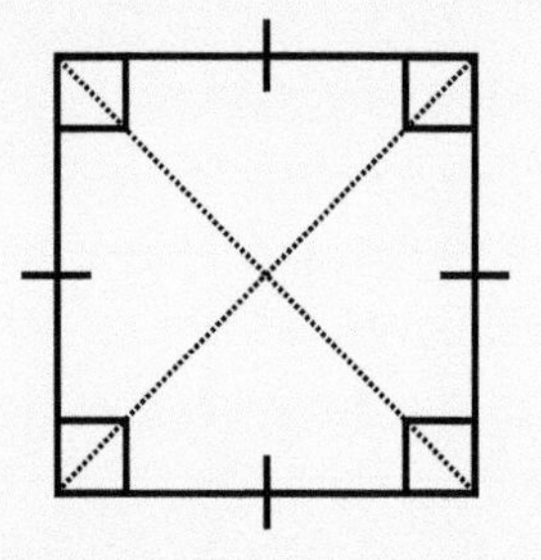

ii. To multiply a given number by itself.

e.g. 5 squared is 5 × 5 = 25.

Test yourself

1. Which of the following shapes is a square?

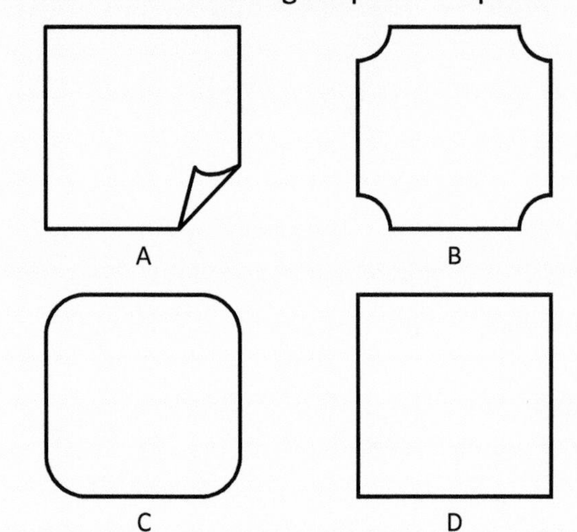

2. What is three squared?

Challenge yourself

1. What is the area of a square with sides of 8cm?

2. How many lines of symmetry does a square have?

3. What is the order of rotational symmetry of a square?

4. What is 36 squared?

square centimetre (cm^2)

A *metric unit* of area *equivalent* to the *area* of a *square* that has *sides* of 1cm.

e.g. If each side of a square is 5cm, the total area of the square is 5cm × 5cm = 25cm^2.

Test yourself

1. If each side of a square is 3cm, what is the total area of the square in cm^2?

2. If each side of a square is 9cm, what is the total area of the square in cm^2?

Challenge yourself

1. What is 12cm × 0.5m? Give your answer in cm^2.

2. Convert 5720cm^2 into m^2.

square kilometre (km^2)

A *metric unit* of area *equivalent* to the *area* of a *square* that has *sides* of 1km.

e.g. The area of the UK is approximately 240,000km^2.

Test yourself

1. If a national park is assumed to be a square with sides of 7km, what is its area in km^2?

2. What is 8km × 6km? Give your answer in km^2.

Challenge yourself

1. What is 2km × 120m? Give your answer in km^2.

2. Convert 2.7km^2 into m^2.

square metre (m^2)

A *metric unit* of area *equivalent* to the *area* of a *square* that has *sides* of 1m.

e.g. If the top and bottom sides of a parallelogram each measure 1m and the two sides are 2m apart, the area of the parallelogram is given by:

$1m \times 2m = 2m^2$.

Test yourself

1. What is 4m × 10m?

2. A square has sides of 11m. Calculate its area in m^2.

Challenge yourself

1. What is 5010mm × 3m? Give your answer in m^2.

2. Convert $3.7m^2$ into mm^2?

square millimetre (mm^2)

A *metric unit* of area *equivalent* to the *area* of a *square* that has *sides* of 1mm.

e.g. If the base of a triangle is 3mm and its height is 8mm, the area of the triangle is $^1/_2 \times 3 \times 8 = 12mm^2$.

Test yourself

1. What is 8mm × 2mm?

2. An MP3 player has a square screen with each side measuring 6mm. What is the area of the screen in mm^2?

Challenge yourself

1. What is 51mm × 7cm? Give your answer in mm^2.

2. Convert $3780mm^2$ into cm^2?

square number

A *positive number* which is calculated by multiplying a *whole number* by itself.

e.g. 1, 4, 9, 16, 25, 36, 49,...

Test yourself

1. What is the sum of the first five square numbers?

2. What is the twelfth square number?

3. What is the difference between the ninth and tenth square numbers?

4. What is the twentieth square number?

Challenge yourself

1. What is the sum of the seventh and eleventh square numbers?

2. What is the sum of the first five odd square numbers?

3. What are the square numbers between 250 and 290?

square prism

See *cube*.

***

square pyramid (square-based pyramid)

See *pyramid*.

***

square root

A *value* that results from carrying out the *inverse operation* of squaring, i.e. finding the number that, when multiplied by itself, gives the original number. It has the symbol '√'.

e.g. Since 2 × 2 = 4, the square root of 4 is 2, i.e. $\sqrt{4} = 2$.

Test yourself

1. Given that 12 × 12 = 144, what is the square root of 144?

2. What is the square root of 81?

3. What is the square root of 49?

Challenge yourself

1. What is the square root of 225?

2. What is the square root of 361?

3. What is the square root of 196?

4. If the area of a square is $441cm^2$, what is the length of one of its sides?

standard form (standard index form)

A method of writing very large and very small numbers. It is written in the form $D \times 10^n$, where D is a number between 1 and 9 and n is the number of columns the *decimal point* has to be shifted across.

Note: n is positive if the decimal point needs to be moved to the left, and negative if it needs to be moved to the right.

e.g. Write 22000 in standard form.

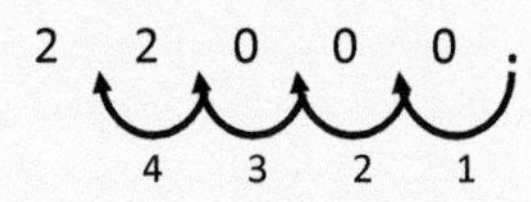

The decimal point is moved across four columns to the left, so n = 4 and D = 2.2.
Therefore, 22000 in standard form is 2.2×10^4.

Test yourself

1. Write 50,000 in standard form.

Challenge yourself

1. Write 250,000 in standard form.

2. Write 0.00025 in standard form.

statistical diagram

A *figure* representing *data* in the form of a diagram such as a graph, chart, *Venn diagram* or *pictogram*.

e.g. The Venn diagram below shows the first four square and triangular numbers.

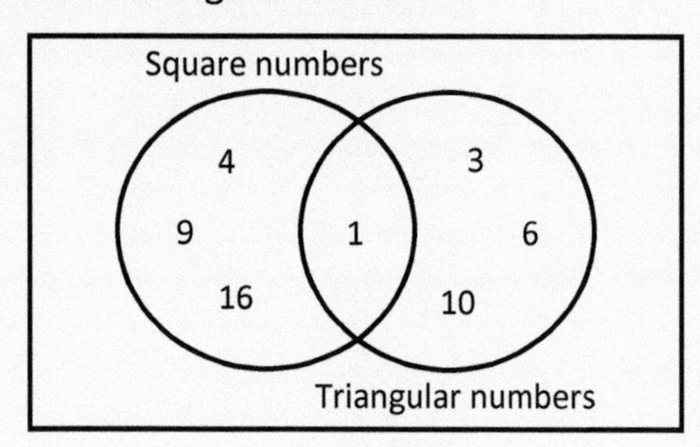

Test yourself

Answer the following questions using the Venn diagram in the example above.

1. List the first four square numbers.

2. List the first four triangular numbers.

3. Which number is both a square and a triangular number?

Challenge yourself

Using the pictogram below answer the following questions.

The pictogram shows the number of apples sold by a shop over a four-month period.

June	
July	
August	
September	

= 20 apples

1. How many apples were sold in June?

2. How many apples were sold in September?

3. What is the difference in the number of apples sold between August and September?

4. Calculate the mean number of apples sold per month to the nearest whole number.

stone (st)

An *imperial unit* of *mass equivalent* to 14 *pounds*, and approximately 6.4 *kilograms*.

e.g. 13st is equivalent to 182lbs.

Test yourself

1. What is 28 pounds expressed in stone?

2. Given that 1st = 6.4kg, how many kilograms are there in 3 stone?

Challenge yourself

1. Given that 1st = 6.4kg, convert 39 stone into kilograms.

2. Given that 1st = 14lbs, convert 784 pounds into stone.

straight angle

See *flat angle*.

***

subset

A set of numbers that is a part of a larger *set*.
e.g. If set A = {1, 2, 3, 4, 5, 6} and set B = {2, 4, 6}, then B is a subset of A.

Test yourself

1. If set C = {5, 8, 9} and set D = {8}, is set D a subset of set C?

Challenge yourself

1. If set E = {3, 4, 1} and set F = {3, 4, -1, 5}, is set E a subset of set F?

2. Are even numbers a subset of integers?

substitution

The replacement of a letter (a *variable*) in an *algebraic equation* or *expression* with a *value* or another variable.
e.g. Substituting the values $x = 2$ and $z = 5$ into the algebraic equation $y = x + 5z$ gives $y = 2 + 25 = 27$.

Test yourself

1. Given that $x = 3$, use substitution to find the value of y in the equation $y = x + 10$.

2. Given that $x = 5$, use substitution to find the value of y in the equation $y = 2x - 7$.

3. Given that $x = 6$, use substitution to find the value of y in the equation $y = 3x + 7$.

Challenge yourself

1. Given that $y = 2$ and $h = 3$, find the value of x in the following equation.

$$3x + 5y^2 - h^3 = 0$$

2. Given that $w = 0$, $y = x$ and $z = 6$, find the value of y in the following equation.

$$y = 9x + x - 33 + z + 15w$$

subtraction (minus)

An *arithmetic operation* used to calculate the *difference* between two or more numbers by taking one number away from another. It has the symbol '-'.
e.g. Subtracting 6 from 30 gives 24. This calculation can be written as 30 - 6 = 24.

Test yourself

1. What is 14 - 8?

2. Calculate 33 - 11.

Challenge yourself

1. What is 1809 - 324?

2. Calculate 25.21 - 15.98.

3. If the temperature of London on a given day is 5°C less than the one shown on the thermometer below, what is the actual temperature?

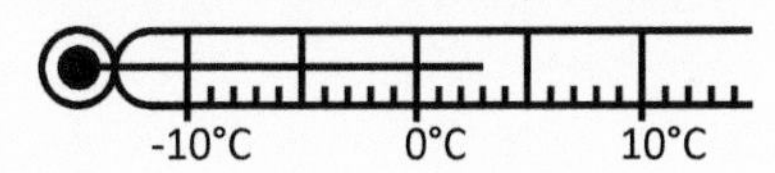

4. There are forty-seven cars in a car park. Every hour, five cars leave and three cars come in. How many cars are there in the car park after 7 hours?

sum

The result obtained by adding two or more numbers together.
e.g. The sum of 3, 5 and 8 is 3 + 5 + 8 = 16.

Test yourself

1. What is the sum of 4, 11 and 12?

2. What is the sum of 110 and 26?

Challenge yourself

1. What is the sum of 15.087 and 25.49?

2. What is the sum of the first 5 cube numbers?

3. What is the sum of the fifth square number and the eighth cube number?

supplementary angles

Any two *angles* that have a *sum* of 180°. See also *flat angle*.
e.g.

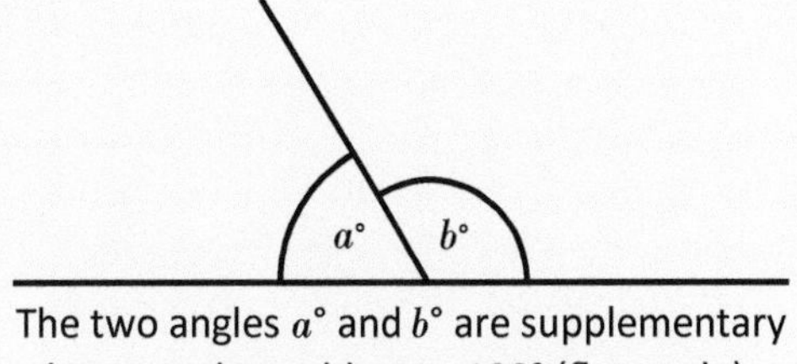

The two angles $a°$ and $b°$ are supplementary because they add up to 180° (flat angle), i.e. $a° + b° = 180°$.

A B C D E F G H I J K L M N O P Q R S T U V W X Y Z

<u>Test yourself</u>

Answer the following questions using the diagram below.

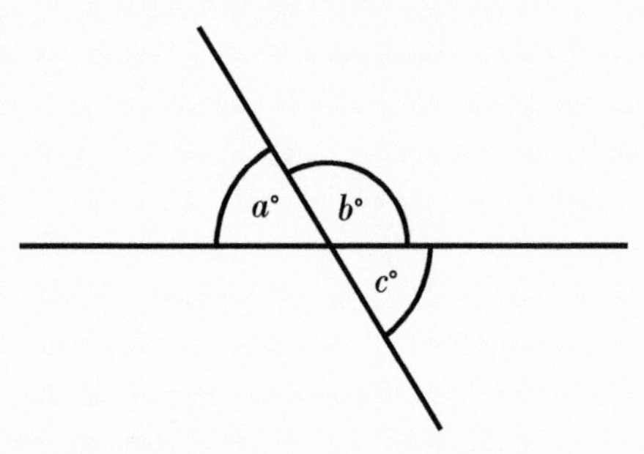

1. Are $a°$ and $b°$ supplementary angles?

2. Are $a°$ and $c°$ supplementary angles?

3. Are $b°$ and $c°$ supplementary angles?

<u>Challenge yourself</u>

1. What is the supplementary angle of 45°?

2. Which of the angles below are supplementary when added together?

40° 220° 86° 84° 120° 140°

surface

See *face*.

***

surface area

The total *area* of a *three-dimensional* shape given by the *sum* of the areas of all its *faces*.

e.g.

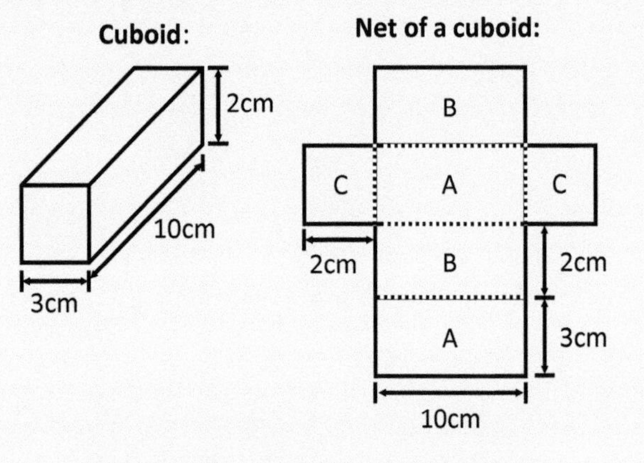

Area of surface A is 3cm × 10cm = 30cm^2.
Area of surface B is 2cm × 10cm = 20cm^2.
Area of surface C is 2cm × 3cm = 6cm^2.
Since there are two of each surface area, the total surface area is
2 × (30cm^2 + 20cm^2 + 6cm^2) = 112cm^2.

<u>Test yourself</u>

1. Calculate the surface area of the cuboid shown below.

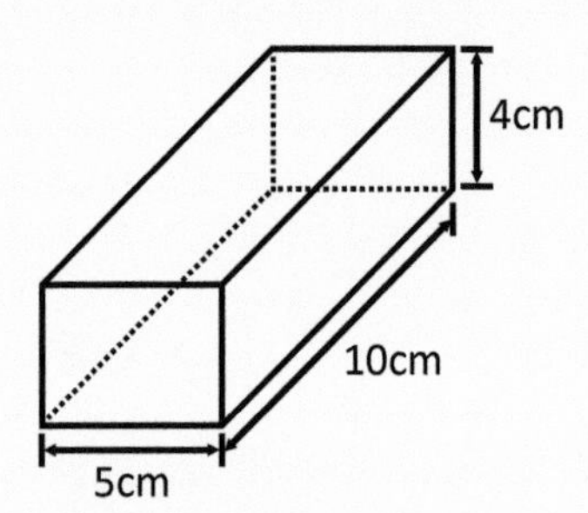

2. What is the surface area of the cube shown below? Give your answer in cm^2.

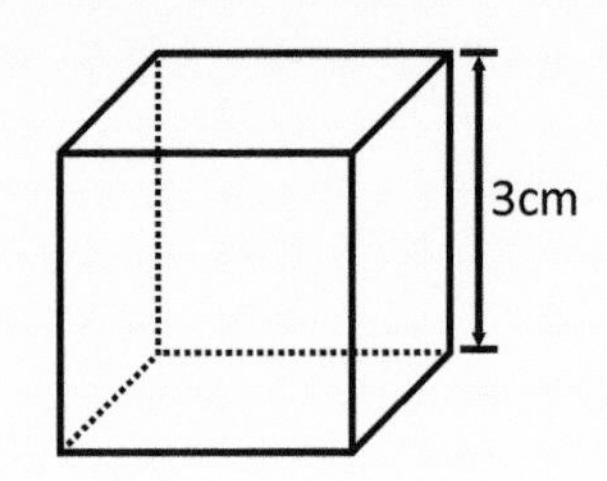

<u>Challenge yourself</u>

1. If the circumference of the circular face on the cylinder below is 10πcm and its cross-sectional area is 25πcm^2, what is the total surface area of the cylinder? Give your answer in πcm^2?

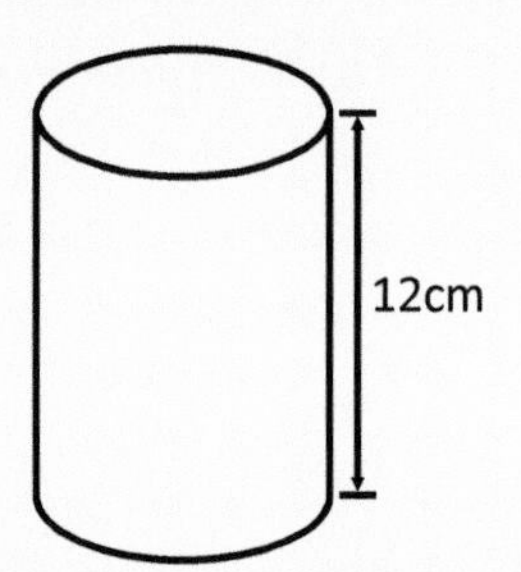

2. Calculate the surface area of the hexagonal prism shown below.

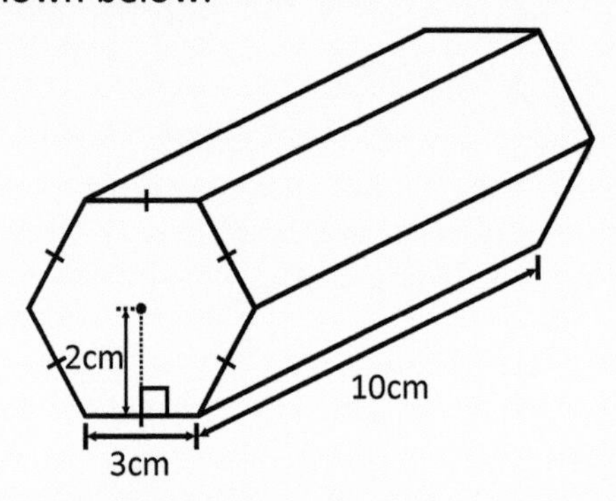

symmetry

i. See *reflective symmetry*.

ii. See *rotational symmetry*.

***

tally chart

A method of recording *data* using a tally, whereby the first four counts are *vertical* lines followed by a *diagonal* on the fifth.
Note: Each line or tally represents one count.
e.g.

A tally chart showing the favourite sports activities of children in a class.

Sport	Tally	Frequency
Football	𝍸 𝍸 𝍸	15
Basketball	𝍸 𝍸 |	11

Test yourself

Answer the following questions using the tally chart in the example above.
1. How many children favour football?

2. How many children favour basketball?

3. How many more children favour football compared to basketball?

Challenge yourself

Answer the following questions using the tally chart below.

A tally chart showing the gender of the students in a class

Gender	Tally
Boys	𝍸 𝍸 𝍸 |||
Girls	𝍸 𝍸 ||||

1. How many children are there in the class all together?

2. What is the ratio of girls to boys in the classroom?

3. If five girls and four boys permanently left the class, how many more boys would there be compared to girls?

tangent

A straight line that touches a curve at a single point but does not cross it.
e.g.

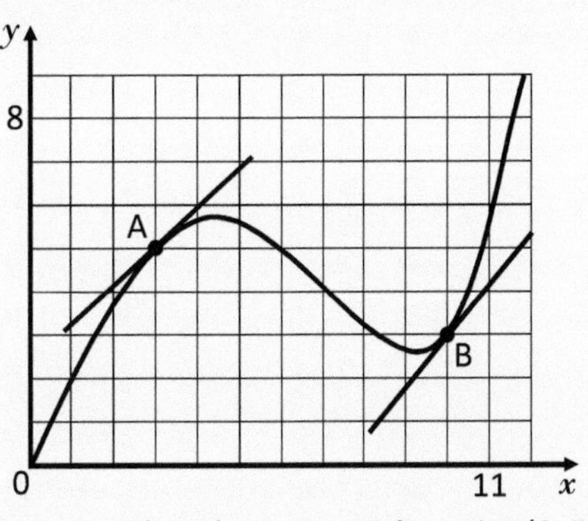

Tangent A touches the curve at the point (3, 5) and tangent B touches the curve at the point (10, 3).

Test yourself

1. Tangents C and D are shown below. What are the coordinates of the points at which tangents C and D touch the curve?

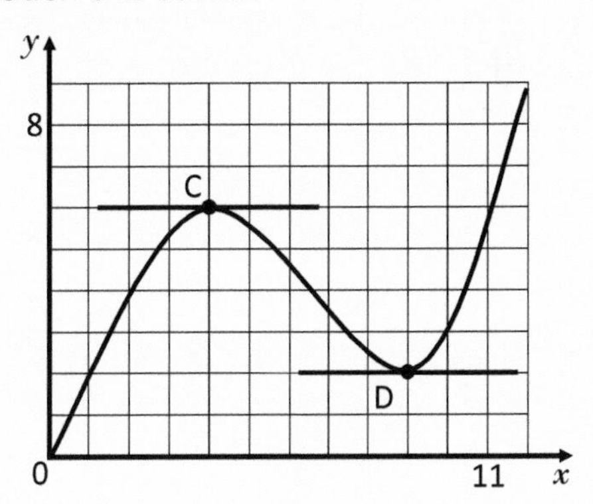

Challenge yourself

1. Which of the lines shown on the diagram below is a tangent to the circle?

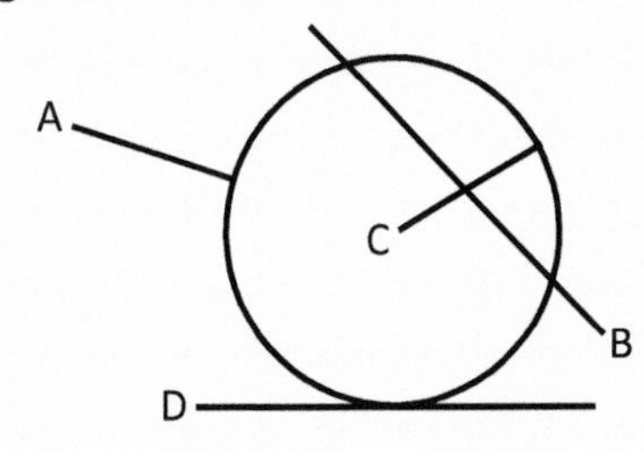

2. On the graph below, draw tangents to the curve at points A and B.

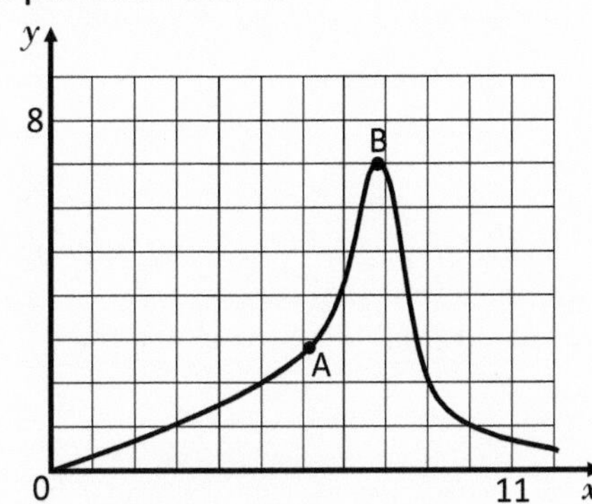

temperature

A numerical measure of how hot or cold something is, usually in *degree Celsius* (°C), Kelvin (K) or degree Fahrenheit (°F).

e.g. The boiling point of water is 100°C at sea level.

Test yourself

1. Boiling water was left to cool to a temperature of 25°C. If the boiling point of water is 100°C, what is the temperature change of the water?

2. Drashti has a fever and she measures her body temperature using a thermometer. According to the thermometer below, what is her body temperature?

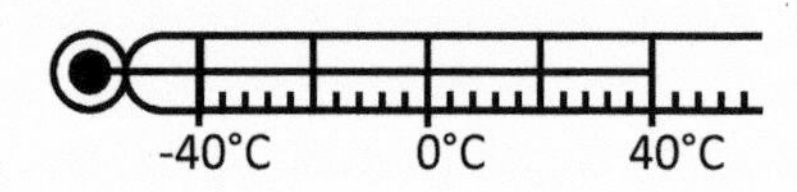

Challenge yourself

1. The temperature in Kelvin, T_k, can be found using the equation $T_k = T_c + 273.15$, where T_c is the temperature in degrees Celsius. Express 34°C in Kelvin.

2. Which of the following is the most reasonable approximation of room temperature?

0°C   -2°C   55°C   100°C   25°C

3. In a lake, a crocodile's body temperature drops from 30°C at a rate of 2°C every hour. If the crocodile's body temperature goes below 20 °C, its organs malfunction. How long can the crocodile stay in the lake before its organs start to malfunction?

tenth

i. A single part of something that has been divided into ten *equal* parts. It is expressed as $^1/_{10}$.

e.g. A tenth of 40 is $^1/_{10} \times 40 = 4$.

ii. The *ordinal number* of ten, i.e. 10th.

e.g. October is the tenth month of the year.

Test yourself

1. What is $^1/_{10}$ of 50?

2. Given that the first 5 square numbers are 1, 4, 9, 16 and 25, what is the tenth square number?

Challenge yourself

1. What is a tenth of 302?

2. Two hundred and twenty people sit an exam. A tenth of these people get below 40% and a tenth get above 90%. How many people get neither below 40% or above 90%?

3. Which of the following numbers is the tenth greatest: -0.3, 4, 100, 5^3, 89, 121, 2, -900, 79 and 123?

term

i. A single part of an *expression* that is separated from other parts by either a *plus* or *minus sign*. See also *coefficient*, *like terms*, *unlike terms*, *variable*.

e.g. In the expression $4x + 5y + 1$, the terms are $4x$, $5y$ and 1.

ii. A number in a sequence.

e.g. The geometric sequence: 2, 4, 8, 16, 32, comprises 5 terms.

Test yourself

1. Write the term that contains the x variable in the expression below.

$$4x + y$$

2. Write the term that contains the y variable in the expression below.

$$x + x + 7y$$

3. How many terms are in the sequence below, given that it terminates at 19?

1, 3, 5, 7, 9, 11,...

Challenge yourself

1. Which is the modal term in the list below?

$x, x, y, w, z, z, x, z, x, z, w, w, x$

2. Simplify the following expression and identify the coefficient of the term that has the x variable.

$$5x + 3y - x + x^2$$

3. Complete the sequence below by identifying the missing terms.

6	0	12		24	10		15

tetrahedron
See *triangular pyramid*.

***

thousandth
i. A single part of something that has been divided into one thousand *equal* parts. It is expressed as $^1/_{1000}$.
e.g. A gram is a thousandth of a kilogram.

ii. The *ordinal number* of one thousand (1000th).
e.g. Finishing a marathon in one thousandth place.

Test yourself

1. What is one thousandth of 2000?

2. What is the thousandth positive integer?

Challenge yourself

1. How many thousandths are there in two tenths?

2. How may thousandths do you need to make five?

three-dimensional (3D)
Figures with three dimensions: *length*, *width* and *height*.
e.g.

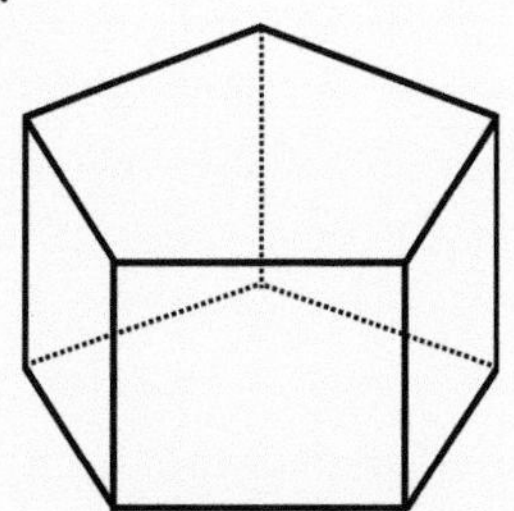

Pentagonal Prism:
It has 7 faces.
It has 10 vertices.
It has 15 edges.

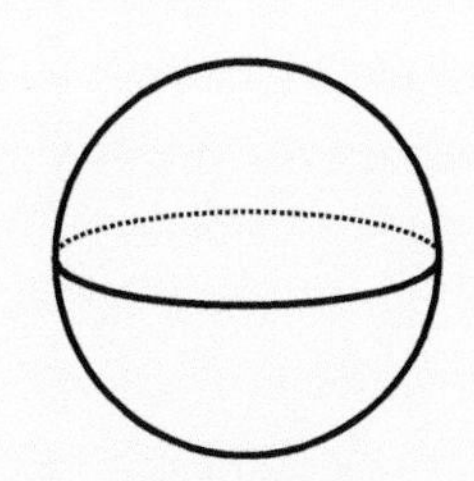

Sphere:
It has no flat faces.
It has 1 curved face.
It has no edges.

Both the pentagonal prism and sphere have a volume. Therefore, it is a three-dimensional shape.

Test yourself

1. Which of the following statements are true?
a. Three-dimensional shapes have length and width only.
b. Three-dimensional shapes have a volume.
c. Three-dimensional shapes have a surface area.
d. Three-dimensional shapes always have 2 faces.

Challenge yourself

1. How many of the shapes listed below are three -dimensional?

Trapezium	Rectangle	Cube
Pentagonal pyramid	Octahedron	Triangle

2. What is the name of the shape that has nine edges, six vertices and five faces?

3. What is the volume of a pentagonal prism if the cross-sectional area is 50cm^2 and the length is 1.5m? Give your answer in cm^3.

ton
An *imperial unit* of *mass equivalent* to 160 *stones*. See also *tonne*.
e.g. The British ton is approximately 1016kg.

Test yourself

1. What is 80 stone expressed in tons?

2. How many stone are there in 5 tons?

Challenge yourself

1. What is 1120 stone in tons?

2. What is 43 tons in stone?

tonne
A *metric unit* of *mass equivalent* to 1000 *kilograms*. See also *ton*.
e.g. 3.5 tonne is equivalent to 3500kg.

Test yourself

1. Convert 10 tonnes into kilograms.

2. Convert 700 kilograms into tonnes.

Challenge yourself

1. What is 300 grams in tonnes?

2. What is 53 tonnes in kilograms?

top-heavy fraction
See *improper fraction*.

***

A B C D E F G H I J K L M N O P Q R S T U V W X Y Z

transformation

A process of changing the position, orientation and/or size of a *figure*.
Note: The four types of transformations are *reflection*, *rotation*, *translation* and *enlargement*. The size of a shape does not change after reflection, rotation or translation.

e.g.

Shape A can be rotated 180° anticlockwise or clockwise to give shape B. Alternatively, shape A can be translated 4 units left and 4 units down, or reflected across the line $y = -x$ to give shape B.

Test yourself

1. Which transformations change the size of a shape?

2. Which transformations change the position of a shape about a given point?

3. Which transformations change the position of a shape relative to a mirror line?

Challenge yourself

1. What type of transformation is applied to shape A to give shape B?

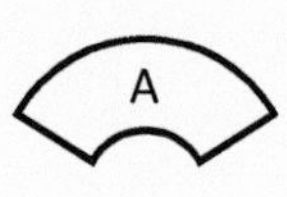

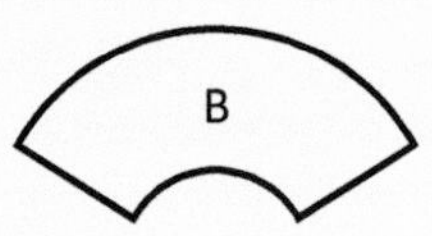

2. Reflect the dot on the graph below across the y-axis and then the x-axis. Finally, identify the coordinates of its new position.

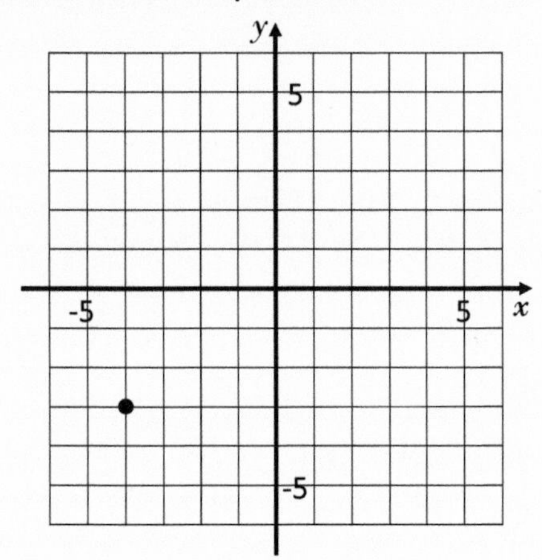

3. Rotate point A(2, 4) 180°C anticlockwise about the point (0, 2) and identify the coordinates of its new position.

translation

Changing the position of an object without rotating or resizing it. See also *column vector*.
Rule: A *positive number* represents a movement to the right or upwards and a *negative number* represents a movement to the left or downwards. The first number represents *horizontal* movement, and the second represents *vertical* movement.

e.g. If a point at the origin is translated 2 units right and 5 units down, the new position of the point is (2, -5). The vector form of this translation is $\begin{pmatrix} 2 \\ -5 \end{pmatrix}$.

Test yourself

1. Point A is translated to a new position B. Describe the transformation.

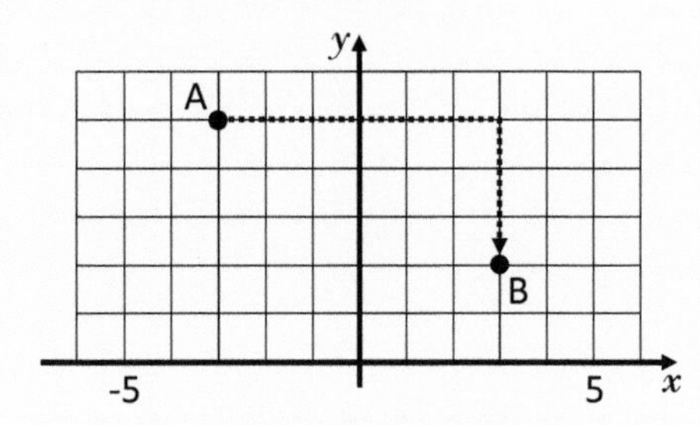

Challenge yourself

1. What are the new coordinates of point A (3, 5) after a translation of 6 units left, 9 units right, 4 units up and 3 units down?

2. Translate the dot on the graph below 5 units right and 8 units down. Identify the coordinates of its new position and express the translation using a column vector.

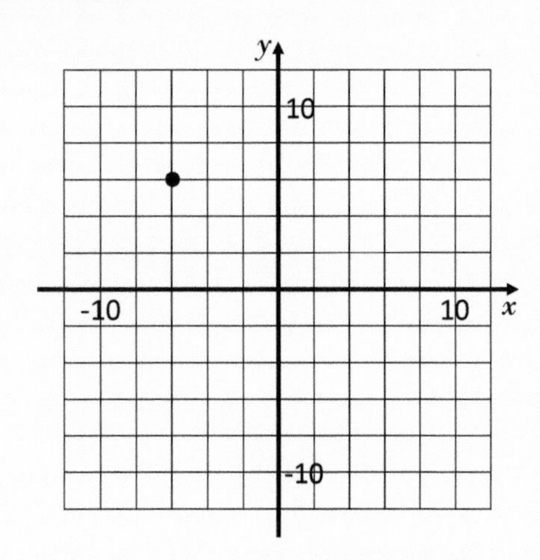

transversal

A straight line that intersects at least two other lines at two distinct points. See *intersection*.

e.g.

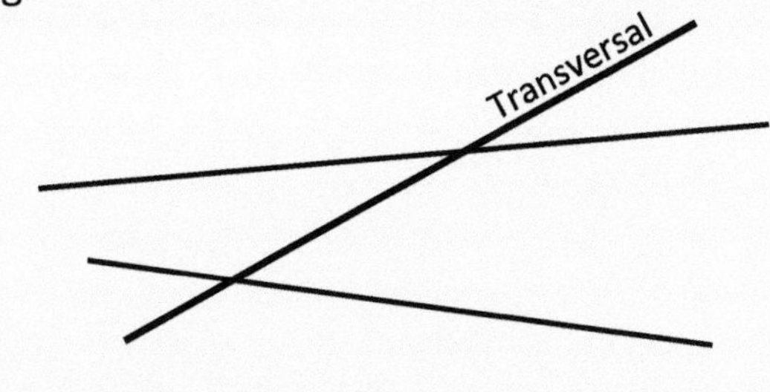

Test yourself

1. Which of the lines below is a transversal?

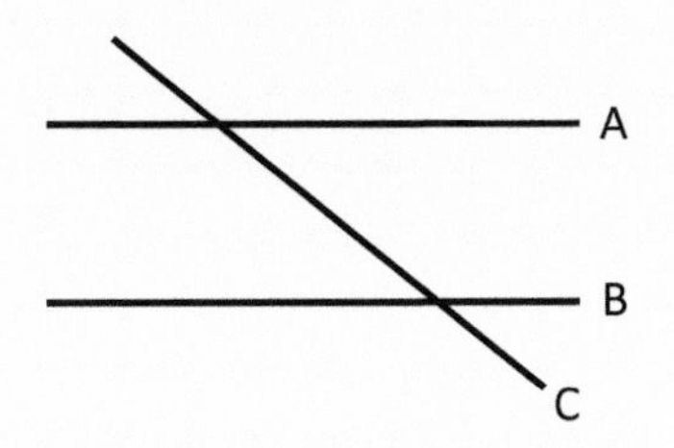

Challenge yourself

1. How many of the lines below are transversals?

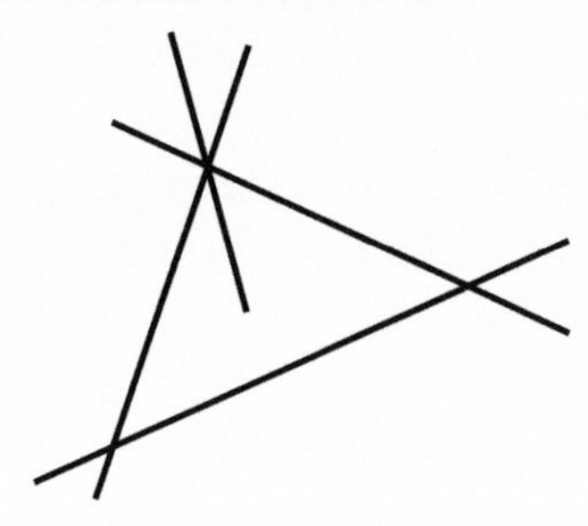

2. How many angles does a transversal produce?

trapezium (trapezoid)

A *quadrilateral* with one pair of *parallel* lines of different lengths.

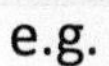

e.g.

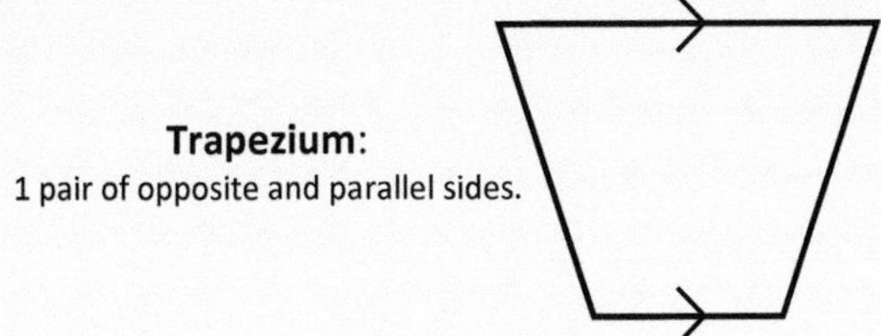

Test yourself

1. Is the shape below a trapezium?

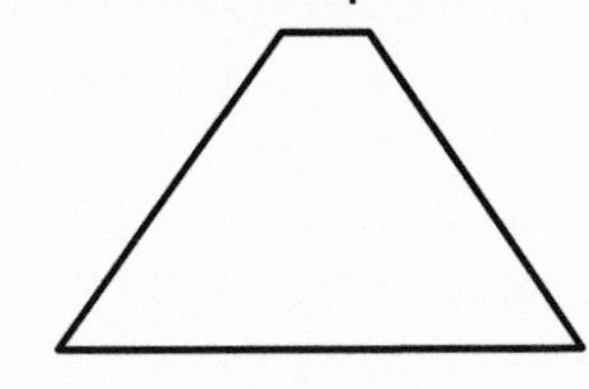

Challenge yourself

1. What is the sum of the interior angles of a trapezium?

2. What is the order of rotational symmetry of an isosceles trapezium?

3. Calculate the area of the shape below in cm^2.

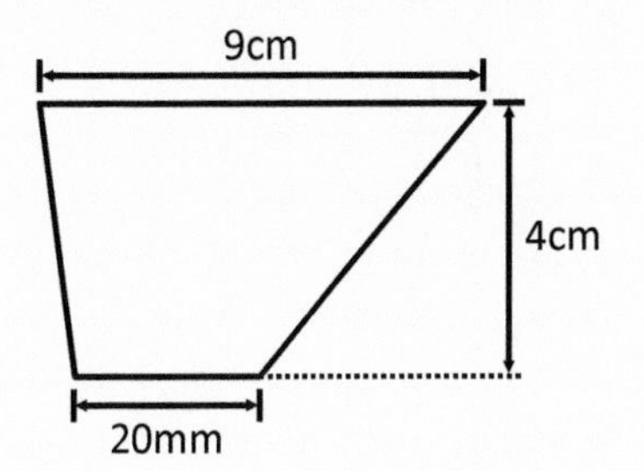

tree diagram

A way of illustrating *probabilities* of *consecutive events* using branches.

Note: You can use the 'and' rule and 'or' rule with a tree diagram.

Rule: The word 'or' is replaced by an *addition* sign. The word 'and' is replaced by a *multiplication* sign. When using a tree diagram, multiply probabilities along the branches, and add probabilities down the columns.

e.g. Tree diagram illustrating two tosses of a biased coin.

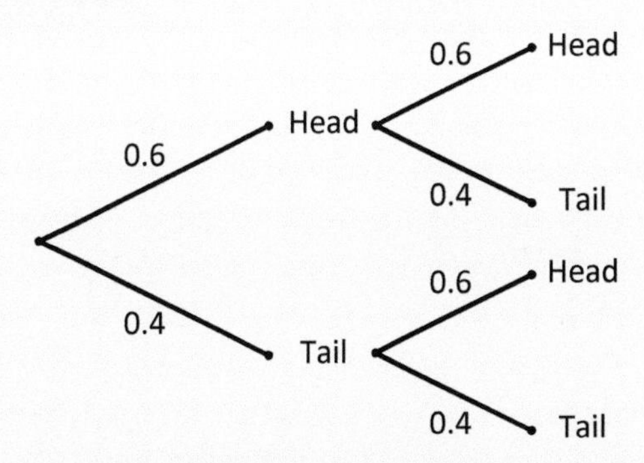

Multiply probabilities along the branches, and add probabilities down columns.

Test yourself

Answer the following questions using the tree diagram in the example above.

1. Is the coin fair?

2. What is the probability of the coin landing on heads on the first toss?

3. What is the probability of the coin landing on heads twice in a row?

A B C D E F G H I J K L M N O P Q R S T U V W X Y Z

Challenge yourself

1. According to the tree diagram in the example, what is the probability of the coin landing on heads and then tails or landing on tails twice?

2. Look at the tree diagram below. A factory produces toys of two different colours, red and blue. A toy can either be defective or not. What is the probability of manufacturing a red toy that is not defective?

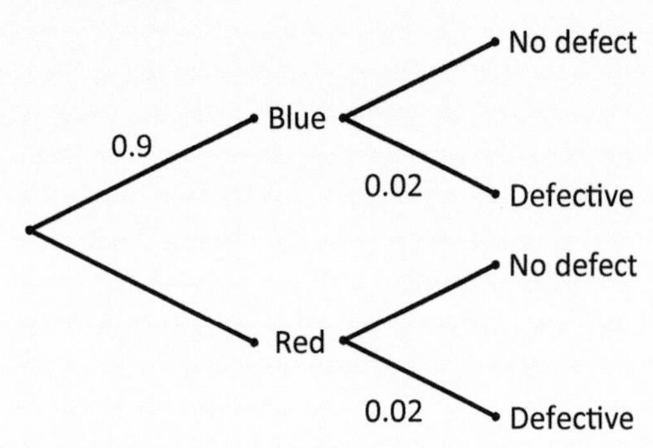

triangle

A three-sided *polygon*.

e.g.

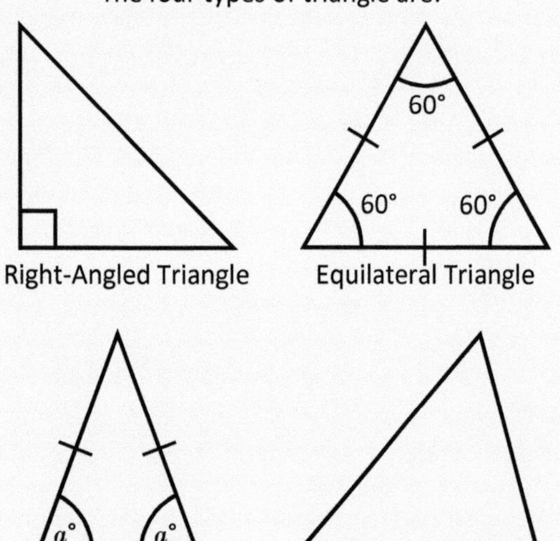

Test yourself

1. What is the name given to a triangle with 3 equal sides?

2. What is the name given to a triangle with a right angle?

3. What is the name given to a triangle with no equal sides?

4. What is the name given to a triangle with two equal sides and two equal interior angles?

Challenge yourself

1. How many triangles can you see in the diagram below?

2. If the angles of a triangle are in the ratio 1:1:2, what is the size of the largest angle?

triangular number

A positive *integer* which is the *sum* of *consecutive whole numbers*. This can be illustrated by drawing a triangular dot pattern.

e.g. 1, 3, 6, 10, 15, 21,...

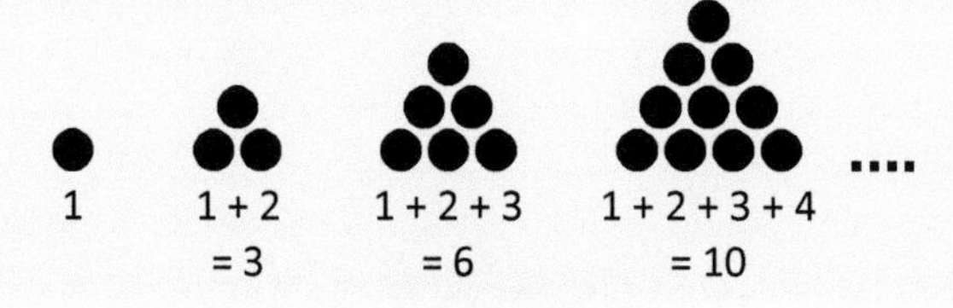

Test yourself

1. What is the fifth triangular number?

2. What is the sum of the first five triangular numbers?

Challenge yourself

1. The general formula for the nth term of the triangular number sequence is $x_n = n(n + 1) \div 2$. What is the 30th triangular number?

2. What is the product of the second, fifth and seventh triangular numbers?

triangular prism

A *three-dimensional figure* with two *parallel* triangular *faces* that are joined by *rectangles*. It has a triangular *cross-section*.

e.g.

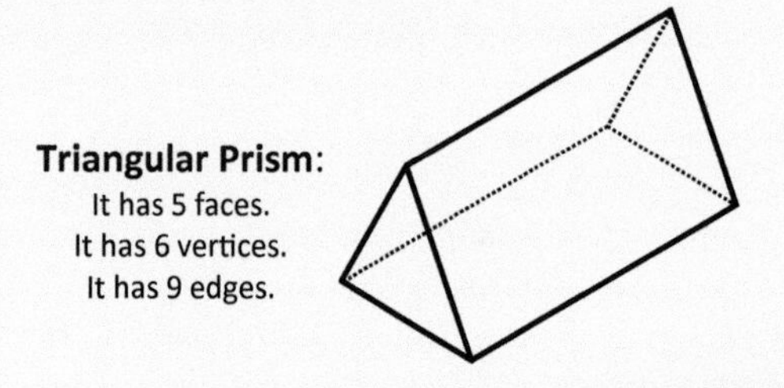

Test yourself

1. What is the sum of the numbers of faces, vertices and edges of a triangular prism?

Challenge yourself

1. If the cross-sectional area of a triangular prism is $17cm^2$ and the length is 22cm, what is its volume?

2. If the volume of a triangular prism is $180cm^3$ and its length is 15cm, what is its cross-sectional area?

triangular pyramid (tetrahedron)

A *three-dimensional* shape made up of four triangular *faces*.

e.g.

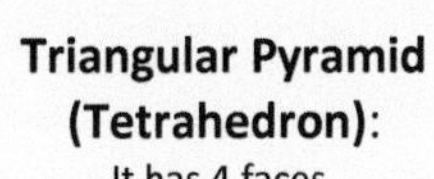

It has 4 faces.
It has 4 vertices.
It has 6 edges.

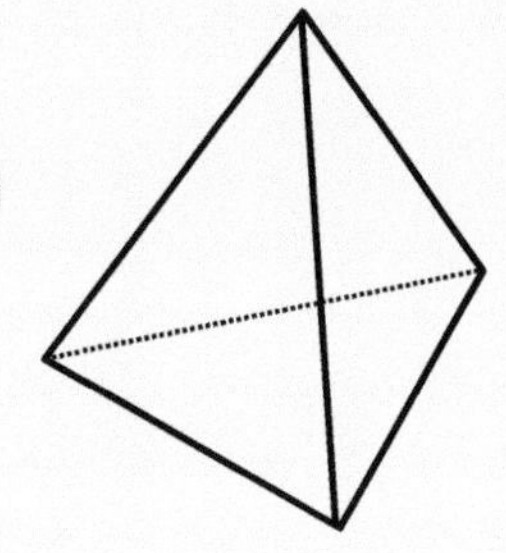

Test yourself

1. How many triangular faces are required to construct a tetrahedron?

2. What is the sum of the numbers of faces and edges of a triangular pyramid?

Challenge yourself

1. What is the name given to the triangles that make up the faces of a regular tetrahedron?

2. If equilateral triangles of area $50cm^2$ are used to make a tetrahedron, what is its total surface area?

trinomial

An algebraic *expression* consisting of three *terms*, each with a unique letter (*variable*).

e.g. In the expression $7x + 5y + 2z$, there are three unique terms, $7x$, $5y$ and $2z$, so it is a trinomial.

Test yourself

1. Is $x + y - 2z$ a trinomial expression?

Challenge yourself

1. Which of the expressions below is a trinomial but not in its simplest form?

$x^2 + y^2$ $\quad$ $a + 2a + b - c$ $\quad$ $3a^2 + b$

triple

Increasing a *value* by a *factor* of three, i.e. multiplying a value by 3.

e.g. Triple 2 is 2 × 3 = 6.

Test yourself

1. What value is obtained when 12 is tripled?

Challenge yourself

1. What value is obtained when 5^4 is tripled?

two-dimensional (2D)

Figures with two dimensions: *length* and *width*, but no depth.

e.g.

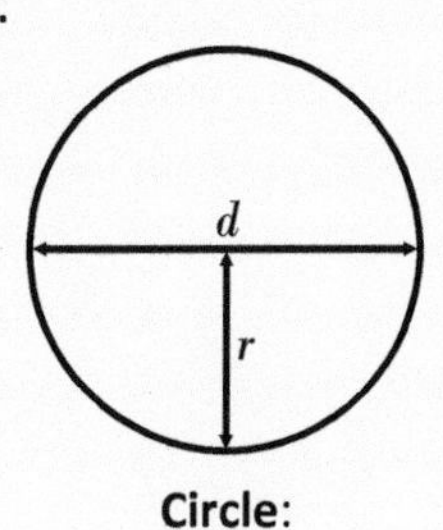

Circle:
r = radius
d = diameter
Circumference = $2\pi r$
Area = πr^2

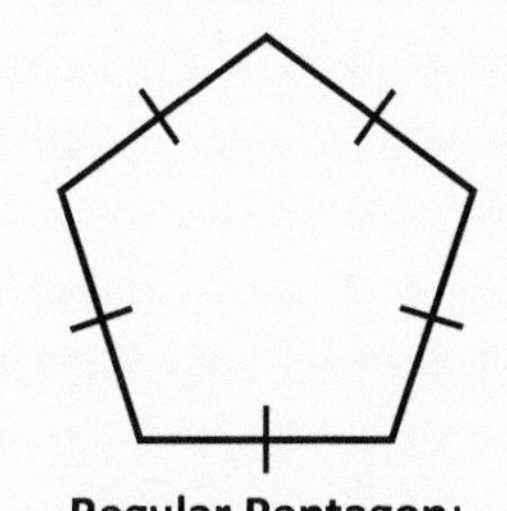

Regular Pentagon:
All 5 angles are equal.
All 5 sides are of equal length.
The sum of the interior angles is 540°.

Test yourself

1. A shape has four pairs of parallel sides. What 2D shape could this be?

2. Which of the following shapes is two-dimensional?

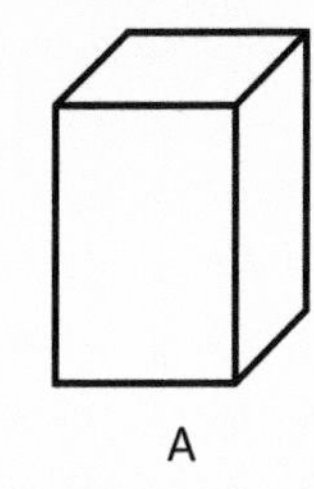

A

B

C

Challenge yourself

1. How many edges does a nonagon have?

2. What is the name of a shape that has one pair of parallel sides and one pair of sides of equal length?

A
B
C
D
E
F
G
H
I
J
K
L
M
N
O
P
Q
R
S
T
U
V
W
X
Y
Z

U

unbiased

See *fair*.

***

unfair

An item or *event* that is not free from *bias*, i.e. marked by partiality.

e.g. When an unfair die is rolled, the probability of rolling an even number is not 0.5.

Test yourself

1. A deck of cards consists of six Jacks. Is this a fair deck?

2. A coin lands on heads twenty times out of twenty tosses. Can the coin be described as unfair?

Challenge yourself

1. An unfair coin lands on tails sixty times out of a hundred tosses. What is the probability of getting a tail followed by a head?

uniform

Something that has the same structure throughout, i.e. having an unchanging form.

e.g. A cylinder has a uniform circular cross-section.

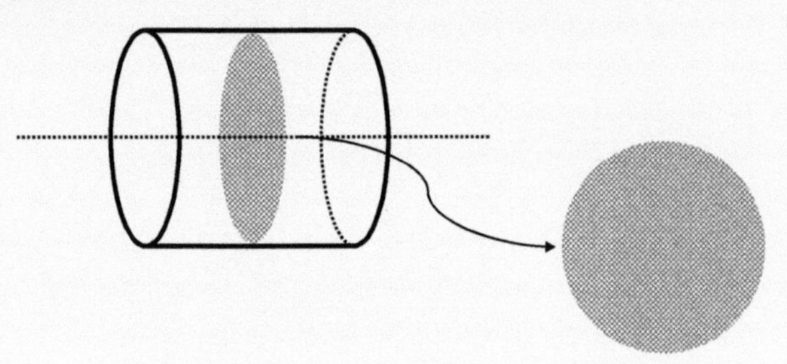

The cross-section of a cylinder is a circle.

Test yourself

1. Which shape represents the uniform cross-section of a cube?

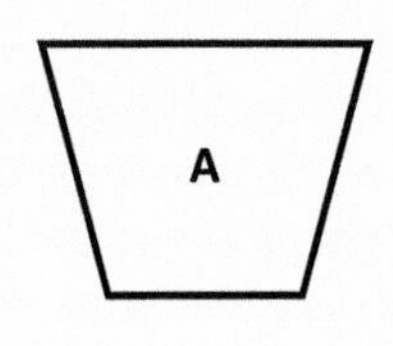

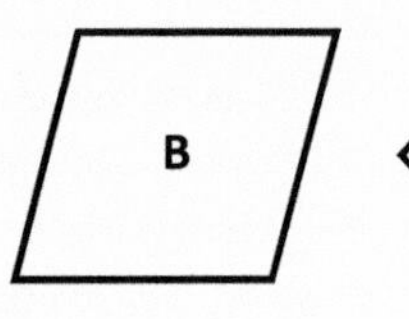

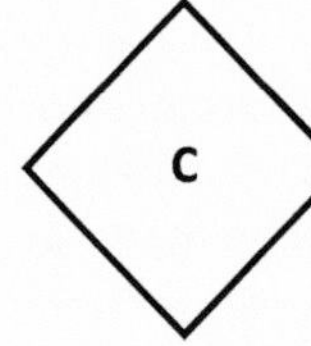

Challenge yourself

1. A prism has a uniform triangular cross-section. Sketch the shape.

2. What is the name given to the shape in question 1?

3. What is the name given to a prism with a pentagon as its cross-section?

4. What is the name given to a prism with a heptagon as its cross-section?

unit

i. A quantity used as a standard of measurement.

e.g. metre, kilogram, second etc.

ii. The *digit* that is positioned immediately left of the *decimal point*.

e.g. In the figure 125.12, the unit is 5.

Test yourself

1. From the options below, which is a unit of distance?

A	B	C
mm	m^2	cm^3

2. Which value is in the unit column in 512?

Challenge yourself

1. What unit is most commonly used when measuring the volume of a cup of water?

2. Which value is in the unit column in 9483.074?

unlikely

Having a *probability* that is less that 0.5, i.e. *improbable*.

e.g. Tossing a fair coin and obtaining ten straight heads is unlikely.

Test yourself

1. Is it unlikely to get ten sixes in a row when a fair die is thrown?

2. Is it unlikely to pick a heart or a diamond from a deck of playing cards?

Challenge yourself

1. On the probability scale below, circle the letter which marks the probability of an unlikely event occurring.

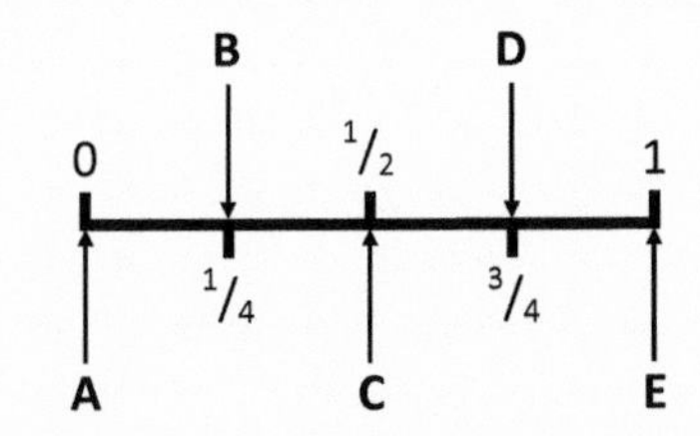

2. Which of the following events are unlikely?

a. The Sun will rise tomorrow.
b. It will snow in June in the UK.
c. Getting a tail when tossing a fair coin.
d. Rolling an even number with a six-sided fair die.

unlike terms

Terms with different *variables*, or with the same variables but raised to different *powers*.

e.g. In the expression $y + y^2$, y and y^2 are unlike terms because they are raised to different powers of y.

Test yourself

1. In the expression below, how many unlike terms are there?

$$x + x^2 - y$$

2. In the expression below, how many unlike terms are there?

$$7x + x - y - 2y$$

Challenge yourself

1. In the expression below, how many unlike terms are there?

$$2x + x^2 - y + xy + 10 - 2y - 5 + 5y$$

2. In the expression below, how many unlike terms are there?

$$7x + x^7 - y - 2y$$

value

i. A numerical amount showing how much something is worth.

e.g. If the price of a car was £10,000 and it was reduced by 25%, the value of the car is now:
$^3/_4 \times$ £10,000 = £7,500.

ii. A numerical quantity.

e.g. 4 × 3 ÷ 2 × 5 gives the value 30.

Test yourself

1. What is the value of 12 multiplied by 6?

2. Determine the value of 3 in £4367.

3. Assuming £1 = € 1.50, what is the value of £350 in euros?

Challenge yourself

1. If a pair of shoes costs £50 and they are reduced by 30%, what is the value of the shoes now?

2. What is the value of the digit 4 in 5493?

3. What is the value of the digit 9 in 2.509?

variable

A symbol that is used in mathematical *expressions* that can take a *range* of *values*.

e.g. In the equation $y = x$, both y and x are variables.

Test yourself

1. In the equation $4x + 5 = 11$, identify the variable.

2. What are the variables in $5y - 2x = 10$?

Challenge yourself

1. Count the number of different variables in the expression $y + y + y^2 + \pi x^2 + 5 = 0$.

2. Given that $y = 5$ and $x = 6$, find the value of z.
$z = 10y - 2x$

A
B
C
D
E
F
G
H
I
J
K
L
M
N
O
P
Q
R
S
T
U
V
W
X
Y
Z

vector
A quantity that gives information about the *direction* and *distance* of one point from another. See also *column vector*.
e.g.

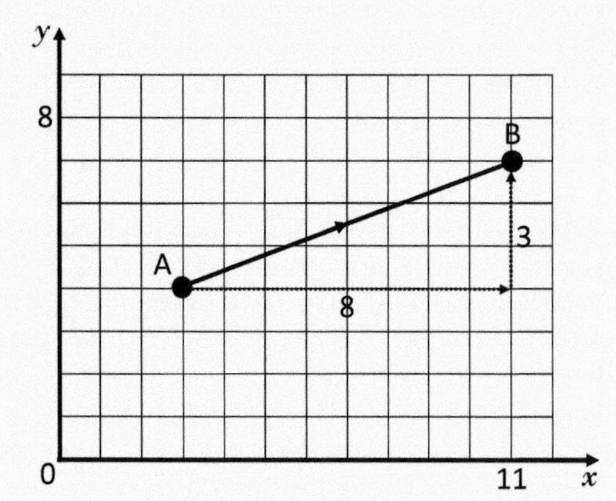

To translate point A to point B, point A must be translated 8 units right and 3 units up, that is $\binom{8}{3}$ in vector form.

Test yourself

1. A point at the origin is translated to a new position with coordinates (3, 8). Describe the translation in words.

Challenge yourself

Answer the following questions using the graph below.

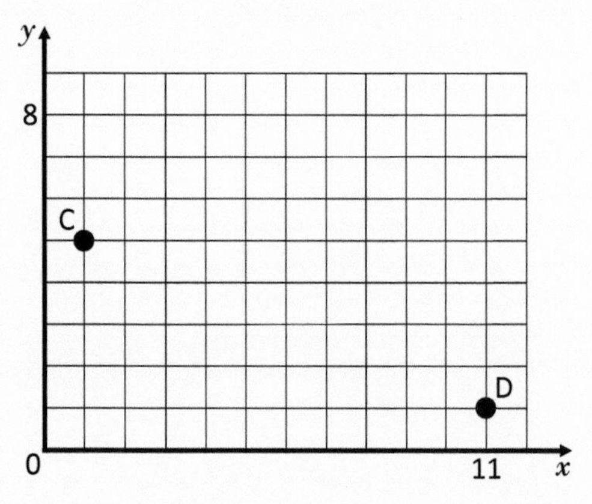

1. What is the translation required to move point C to point D? Give your answer in vector form.

2. What is the translation required to move point D to point C? Give your answer in vector form.

3. A point is translated 11 units left and 5 units down. Express the translation in vector form.

4. A point is translated 8 units up and 1 unit right. What is the translation in vector form?

velocity
See *speed*.

***

Venn diagram
A diagram showing all logical relations for a collection of *sets* using overlapping *circles*, non-overlapping circles and a rectangular boundary.
e.g. Venn diagram showing the first ten positive integers.

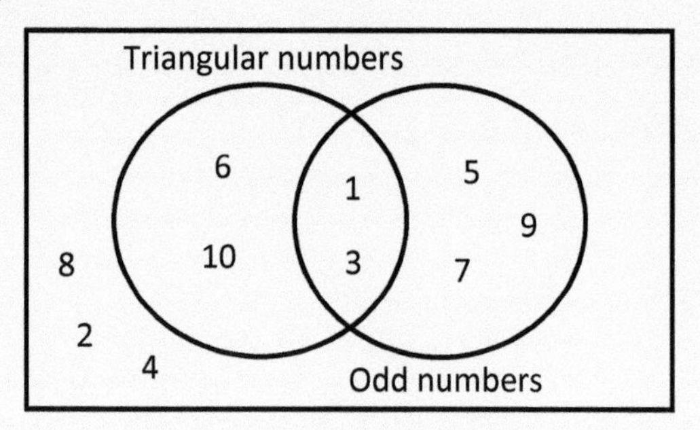

Test yourself

Answer the following questions using the Venn diagram in the example above.

1. How many numbers are triangular numbers?

2. How many numbers are odd numbers?

3. How many numbers are both triangular and odd numbers?

4. How many numbers are neither triangular nor odd numbers?

Challenge yourself

Answer the following questions using the incomplete Venn diagram below.

Venn diagram illustrating the relations of integers between 1 and 25

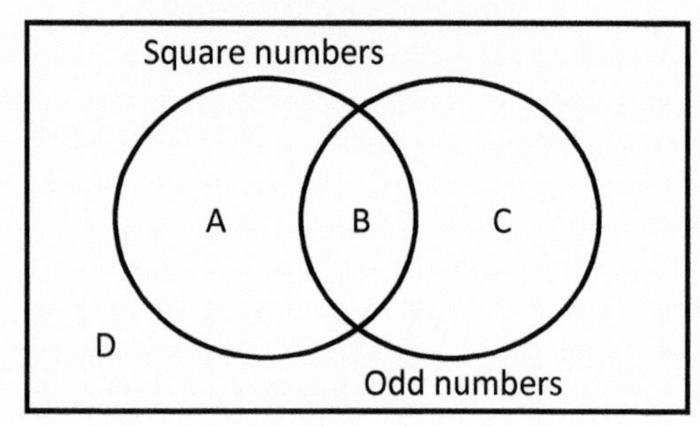

1. List the numbers that should go into D.

2. List the numbers that should go into C.

3. List the numbers that should go into B.

vertex (plural: vertices)

A point or a corner where two or more straight lines meet.

e.g.

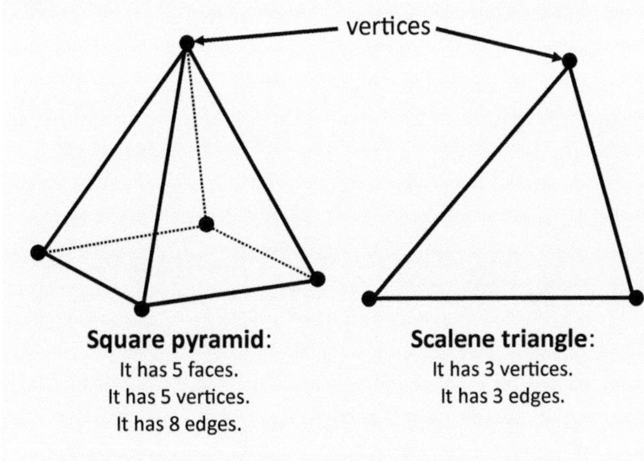

<u>Test yourself</u>

1. How many vertices does the following shape have?

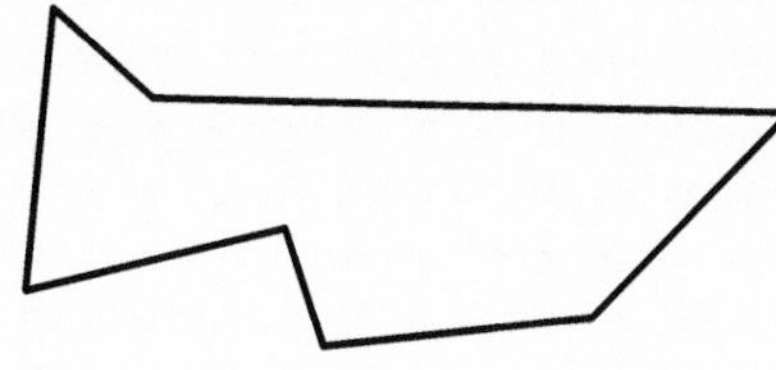

2. How many vertices does the following shape have?

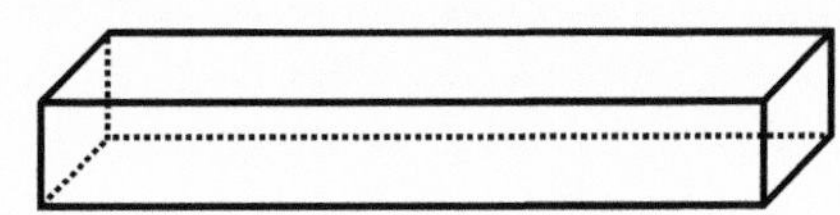

<u>Challenge yourself</u>

1. How many vertices does a tetrahedron have?

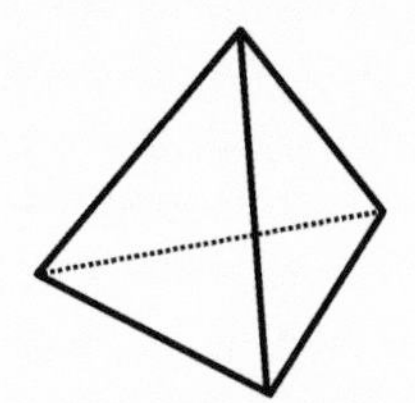

2. How many vertices does a decagonal prism have?

3. How many vertices does a circle have?

4. How many vertices does the following shape have?

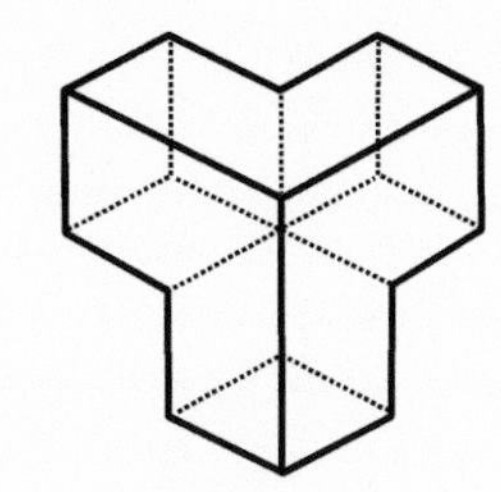

vertical

A line that is perpendicular to a horizontal line or a flat surface.

e.g.

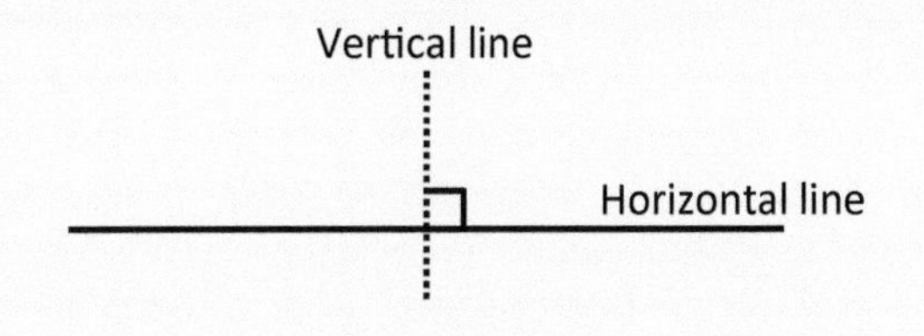

<u>Test yourself</u>

1. What is the angle between a horizontal line and a vertical line?

2. An octagon is sitting on a plane as shown below. How many vertical lines are there in the octagon?

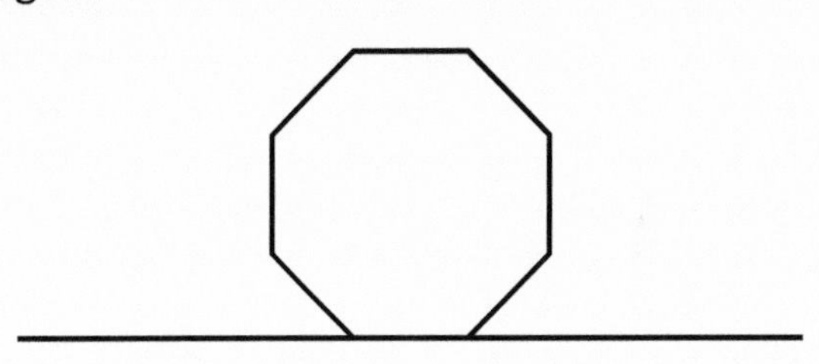

<u>Challenge yourself</u>

1. Draw a line that is vertical to the x-axis and goes through (4, 4).

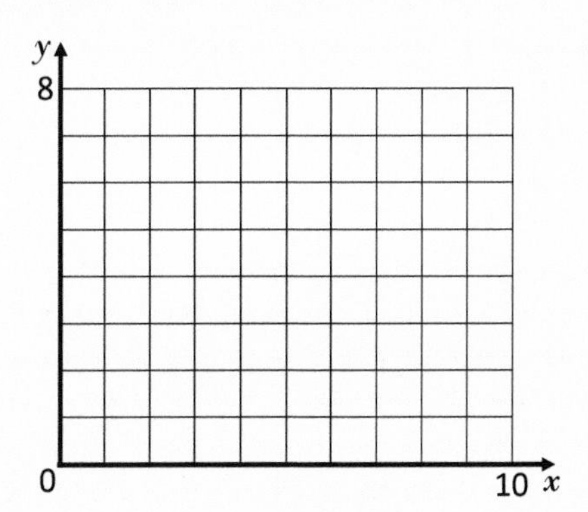

vertically opposite angle

Equal angles that are opposite each other when two lines cross (intersect).

e.g.

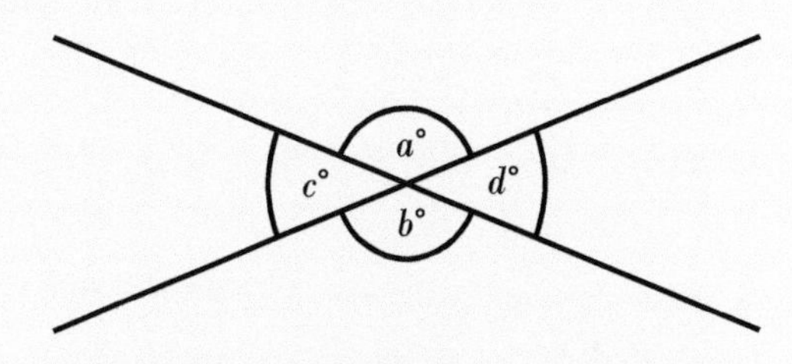

Vertically opposite angles are always equal, i.e. $a° = b°$ and $c° = d°$.

A B C D E F G H I J K L M N O P Q R S T U **V** W X Y Z

<u>Test yourself</u>

Answer the following questions using the diagram below.

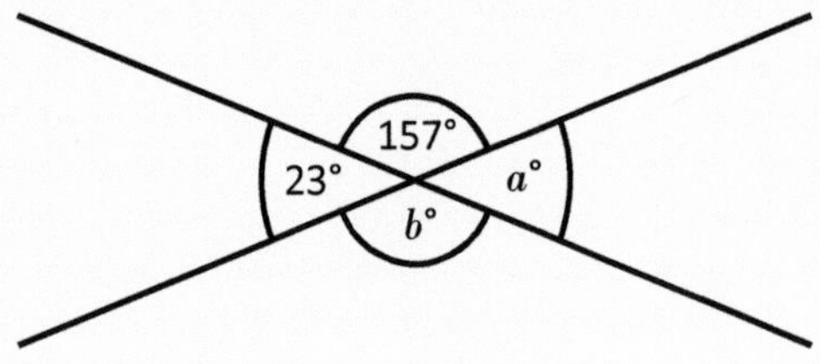

1.What is the size of angle a°?

2. What is the size of angle b°?

<u>Challenge yourself</u>

1. Look at the diagram below. What is the value of angle x°?

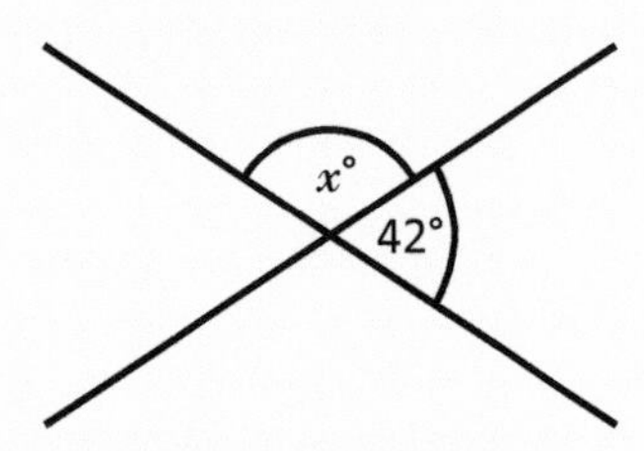

volume

The amount of space a *three-dimensional* shape occupies, i.e. the amount of space contained within it.

<u>Note:</u> Volume is measured in cubed *units* such as cm^3 and m^3.

e.g.

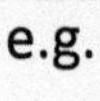

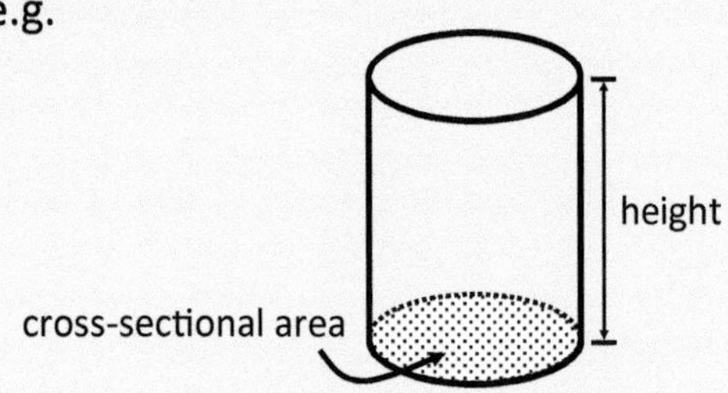

The volume of a cylinder is given by:
cross-sectional area × height.

<u>Test yourself</u>

Using the formula sheet to help you, answer the following questions.

1. What is 5cm × 8cm × 2cm?

2. What is the volume of a cube with sides of 7cm?

3. If a cylinder has a cross-sectional area of $12mm^2$ and a height of 10mm, what is its volume?

<u>Challenge yourself</u>

1. If the cross-sectional area of a hexagonal prism is $15cm^2$ and its length is 8cm, what is the maximum number of marbles of volume $10cm^3$ that can potentially fit inside it?

2. How many small cubes with sides of 4cm can fit inside a cuboid with a volume of $704cm^3$.

3. Jenar plans to divide his large living room into two smaller separate rooms. The living room has a volume of $169m^3$ and it is 12m wide. He decides to divide the room at 4m from the end by inserting a sliding door. Ignoring the thickness of the doors, what will be the new volume of the smaller room?

vulgar fraction

A *fraction* that is expressed with a *numerator* and a *denominator* that are both *integers*.

e.g. $^5/_6$, $^7/_8$, $^{11}/_{13}$ etc.

<u>Test yourself</u>

1. Which of the following are vulgar fractions?

A	B	C	D
$^{4.1}/_5$	$^2/_{8.1}$	$^{20}/_{13}$	$^1/_{20}$

<u>Challenge yourself</u>

1. Express 4 ÷ 84 as a vulgar fraction in its simplest form.

2. Express 12 ÷ 120 as a vulgar fraction in its simplest form.

3. Convert the vulgar fraction $^{77}/_4$ into a mixed fraction.

4. What is the sum of the two vulgar fractions below?

$$^2/_3 + {}^3/_2$$

week

A period of seven *consecutive* days. A week is comprised of weekdays and a weekend.
Note: Any day other than Saturday and Sunday is known as a weekday.
e.g. There are 14 days in 2 weeks.

Test yourself

1. How many days are there in 5 weeks?

2. How many weeks are there in 49 days?

Challenge yourself

1. Approximately, how many weeks are there in a year?

2. How many days are there in 9.5 weeks?

weight

This is how heavy an object is. The weight of an object changes according to the force of gravity acting on it. However, it is commonly used to refer to the mass of an object.
e.g.

The scale shows that 3.5 pints of milk weigh approximately 2kg.

Test yourself

1. Which of the following weighs the most?
   a. Basketball
   b. Tennis ball
   c. Volleyball

2. Assume 1lb = 0.45kg. Pooja weighs 90lb to the nearest whole number. How much does she weigh in kilograms (kg)?

Challenge yourself

1. What is 9.5kg in grams?

2. What is 583.2g in kilograms?

3. What is the weight of the two bricks shown on the scale below?

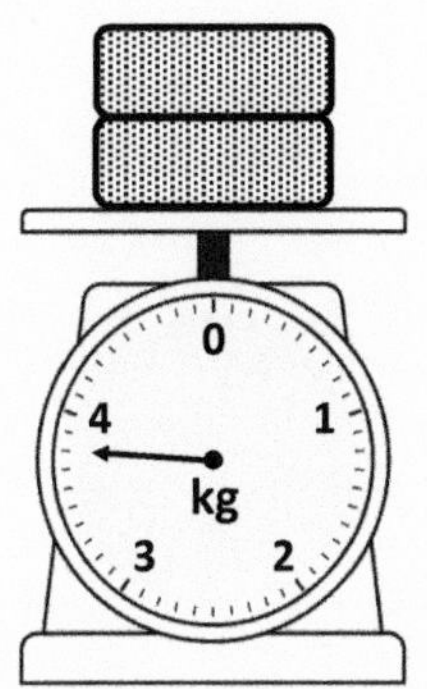

4. Given that the two bricks are identical, if one of the bricks was removed from the scale above, what would the scale read?

west

The *direction* corresponding to the compass point which is 90° *anticlockwise* of *north* and 180° *clockwise* of *east*.
e.g.

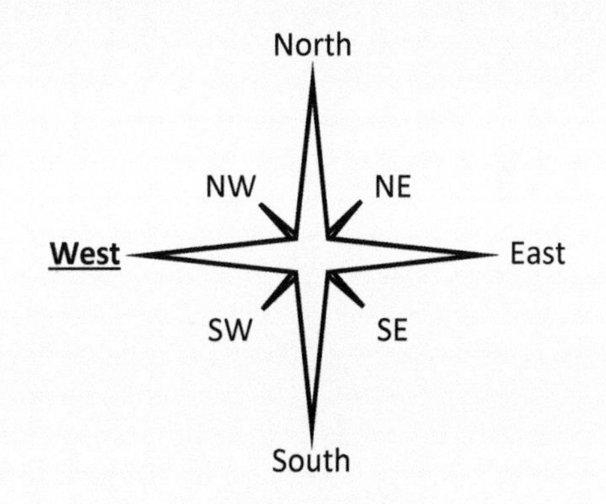

Test yourself

1. Is west 90° clockwise of south?

2. Through how many degrees must one turn to face west if one is initially facing east?

3. Tony is facing west. If he turns 90° clockwise, in which direction is he now facing?

Challenge yourself

1. What is the bearing that corresponds to west on a compass?

A
B
C
D
E
F
G
H
I
J
K
L
M
N
O
P
Q
R
S
T
U
V
W
X
Y
Z

2. Kevin is facing west. In which direction will he be facing after turning 405° anticlockwise?

3. Look at the diagram below. Which point is directly west of C?

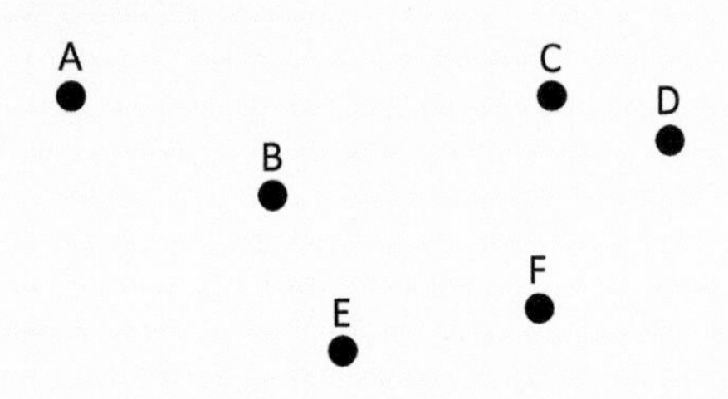

whole

The full amount or total quantity.

e.g. $^{7}/_{8}$ of the whole pizza was eaten. Therefore, there is $^{1}/_{8}$ of the pizza left.

Test yourself

1. If $^{1}/_{4}$ of a pizza was eaten, how much is left?

2. What is 1 - 2/5?

Challenge yourself

1. The total capacity of seats in a cinema is 800. A quarter of the tickets were sold online. How many more tickets must be sold to sell-out the whole capacity of the cinema?

2. John and Ben sliced a cake into 10 equal slices. If John ate $^{3}/_{5}$ of the cake, how many slices must Ben eat to finish the whole cake?

3. If $^{5}/_{6}$ of a cake weighs 500g, how much would the whole cake weigh?

4. If a jug of water is $^{7}/_{9}$ full and weighs 756g, how much would the whole jug weigh if it were full?

whole number

There is no general agreement on the definition of a whole number. Whole numbers are *natural numbers* and may refer to:

i. The positive *integers*.

e.g. {1, 2, 3, 4,...}

ii. The non-negative integers.

e.g. {0, 1, 2, 3, 4,...}

Test yourself

1. Round 98.1 to the nearest whole number.

2. Round 5.656 to the nearest whole number.

Challenge yourself

1. Round 5.23 × 1.5 to the nearest whole number.

2. Round 155 ÷ 25 to the nearest whole number.

width

The measurement of an object from side to side.

e.g.

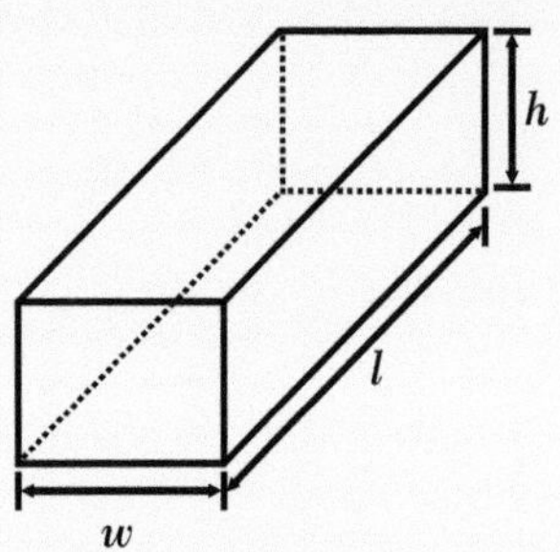

Volume of a cuboid = length (l) × width (w) × height (h)

Test yourself

1. Which of the following units can be used to measure the width of an object?

a. mm
b. cm^2
c. ml
d. cm

2. A block of wood has a volume of $420cm^3$. If the length of the wooden block is 7cm and its height is 10cm, what is the width of the wooden block?

Challenge yourself

1. If the length and height of a $60cm^3$ cuboid are 1cm and 60cm respectively, what is its width in cm?

2. If the length of a rectangular tile is 12cm and it has an area of $96cm^2$, what is its width in cm?

3. What is the volume of a cuboid with a length of 6cm, a width of 0.5m and a height of 8cm? Give your answer in cm^3.

x-axis

The *horizontal axis* on a graph.

e.g.

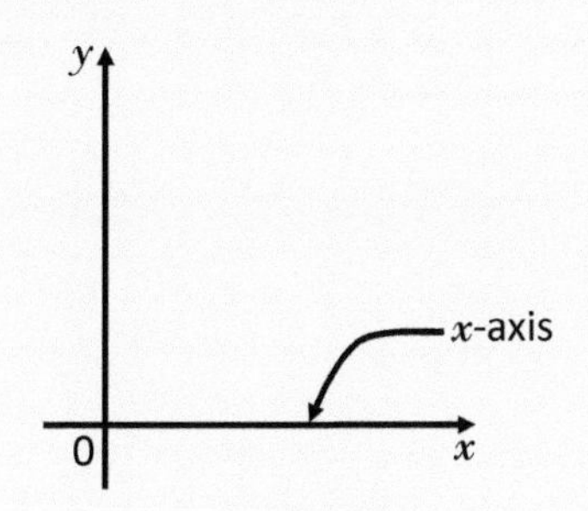

Test yourself

1. What is the angle between the y-axis and the x-axis?

2. Which of the lines below is perpendicular to the x-axis?

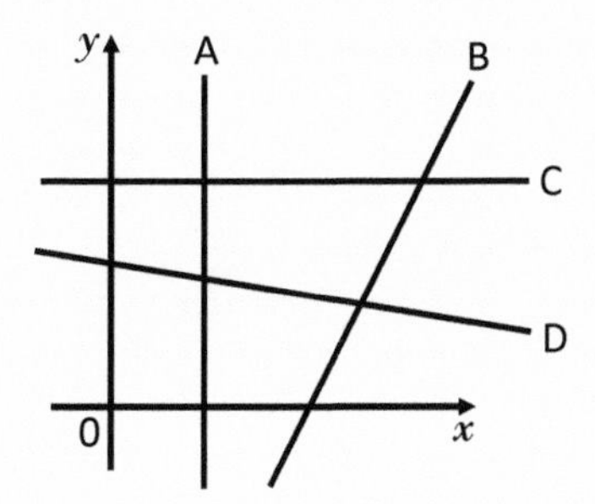

Challenge yourself

1. Which of the following statements are true?

a. The x-axis is always perpendicular to the y-axis.

b. The x-axis is always parallel to the y-axis.

c. The point where the x-axis and the y-axis meet is called the origin.

d. The x-axis is always drawn longer than the y-axis.

2. Reflect the trapezium across the x-axis and identify the new coordinates of A.

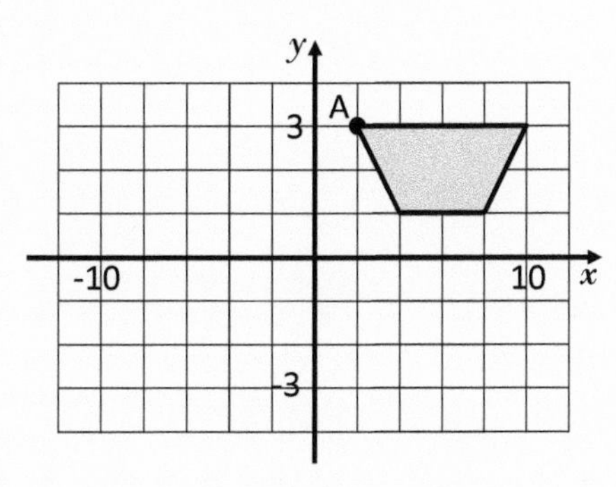

x-intercept

The point at which a line on a graph crosses the *x-axis*.

e.g.

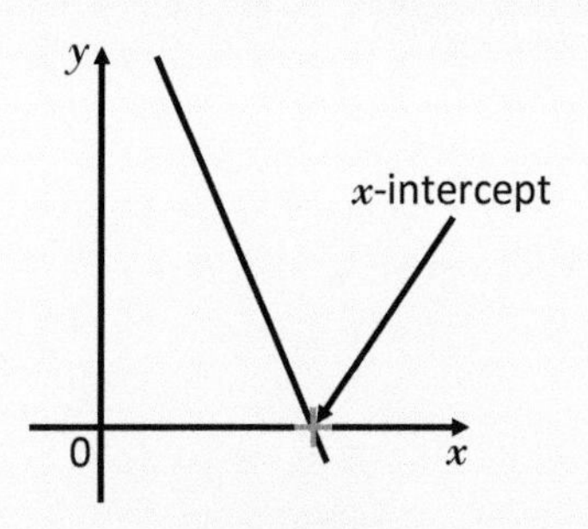

Test yourself

1. How many x-intercepts are there on the graph below?

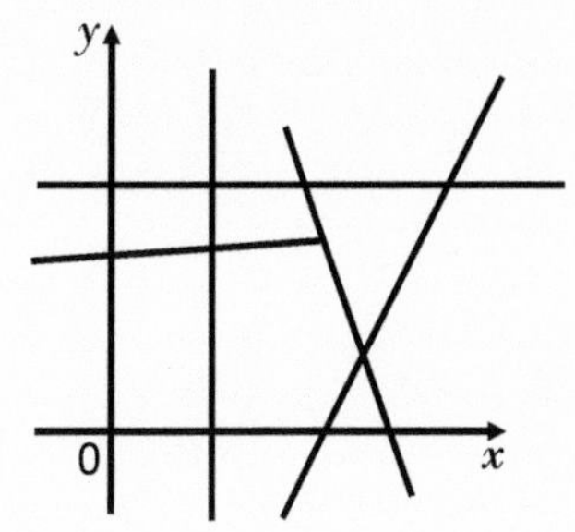

2. Which of the following statements is true?

a. A horizontal line that is above the x-axis never intersects the x-axis.

b. A vertical line that is on the right-hand side of the y-axis will never intersect the x-axis.

c. An x-intercept has coordinates of the form $(0, y)$.

Challenge yourself

Answer the following questions using the graph below.

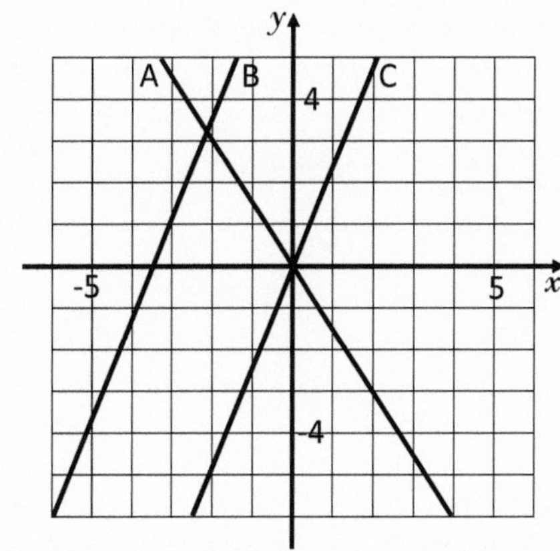

1. What are the coordinates of the x-intercept of lines A and C?

2. What are the coordinates of the x-intercept of line B?

A
B
C
D
E
F
G
H
I
J
K
L
M
N
O
P
Q
R
S
T
U
V
W
X
Y
Z

yard (yd)

An *imperial unit* of *length equivalent* to 3 *feet*, and approximately 0.9 *metres*.
e.g. 12yd is approximately 11m.

Test yourself

1. What is 24 feet expressed in yards?

2. How many feet are there in 12 yards?

3. What is 6 yards divided by 6 feet? Give your answer in ft.

Challenge yourself

1. If 1 yard = 0.9 metres, how many metres are there in 15 yards?

2. If 12 yards are approximately equal to 11 metres, how many yards are there in 176 metres?

3. Drashtic Measures Ltd wants to find out how big their car park is. They find that the car park is 300 feet long and 267 feet wide. Assuming that a yard is equal to 3 feet and also equal to 0.9 metres, what is the area of the car park in m^2?

y-axis

The *vertical axis* on a graph.
e.g.

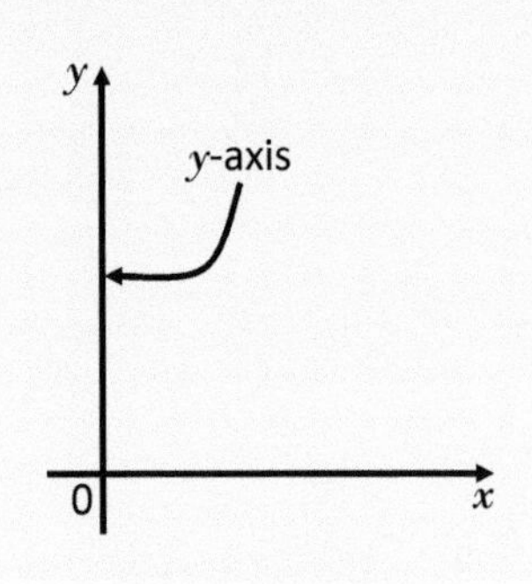

Test yourself

1. Which of the following statements is true?
a. The y-axis is not always perpendicular to the x-axis.
b. The y-axis can be parallel to the x-axis.
c. The x-axis and the y-axis meet at the coordinates (0, 0).

2. How many of the lines below are parallel to the y-axis?

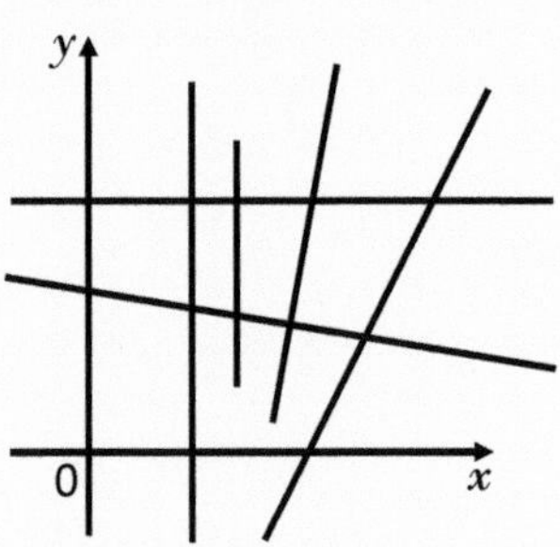

Challenge yourself

Answer the following questions using the graph below.

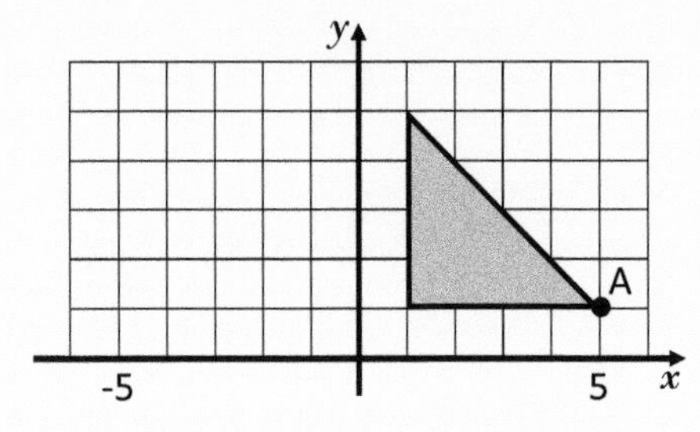

1. What are the coordinates of point A?

2. Reflect the triangle across the y-axis.

3. What are the new coordinates of point A?

4. What is the area of the reflected triangle?

year

A period of time lasting 365 *days*, or 366 days in a *leap year*. This is the time taken for the Earth to orbit around the Sun once.
e.g. There are approximately 8760 hours in a year.

Test yourself

1. If the year is 2015, how many years ago was 1992?

2. How many days are there in 3 non-leap years?

Challenge yourself

1. Round 4593 days to the nearest number of years.

2. How many weeks are there in a year?

3. If it takes the moon 27 days to orbit the Earth, how many times does the moon orbit the Earth in a year?

y-intercept

The point at which a line on a graph crosses the *y-axis*.

e.g.

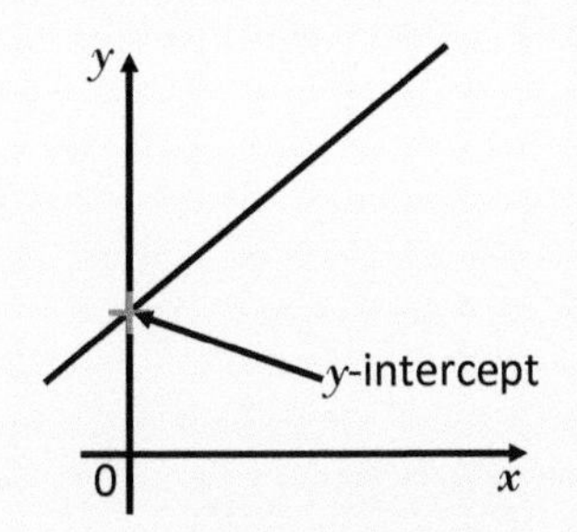

Test yourself

1. Which of the lines below intersects the y-axis?

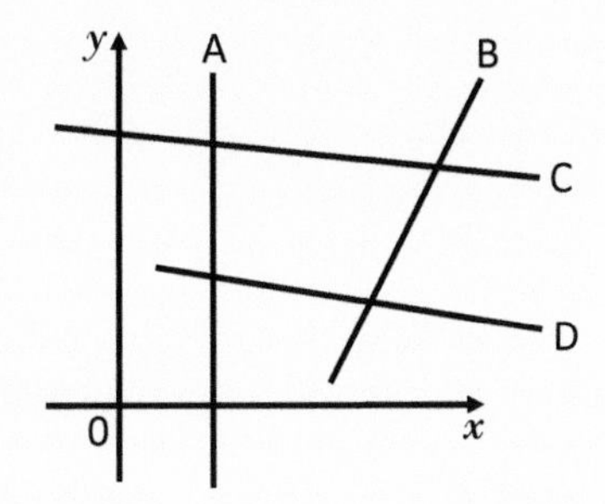

2. Which one of the following statements is false?

a. A vertical line that lies on the positive side of the x-axis will never intersect the y-axis.

b. A horizontal line that goes through the coordinates (0, 0) never intersects the y-axis.

c. A y-intercept has coordinates of the form (0, y).

Challenge yourself

Answer the following questions using the graph below.

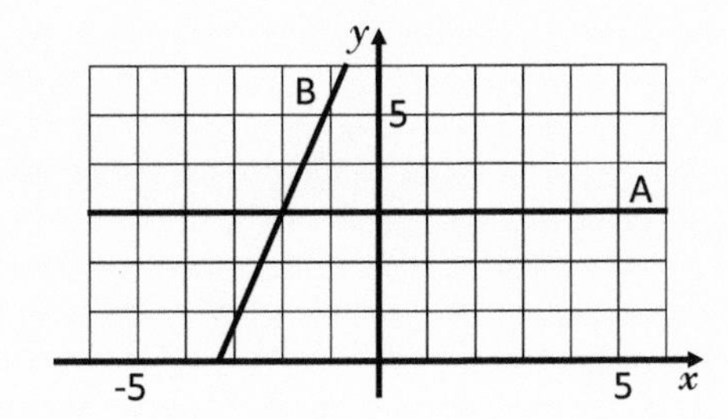

1. What are the coordinates of the y-intercept of line A?

2. What are the coordinates of the intersection of lines A and B?

3. If a horizontal line with an equation $y = 9$ intersects the y-axis at point A. What are the coordinates of point A?

Z

Z-angle

See *alternate angle*.

***

zero

A numerical *digit* used to represent no amount.

Note: Zero is neither positive nor negative. Also, when a digit in a particular column of a number is zero, it is acting as a *placeholder*.

e.g. 150 + 0 = 150 and 150 × 0 = 0.

Test yourself

1. What is 157 × 0?

2. In the number four hundred thousand, how many zeros are used as placeholders?

Challenge yourself

1. Calculate (58 × 0.5874) × 0.

2. What is 5(71 + 52 + 0) + 0?

3. Calculate 654 × 0 + 34 - 0.

4. In statistics, what does a probability of zero represent?

zero angle

An *angle* of size 0°.

e.g.

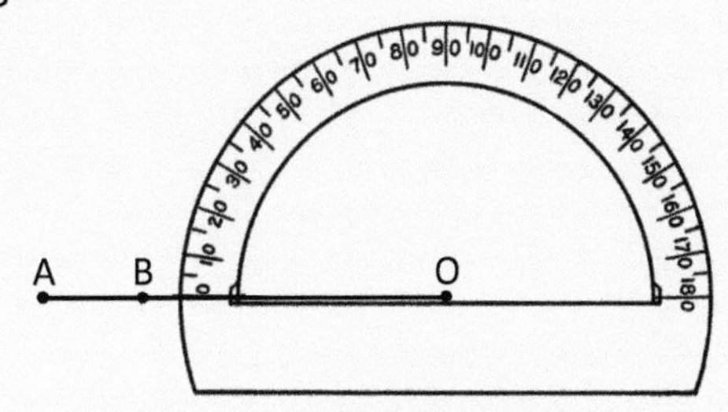

The lines AO and BO lie on the same axis, and point B lies on line AO.
Therefore, the angle AÔB is 0°.

Test yourself

1. James is facing north. He walks 20m straight then rotates 0°. In which direction is he facing now?

A
B
C
D
E
F
G
H
I
J
K
L
M
N
O
P
Q
R
S
T
U
V
W
X
Y
Z

Challenge yourself

1. Which of the following statements is true?

a. The angle between two perpendicular lines is zero.

b. There can be a zero angle in a triangle.

c. Two different lines with zero angle between them always intersect.

d. Two straight lines with zero angle between them have the same gradient.

2. A straight line makes 0° to the horizontal. What is the magnitude of the gradient of the line?

zero index rule

A rule stating that any number raised to the *power* of *zero* is *equivalent* to one.

e.g. $5641^0 = 100^0 = 10^0 = 5^0 = 1^0 = 1$

Test yourself

1. What is 3^0?

2. Calculate $4^0 + 7$.

Challenge yourself

1. Calculate $754^0 \times 23^0 \times 1$.

2. Calculate $25(78x^0 \times 51^0 + 3)$.

zigzag

A line made of alternating sharp turns.

Note: This can be used to represent missing numbers on a *number line* or an *axis*. Here, it is known as a break.

e.g.

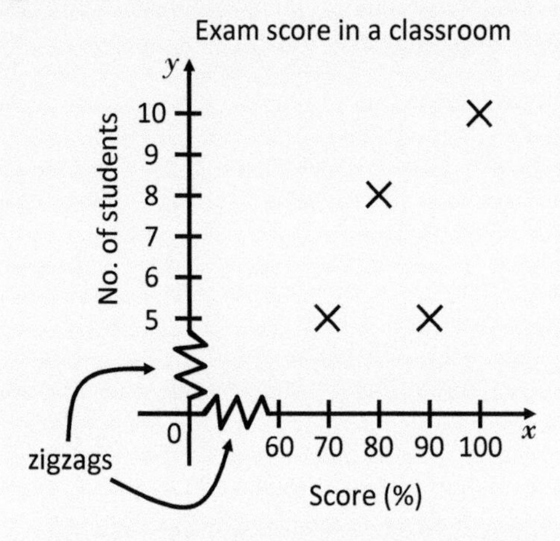

In this example, 5 students achieved 70% and 90%, 8 students achieved 80%, and 10 students achieved 100%. In total, there are 28 students.

Test yourself

Answer the following questions using the graph below.

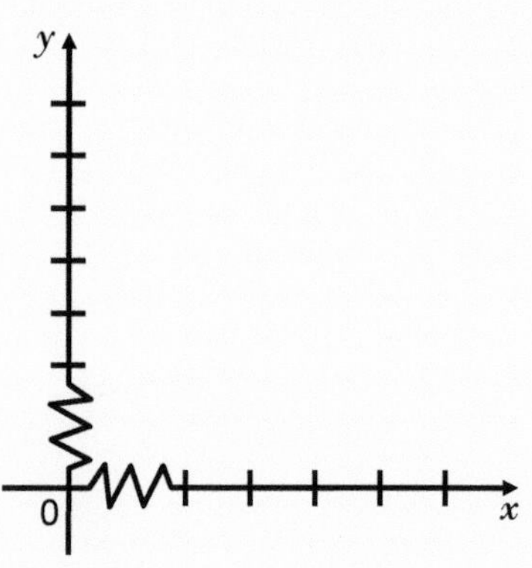

1. A set of data is given in which the values range from 25 to 105 for the x-axis and 15 to 90 for the y-axis. Label the axes of the graph with appropriate values so that it is able to represent the data set described above.

2. Plot the following points on the graph:
A(25, 30), B(45, 60) and C(105, 90).

Challenge yourself

Answer the following questions using the graph below.

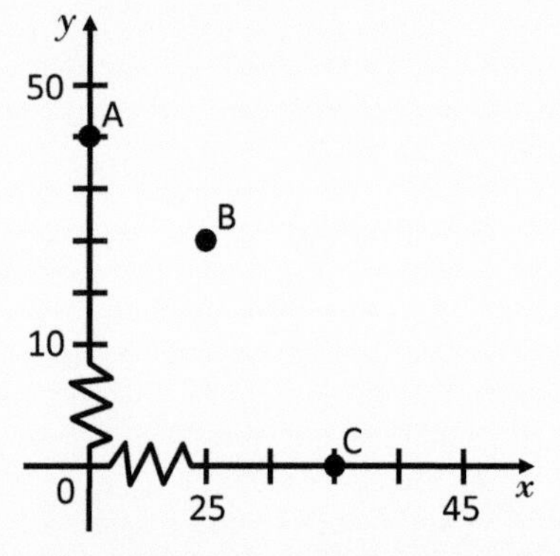

1. Determine the coordinates of points A, B and C.

2. Write the column vector that describes the translation of point A to C.

3. Plot the following points on the graph:
D(30, 18) and E(40, 50).

Index & Answers

including

Diagram Answers

Index & Answers

A

B

C

common multiple - page 15

1) 45 2) 30, 60 3) 165

1) 80 2) 60

common ratio - page 15

1) +3 2) +3

1) $^{1}/_{2} + ^{1}/_{10} = ^{3}/_{5}$ 2) 64 3) 55

complementary angles - page 16

1) yes

1) 33° 2) 720°

composite number - page 16

1) 10

1) 5

concave polygon - page 16

1) yes

1) x° = 257°

concentric shapes - page 16

1) no

1) 6

cone - page 17

1) 1 2) 0

1) 211m^2

congruent - page 17

1) yes 2) no

1) A and C 2) A and C

consecutive numbers - page 17

1) 11, 12, 13

1) 3, 5, 7, 9 2) 27, 64, 125

constant - page 17

1) +1 2) -9

1) -9 2) -9

conversion graph - page 18

1) yes 2) 80km/h

1) 100°C

coordinate - page 18

1) E(0, 0) 2) F(3, 0)

1) A(2, -3), B(-4, 2)

2) D(-5, -5)

corresponding angles - page 18

1) y° = 57° 2) w° + z° = 24°

1) C° = 57° 2) y° = 65°, z° = 115°

counter-clockwise - page 19

cross cancel - page 19

cross-section - page 19

1) diagram 14

1) 108cm^3

cube - page 19

1) 8cm

1) 26 2) 1 cube

cube number - page 19

1) 8

1) 216 2) 512

cube root - page 19

1) 3

1) 5 2) 12 3) 11cm

cubic centimetre (cm^3) - page 20

1) 2ml 2) 3cm^3

1) 1.54ml 2) 3740mm^3

cubic metre (m^3) - page 20

1) 4000l 2) 6m^3

1) 245l 2) 53,000cm^3

cubic millimetre - page 20

1) 0.007ml 2) 5mm^3

1) 0.547ml 2) 48cm^3

cuboid - page 20

1) yes 2) 6

1) 54cm^3 2) 324mm^3

cyclic quadrilateral - page 20

1) 160° 2) 180°

1) 360° 2) 179°

3) diagram 15, square

cylinder - page 21

1) 0 2) 3 3) 0

1) circle 2) 300cm^3

3) 350cm^3

D

datum - page 21

1) mass and height 2) mood

1) gender

2) shoe size, no. of siblings

dataset - page 21

1) 2 2) 48%

1) 17.5 2) 0.62 3) 83%

4) 73%

day - page 22

1) 350 days 2) 751 days

3) 144hrs 4) 1440mins

1) 86,400secs 2) 8760hrs

3) Saturday 4) Tuesday

decagon - page 22

1) 4

1) 10 2) 4:1

decimal number - page 22

1) 1.05 2) 0.32

3) 0.28 4) 0.44

1) 0.15 2) 10.75

3) 58.71 4) 0.4004

decimal place - page 23

1) 6 2) 3.3

1) 3.01 2) 78.9%

decimal point - page 23

1) 16.48

1) 0.77

decrease - page 23

1) £19 2) £20 3) 250ml

1) 86.01 2) £382.50

decreasing order - page 23

degree - page 23

1) yes 2) yes

1) degree of x and z is 5, y is 10

denary - page 23

1) 112 2) 76

1) 5,074,050 2) 8007.1

denominator - page 24

1) 10 2) 19

1) $^{17}/_{30}$ so 30 2) 8 3) 208

dependant event - page 24

1) no

1) $^{4}/_{11}$ 2) $^{4}/_{51}$

descending order - page 24

1) 10, 9, 5, 3, 1

2) 52, 30, 20, 11, 0

1) 99, 21, 2, 1, 0, -5, -14

2) 23.2, 11, 10, 2.3, -25

diagonal - page 24

1) 2 2) 5

1) 24cm^2

diameter - page 24

1) 20mm 2) 5mm

1) 28cm 2) 56mm

diamond - page 25

difference - page 25

1) 3 2) 134 3) 4

1) 5386 2) 298 3) 0.702

digit - page 25

1) 3 2) 5

1) 324 2) 343

dimension - page 25

1) B, C and D

1) 3 2) 1 3) 2

direction - page 26

1) N, NE, E, SE, S, SW, W, NW

1) (11, 4) 2) south-west

disjoint set - page 26

1) no 2) yes

1) A and C

distance - page 26

1) 3 units 2) 2 units 3) B, D

distance-time graph - page 26

1) 125m/s 2) 250m

3) diagram 16

distribution table - page 27

dividend - page 27

1) 66 2) 24

1) $^{1}/_{8}$ so 1 2) $^{11}/_{39}$ so 11

3) x = 65 4) x = 133

divisible - page 27

1) yes 2) no

3) 2, 4, 6, 8, 10 4) 15

1) no 2) 24 3) yes 4) 12

division - page 27

1) 2 2) 4

3) 5 pencils 4) 8

1) 42 2) 12 3) x = -1

divisor - page 27

1) 2 2) 4

1) $x = 4$ 2) 12

3) 1000mm^3 4) $x = 35$

double - page 28

1) 24 2) 16 3) 24 4) 60

1) 112.5 2) 43.5

3) 3 4) 12

dozen - page 28

1) 24 2) 6 3) 9 4) 7

1) 0.7kg 2) £3

3) 126 4) 42,120secs

E

east - page 29

1) north 2) north

1) 3 2) west

edge - page 29

1) 4 2) 12

1) 50 2) 8

element - page 29

1) yes 2) yes

1) 3 2) 1, 3, 6, 10, 15

3) 5 and 25

elevation - page 30

1) diagram 17

1) 7 2) 5

ellipse - page 30

enlargement - page 30

1) B

1) C and E

equally likely - page 31

1) 0.3 2) yes

1) B

equals - page 31

1) yes 2) no

1) -1 2) 10

equation - page 31

1) $x = 10$ 2) $y = 13$

1) $x = 2$ 2) $x = 56$

equidistant - page31

1) F

1) E 2) E 3) A and E

equilateral triangle - page 32

1) 180 ° 2) 6cm

1) 48mm 2) 0.19m

equivalent - page 32

1) yes 2) no 3) yes 4) no

1) $^{10}/_{15}$, $^{40}/_{60}$ 2) 7.21pm

equivalent fractions - page 32

1) no 2) yes

1) $^{350}/_{280}$ 2) $^{25}/_{100}$, $^{10}/_{40}$

equivalent ratios - page 32

1) yes 2) no

1) 62:33 2) 7:8

estimation - page 33

Euler's polyhedral formula - page 33

1) yes

1) 6 2) 8 3) yes

evaluate - page 33

1) 23 2) 42

1) $x = 15$ 2) $y = -41$

even chance - page 33

even number - page 33

1) 0, 2, 4, 6, 8 2) 20

1) yes 2) yes 3) no

event - page 33

1) e.g. heads when tossing a fair coin

2) unlikely

1) $^{14}/_{25}$ 2) $^{1}/_{32}$

explanatory variable - page 34

exponent - page 34

expression - page 34

1) b

1) 15 2) 209 3) $3S$

exterior angle - page 34

1) 72° 2) 45°

1) 360° 2) 9 3) 36°

external angle - page 34

F

face - page 35

1) 7 2) 6

1) 5 2) 8 3) 5 4) 1

factor - page 35

1) 1, 3 2) 1, 2, 3, 6 3) 1, 2, 5, 10

1) 1, 2, 4, 8, 16, 32 2) 32 3) 6

factorise - page 35

1) $4(2x + 3)$ 2) $2(4x + 1)$

1) $18(2y + x)$ 2) $2x^2(x + 3)$

fair - page 35

1) no

1) $^{1}/_{4}$ 2) $^{1}/_{4}$

F-angles - page 35

Fibonacci sequence - page 36

1) 11 2) 32

1) 10, 10, 20, 30, 50, 80, 130

2) 4, 4, 8, 12, 20, 32, 52

fifty-fifty - page 36

1) £5 and £5 2) no

1) £425 2) 0.5 3) 50%

figure - page 36

1) diagram 18 2) 20

1) kite 2) trapezium

3) 80 4) $-^{8}/_{100} = -0.08$

finite decimal - page 36

1) yes 2) no

1) 0.75 2) 15 3) B, C

flat angle - page 37

1) 2

1) south-west 2) $^{3}/_{2}$

flow chart - page 37

1) 40 2) 9

1) -2 2) 104

foot (ft or ') - page 37

1) 24 inches 2) 6 feet

1) 132 inches 2) 122cm

formula - page 38

1) 8cm^3 2) 40mm^3

3) 140cm^3

1) $x = (d + y) \times {}^{1}/_{2}$ 2) $r = 5t \times {}^{1}/_{18}$

3) 154yd 4) 69ft

fraction - page 38

1) $^{1}/_{3}$ 2) $^{3}/_{4}$

1) $^{37}/_{24}$ 2) $^{2}/_{5}$ 3) $^{2}/_{3}$

frequency - page 38

1) 10 2) 7

1) 59 2) 44

frequency distribution table - page 38

1) 20 2) 2

1) 20 2) 360 3) 18 goals

full turn - page 39

function - page 39

1) 25 2) 2

1) 28.26cm^2 2) 628mm

G

gallon - page 39

1) 2 pints 2) 1.5 gallons

1) 28 pints 2) 6 $^{1}/_{4}$ gallons

geometric sequence - page 39

1) 3 2) 5

1) $-^{1}/_{2}$ 2) 2, -10, 50, -250, 1250, -6250, 31250

3) 864, 144, 24, 4, $^{3}/_{2}$, $^{1}/_{9}$, $^{1}/_{54}$

geometry - page 40

1) yes 2) no

1) 6 2) 6

gradient - page 40

1) yes 2) yes 3) B

1) 25m/min 2) 12m/min

3) diagram 19

gram - page 40

1) 3000g 2) $^{1}/_{2}$kg

1) 5.812kg 2) 351g

graph - page 41

1) temp. (°C) 2) temp. (K)

1) yes 2) 312.5K

greater than - page 41

1) yes 2) no 3) yes

1) yes 2) yes 3) no

greater than or equal to - page 41

1) no 2) yes

1) 4 2) 5

greatest common factor - page 41

greatest value - page 41

1) 16 2) 51

1) 27 2) -5

H

height - page 42

1) A

1) 6cm 2) 20mm 3) 34cm

hemisphere - page 42

1) 2

1) $2921cm^3$ 2) $4761cm^2$

heptagon - page 42

1) no 2) 14cm

1) 128.6° 2) $87.5cm^2$

hexagon - page 43

1) no 2) 18cm

1) 120° 2) $147mm^2$

highest common factor (HCF) - page 43

1) 2 2) 2

1) 2 2) 7

histogram - page 43

1) 150cm 2) 90cm

1) 45 2) 60

horizontal - page 43

1) diagram 20

1) 56cm 2) 135°, 315°

hour - page 44

1) 2 hours 2) 30 minutes

1) 168 hours 2) 17 hours

3) 7200 seconds

hundredth - page 44

1) £5 2) 100

1) £84.21 2) 10,000 3) 198

hypotenuse - page 44

1) 5cm

1) 10 units 2) (1, 4) 3) 2:3

I

identical - page 45

1) $x° = 60°$

1) $x° = 24°$ 2) $l = 11mm$

image - page 45

1) yes

1) diagram 21

imperial units - page 46

1) yes 2) yes 3) yes

1) $^4/_9$ m/s 2) 3.355m 3) 324l

impossible - page 46

1) true 2) false

1) true 2) false

improbable - page 46

improper fraction - page 46

1) $^4/_3$ and $^9/_5$ 2) $^9/_4$

1) 8 $^2/_7$ 2) $^{44}/_9$ 3) $^{13}/_2$ 4) $^{11}/_3$

inch (in or ") - page 46

1) yes 2) yes

1) 180 inches 2) 43.18cm

increase - page 46

1) 5 vehicles 2) £24

1) 246.69 2) $^{515}/_{56}$

3) £292,500 4) 15,000

increasing order - page 47

independent event - page 47

1) $^1/_2$

1) c

independent variable - page 47

1) yes

1) time 2) distance

index - page 47

indivisible - page 47

1) no 2) no

1) 121, 65, 49

2) 121, 584, 78, 49

inequality - page 48

1) a and c

1) b and d

infinite decimal - page 48

1) no 2) no 3) yes

1) π, √2 2) yes 3) yes

infinity - page 48

1) infinite

input - page 48

1) 354

1) $x = 684$ 2) $x = 21$ 3) 248

integer - page 49

1) yes 2) yes

1) 183 2) 40

intercept - page 49

1) 4, diagram 22

1) (0, 3) 2) (-3, 0)

interest - page 49

1) £2 2) £5

1) £578.24 2) £234.26

interior angle - page 49

1) $x°$

1) 10 2) 140° 3) 720°

internal angle - page 50

intersection - page 50

1) 2

1) (0, -2)

interval - page 50

1) 10 minutes 2) 10

1) 6hrs 22mins 2) 200m

inverse function - page 50

1) - 3 2) ÷ 2

1) $x = 7$

irrational number - page 51

1) no 2) no

1) no 2) √12

irregular polygon - page 51

1) A and C

1) 360° 2) nonagon

isosceles trapezium - page 51

1) yes 2) 5

1) $b° = 106°$ 2) 360°

3) 54cm 4) $100m^2$

isosceles triangle - page 52

1) yes 2) 5

1) 54° 2) 18.35cm 3) $442mm^2$

J

join - page 52

1) diagram 23

1) scalene triangle

K

kilogram (kg) - page 53

1) 3000g 2) 2kg

1) 5780g 2) 0.986kg

3) 5100g 4) 54.25kg

kilolitre (kl) - page 53

1) 2000l 2) 4kl

1) 78,800l 2) 9.286kl

3) 2 4) 0.01kl

kilometre (km) - page 53

1) 4000m 2) 2km

1) 30.7m 2) 0.002005km

3) 13 hours 4) 80km/h, no

kilometres per hour (km/h) - page 53

1) 48km/h 2) 6km 3) 5m/s

1) $^{100}/_9$ m/s 2) 255km 3) 7km

kite - page 54

1) yes 2) 5

1) 1 2) 1

3) 16.8cm 4) 300°

L

label - page 54

1) x-axis: Average rainfall (mm)
y-axis: Month

1) right-angled triangle

2) A - E, B - F, C - D

leap year - page 54

1) 4 years 2) February

1) 731 2) 2nd March

3) Saturday

least value - page 55

length - page 55

1) 3.5cm 2) C

1) 35 units 2) 29 units

less than - page 55

1) yes 2) A and C

1) no 2) no 3) no

less than or equal to - page 55

1) yes 2) A and C

1) yes 2) 16

likelihood - page 55

likely - page 55

1) A

1) 0.6, yes 2) c

like terms - page 56

1) $2x$ 2) $7y$

3) $y - x$ 4) $12y - 4x$

1) $16y - 3x$ 2) $6x - y$

3) $-27x - 16y$ 4) $4x + y$

linear graph - page 56

1) a constant gradient, i.e. a straight line

2) yes

1) 1000 2) 1:1000

3) no 4) less dense

linear sequence - page 56

line graph - page 57

1) diagram 24

1) 90km 2) 0km 3) 100km

line of best fit - page 57

1) diagram 25

1) 1m 2) 80kg 3) no

line of symmetry - page 57

1) diagram 26 2) 2 3) 4

1) 0 2) B, C 3) D 4) 4:5

line segment - page 58

1) diagram 27 2) 3.2cm

1) 10:13 2) 96cm 3) 66cm

litre (l) - page 58

1) 3l 2) 5000ml

1) 45.87l 2) 2300ml 3) 40l

locus - page 59

1) diagram 28

2) 50.24cm^2 2) 128.5cm^2

lowest common denominator - page 59

1) 6 2) 6

1) 72 so $^{31}/_{24}$ 2) 60 so $^{33}/_{20}$

lowest common multiple (LCM) - page 59

1) 12 2) 2

1) 140 2) 15

lowest terms - page 59

M

major arc - page 60

1) A

1) 165cm 2) 21mm

major sector - page 60

1) B

1) 288mm^2 2) $^{500}/_{11}$ cm^2

3) 187.5cm^2

major segment - page 60

1) B

1) 39mm^2 2) 20m^2

3) 408.8cm^2

map - page 61

1) Radford Flat 2) 3km

1) Warwick castle 2) no

mass - page 61

1) kg and g

1) 200,000g 2) 8.5kg

matrix - page 61

1) $\begin{pmatrix}-9\\5\end{pmatrix}$ 2) $\begin{pmatrix}8\\-4\end{pmatrix}$

maximum point - page 62

1) cross at point (4, 40)

1) 504km 2) 35m/s

maximum value - page 62

mean - page 62

median - page 62

1) 2 2) 4.5

1) 5 2) 3.5 3) 3

metre (m) - page 62

1) 400cm 2) 9m

1) 0.00027m 2) 8730cm

3) 4 boxes 4) 27.468yd

metres per second (m/s) - page 62

1) 10m/s 2) 1000m/s

1) 14,400m 2) $^{25}/_{3}$ m/s

3) 300 seconds 4) 212.5m/s

metric units - page 63

1) inch

1) 0.0581km = 58,100mm

2) 5000g = 5,000,000mg

3) 0.078kl

midday - page 63

1) 12:00 2) 12.00pm

1) 10.15am 2) 16:25

midnight - page 63

1) 00:00 2) 12.00am

1) 5.55am 2) 01:53

midpoint - page 63

1) diagram 29

1) (5, 12) 2) (41, -5)

mile - page 64

1) 10 miles 2) 5280yd

1) 880yd 2) 15 miles 3) 4mph

miles per hour (mph) - page 64

1) 9 miles 2) 23mph

1) 20mph 2) 18.75 miles

3) 14mph

milligram (mg) - page 64

1) 2000mg 2) 5g

1) 700mg 2) 0.00255g

millilitre (ml) - page 64

1) 5000ml 2) 8l

1) 2870ml 2) 0.785l

millimetre (mm) - page 64

1) 9000mm 2) 1m

1) 820,000mm 2) 151,875mm^2

minimum point - page 65

1) hour 1 2) 12 seconds

1) 15m/s 2) 112,500m

3) 50 seconds

minimum value - page 65

1) C 2) D

1) D 2) 15km 3) 35km

minor arc - page 66

1) A 2) no

1) 65cm 2) 40.5mm

3) 48mm

minor sector - page 66

1) B

1) 288mm^2 2) 60cm^2

3) 87cm^2

minor segment - page 66

1) A

1) 102mm^2 2) 150m^2

3) 441cm^2

minus - page 67

minute (min) - page 67

1) 120 seconds 2) 120 minutes

1) 147 minutes 2) 40.5 hours

mirror line - page 67

1) 2

1) 1

mixed number - page 67

1) D and E

1) 3 $^{17}/_{35}$ 2) 10 $^{17}/_{35}$ 3) 6 $^{1}/_{8}$

mixed operation - page 68

1) 24 2) 5

1) 16 2) 51 3) $^{2}/_{3}$

modal group - page 68

1) 17

1) E - F 2) 19

mode - page 68

1) 3 2) 5

1) 5 2) 86

month - page 68

1) 12 2) 24 3) May

1) 56 2) 9 $^{1}/_{2}$ years 3) April

multiple - page 69

1) 3, 6, 9, 12 2) 20

1) 117 2) 19, 38, 57

3) 11

multiplication - page 69

1) 12 2) 30

1) 792 2) 11,193

3) 272 4) 46.2

multiply out - page 69

1) $2a + 2b$ 2) $6a + 6$

3) $10a + 35b$ 4) $-70a - 10b$

1) 225 2) $16a + 88b$

3) $10a - 4b$ 4) $80a + 48b$

mutually exclusive events - page 69

1) no 2) no 3) yes 4) no

1) $^1/_{13}$ 2) yes 3) $^2/_{13}$ 4) 0

N

natural number - page 70

1) 1, 2, 3, 4, 5, 6, 7, 8, 9, 10

2) 20 3) no

1) 5 and 7 2) 7^2, $^{15}/_3$

negative number - page 70

1) -1, -2, -3, -4, -5 2) -7 3) no

1) -(3.1), $^5/_{-3}$, -0.57 2) 18

3) 4 4) 47

net - page 70

1) cuboid 2) cylinder

1) diagram 30 2) diagram 31

3) diagram 32

no chance - page 71

nonagon - page 71

1) 0 2) irregular

1) 9 2) 58.5cm

3) 78.75mm^2 4) 18

noon - page 71

north - page 71

1) north

1) south-west 2) 3 3) 350m

***n*th term** - page 71

1) 2n - 1 2) $^n/_2$ 3) 2n

1) yes 2)3n 3) -4n + 21

number line - page 72

1) A = $^1/_2$, B = $^1/_4$

2) 2) C = 1, D = $-^1/_2$

1) A 2) B

number machine - page 72

1) $x = 25$ 2) 7

1) - 56 or ÷ 4.5 2) $x = 15$

numerator - page 73

1) 2 2) 5 3) 1 4) 1

1) 69 2) 61 3) 39 4) 271

O

oblong - page 73

obtuse angle - page 73

1) $z°$ 2) D, C 3) c

1) b° 2) 308° 3) yes 4) no

obtuse-angled triangle - page 74

1) E

1) c 2) yes 3) yes

octagon - page 74

1) 4 2) no

1) 44cm 2) 224mm^2 3) 8

octahedron - page 75

1) triangle 2) 26

1) 296mm^3 2) 6m^2

odd number - page 75

1) 99 2) 34

1) 4 2) 201 3) no 4) odd

operation - page 75

1) addition (+) 2) addition (+)

3) multiplication (×)

1) 17.5 2) 28 3) division (÷)

order - page 75

1) 11, 10, 9, 5, 2, 1

2) 3, 12, 19, 25, 55

3) -11, 0, 0.22, 3, 5, 10

1) -45, -1, 0, 23, 23, 45

2) 6.20, 5.10, 5.09, 3.99, 2.60

3) $^2/_{45}$, $^1/_2$, $^5/_7$, $^8/_9$

4) 50%, 1%, 0.22%, -0.2%, -40%

order of operations - page 76

order of rotational symmetry - page 76

1) 2 2) 1

1) 6 2) 2 3) A

ordinal number - page 77

1) 12 2) 12 3) 81

1) 15 2) 400 3) 343 4) 17

origin - page 77

1) (0, 0) 2) (-5, -3)

1) (-5, -4) 2) (-6, 9)

ounce (oz) - page 77

1) 32oz 2) $^1/_2$ lbs

1) 4.5lbs 2) 120oz 3) 4284g

outcome - page 77

1) heads, tails 2) 1, 2, 3, 4, 5, 6

1) $^1/_4$ 2) $^1/_8$ 3) $^1/_6$

output - page 77

1) 465 2) 5

1) 64.5 2) 50

oval - page 78

1) A

1) 2 2) 2

P

palindrome - page 78

1) 55 2) 1256521

1) 37584648573

2) 53724

parallel - page 78

1) diagram 33 2) 2 3) 3

1) y, z 2) a and c

3) 28° clockwise

parallelogram - page 79

1) B

1) 0 2) 27cm^2 3) $x° = 8°$

Pascal's triangle - page 79

1) 6

1) A = 110, B = C = 165

pentagon - page 80

1) 5 2) yes

1) 540° 2) 360° 3) 122.5cm^2

per cent - page 80

1) 10 2) 1

1) 200 2) 1.25 3) 30.4

percentage - page 80

1) 90% 2) 4%

1) 572.7% 2) 75% 3) £7.04

percentage change - page 80

1) -20% 2) 20%

1) 175% 2) 60%

perimeter - page 81

1) 24cm 2) 16cm

1) 120cm 2) 48cm 3) 40cm

perpendicular - page 81

1) 90° 2) diagram 34

1) diagram 35 2) c

3) G and F

perpendicular bisector - page 82

1) diagram 36

1) 1:1

pi - page 82

1) $^{\text{circumference}}/_{\text{diameter}}$ 2) 3.14

1) $^C/_{2R}$ 2) πcm 3) 144πmm^2

pictogram - page 82

1) 14 2) 7 3) 30 4) 10

1) 66 2) 6 3) 138

pie chart - page 82

1) yes

1) 4:3 2) $^3/_7$ 3) 57

pint (pt) - page 83

1) 2 gallons 2) 24 pints

1) 52 pints 2) 9.5 gallons

placeholder - page 83

place value - page 83

1) 5 2) 800

1) 9 2) 0.09 3) 80

plan - page 83

1) diagram 37 2) diagram 38

1) diagram 39

plane figure - page 84

1) diagram 40 2) circle

1) diagram 41 2) trapezium

plus - page 84

PM - page 84

1) 15:00 2) 4.00pm

1) 7.59pm 2) 18:35

3) 1.10pm

polygon - page 84

1) pentagon 2) no

3) quadrilateral

1) 6 2) nonagon

3) $^{(AP \times P)}/_2$

polyhedron - page 84

1) tetrahedron 2) 8 3) 6

1) 26 2) cube

population - page 85

1) 177 2) 46

1) 200,000 2) 157,950

positive number - page 85

1) yes 2) A and C

1) A, B, D and F 2) 73

possible - page 85

1) a and c

1) a, b and d

pound (lb or £) - page 85

1) £6 2) 850p 3) 2lbs 4) 80oz

1) £16.80 2) £3

3) 42kg 4) 1112.5lbs

power - page 86

1) 16 2) 125 3) 341

1) 288 2) 1025 3) 16

prime factor - page 86

1) 2 and 5 2) 2 × 2 × 3

1) 2 × 2 × 13 2) 3 3) 2

prime number - page 86

1) 13 2) A, B and E

1) 8 2) 13 and 11

prism - page 86

1) 8 2) 2 3) 11

4) triangle

1) hexagon 2) 6

probability - page 87

1) $^1/_2$ 2) 0.9

1) $^1/_8$ 2) $^7/_8$ 3) $^1/_9$ 4) $^1/_4$

probability scale - page 87

1) B 2) D

1) C 2) D

probable - page 87

1) c

1) d 2) B

product - page 88

1) 50 2) 84

1) 405 2) 15,000

3) 162 4) $^{64}/_9$

proper fraction - page 88

1) $^3/_4$ and $^1/_{13}$ 2) 16

1) $^{12}/_{13}$ and -$^1/_2$ 2) $^2/_3$ 3) yes

proportional - page 88

1) 40 2) 9cm

1) $^{80}/_3$ 2) 135 flowers

pyramid - page 89

1) square (based) pyramid

1) 12 2) 20 3) decagon

Pythagoras' theorem - page 89

1) 10cm

Q

quadrant - page 89

1) 45cm^2 2) D

3) 180mm^2 4) origin

1) $\pi r^2/_4$ 2) $^{\pi r}/_2 + 2r$

3) A-4th, B-1st, C-3rd, D-2nd

quadratic equation - page 90

1) b and d

1) A and C

quadratic sequence - page 90

1) 1 2) 2

1) 1, 2, 4, 7, 11, 16, 22

2) 2, 8, 18, 32, 50, 72, 98

3) 6, 12, 20, 30, 42, 56, 72

quadrilateral - page 90

1) 4 2) square

1) 0 2) 90°

quadruple - page 91

1) 8 2) 28 3) 52 4) 80

1) 11 2) 520

3) x = 12 4) x = 121

quotient - page 91

1) 3 2) 3

1) 11 2) 13 3) 159 4) 1400

R

radius - page 91

1) 3cm 2) 6mm

1) 132cm 2) 3:20

random - page 91

1) b

1) $^1/_2$ 2) bunny 3) $^2/_9$ 4) $^1/_{36}$

range - page 92

1) 8 2) 22

1) 31cm 2) 350 3) 58kg

ratio - page 92

1) 1:2 2) 3:1

1) 6:7 2) 2:1 3) 49

rational number - page 92

1) a and c

1) a, c and d 2) -0.7 = -$^7/_{10}$

3) Belinda with 180

real numbers - page 92

1) 2

1) 7 2) -4

reciprocal - page 93

1) $^1/_5$ 2) 8

1) no 2) $^2/_7$ 3) $^5/_9$

rectangle - page 93

1) 4 2) 360°

1) 10cm^2 2) 18cm^2 3) 8mm

rectangular prism - page 93

recurring decimal - page 93

1) 1 2) 09 3) no 4) no

1) $^7/_9$ 2) 1.08333... = $1.08\dot{3}$

3) 0.0234234... = $0.0\dot{2}3\dot{4}$

reduce - page 94

reflection - page 94

1) square 2) diagram 42

1) (5, 7) 2) (2, 4) 3) (-2, 10)

reflective symmetry - page 94

1) C

1) 7 2) 2:3 3) infinite

reflex angle - page 94

1) A

1) $c°$ 2) $a°$ = 105°, $b°$ = 75°

3) scalene triangle

regular - page 95

1) diagram 43 2) diagram 44

1) 135° 2) 9

3) cube, cuboid 4) octahedron

remainder - page 95

1) 2 2) 3

1) 3 2) 11 3) 7

revolution - page 95

1) 2 2) north 3) 1080°

1) $^9/_2$ 2) south-east

rhombus - page 96

1) Equal opposite angles, all sides of equal length, and diagonals which bisect at 90°.

2) diagram 45

1) 30mm^2 2) 2 3) 2

right angle - page 96

1) 180° 2) 2

1) south-west 2) 14

right-angled triangle - page 96

1) diagram 46

1) 55° and 90° 2) 1.2cm

Roman numerals - page 97

1) V 2) XVII 3) XXIII

1) 24 2) 32 3) 900 4) 65

root - page 97

rotation - page 97

1) clockwise

1) (-5, -7) 2) A'(-2, -3), D'(-2, 0)

3) (-1, 4)

rotational symmetry - page 98

1) 2

1) A - 1, B - infinite, C - 1, D - 5

2) 4 3) 6.5

rounding - page 98

1) 7.6 2) 0.1 3) 1.47 4) 0.50

1) -5.25 2) 2.143

3) 67.9 4) 1520g

S

scale - page 99

1) 10°C 2) 10000cm

1) 17°C 2) 550cm 3) 1.4km

scale drawing - page 99

1) 9cm 2) 4

1) 1.5cm^2

scalene triangle - page 100

1) No equal sides and angles.

2) B

1) 0 2) 1 3) 180° 4) 360°

scatter graph - page 100

1) 11

1) As weight increases, height also increases.

second (sec or 2nd) - page 100

1) 300 secs 2) 3

1) 16,200 secs 2) 72 3) $^{13}/_{21}$

second difference - page 100

1) 3, 7, 14, <u>24</u>, <u>37</u> 2) 1

1) 2

2) <u>15</u>, 10, 15, 30, <u>55</u>, 90, <u>135</u>

sector - page 101

1) A

1) 432cm^2 2) 37.5cm^2

segment - page 101

1) diagram 47

1) 56mm^2 2) 10m^2 3) 12cm^2

semicircle - page 101

1) 5cm^2

1) 376cm^2 2) 25.12cm^2

sequence - page 102

set - page 102

1) 4 2) 6

1) 4 2) 3 3) 2 4) 1, 3, 6, 11

side - page 102

significant figures (s.f.) - page 102

1) 1200 2) 0.333 3) 0.015

1) 585,000 2) 0.27 3) 3

signs - page 102

1) addition (+), subtraction (-), multiplication (×), division (÷)

1) + 2) ÷

similar figures - page 103

1) yes

1) no 2) z° = 120°

simplest form - page 103

1) $^1/_4$ 2) 28x

1) $9x^3 + 7x^2 + 8x$ 2) $2x^2 + 12x$

3) $^{203}/_{160}$

simplify - page 103

1) 20y 2) 16x 3) $^2/_3$

1) $69x - 18y$ 2) $44xy + 5x - 11y$

3) $^{25}/_6$ 4) $^{23}/_4$

slope - page 104

solid - page 104

1) a, e and f

1) 8 2) 18 3) 12 4) 6591mm^3

solve - page 104

1) $x = 25$ 2) $x = -1$

3) $x = 8$ 4) $x = -8$

1) $x = 3$ 2) $x = 26$

3) $x = -^{22}/_5$ 4) $x = -7$

south - page 104

1) south 2) north

1) 2 2) south-west

speed - page 104

sphere - page 105

1) 0 2) 0

1) 50.24cm^2

square - page 105

1) D 2) 9

1) 64cm^2 2) 4

3) 4 4) 1296

square centimetre (cm^2) - page 105

1) 9cm^2 2) 81cm^2

1) 600cm^2 2) 0.572m^2

square kilometre (km^2) - page 105

1) 49km^2 2) 48km^2

1) 0.24km^2 2) 2,700,000m^2

square metre (m^2) - page 106

1) 40m^2 2)121m^2

1) 15.03m^2 2) 3,700,000mm^2

square millimetre (mm^2) - page 106

1) 16mm^2 2) 36mm^2

1) 3570mm^2 2) 37.8cm^2

square number - page 106

1) 55 2) 144 3) 19 4) 400

1) 170 2) 165 3) 256 and 289

square prism - page 106

square pyramid - page 106

square root - page 106

1) 12 2) 9 3) 7

1) 15 2) 19 3) 14 4) 21cm

standard form - page 107

1) 5×10^4

1) 2.5×10^5 1) 2.5×10^{-4}

statistical diagram - page 107

1) 1, 4, 9, 16 2) 1, 3, 6, 10 3) 1

1) 80 2) 65 3) 15 4) 59

stone (st) - page 107

1) 2 stone 2) 19.2kg

1) 249.6kg 2) 56 stone

straight angle - page 107

subset - page 108

1) yes

1) no 2) yes

substitution - page 108

1) $y = 13$ 2) $y = 3$ 3) $y = 25$

1) $x = ^7/_3$ 2) $y = 3$

subtraction - page 108

1) 6 2) 22

1) 1485 2) 9.23

3) -2°C 4) 33 cars

sum - page 108

1) 27 2) 136

1) 40.577 2) 225 3)537

supplementary angles - page 108

1) yes 2) no 3) yes

1) 135° 2) 40° and 140°

surface - page 109

surface area - page 109

1) 220cm^2 2) 54cm^2

1) 170πcm^2 2) 216cm^2

symmetry - page 109

T

tally chart - page 110

1) 15 2) 11 3) 4

1) 32 2) 7:9 3) 5

tangent - page 110

1) C(4, 6), D(9, 2)

1) D 2) diagram 48

temperature - page 111

1) 75°C 2) 40°C

1) 307.15K 2) 25°C 3) 5 hours

tenth - page 111

1) 5 2) 100

1) 30.2 2) 176 3) -900

term - page 111

1) 4x 2) 7y 3) 10

1) x 2) 4

3) 6, 0, 12, <u>5</u>, 24, 10, <u>48</u>, 15

tetrahedron - page 112

thousandth - page 112

1) 2 2) 1000

1) 200 2) 5000

three-dimensional - page 112

1) b and c

1) 3 2) triangular prism

3) 7500cm^3

ton - page 112

1) 0.5 tons 2) 800 stone

1) 7 tons 2) 6880 stone

tonne - page 112

1) 10,000kg 2) 0.7 tonnes

1) 0.0003 tonnes 2) 53,000kg

top-heavy fraction - page 112

transformation - page 113

1) enlargement 2) rotation

3) reflection

1) enlargement 2) (4, 3)

3) (-2, 0)

translation - page 113

1) 6 units right and 3 units down

1) (6, 6) 2) (-1, -2)

transversal - page 114

1) C

1) 3 2) at least 8

trapezium - page 114

1) yes

1) 360° 2) 1 3) 22cm^2

tree diagram - page 114

1) no 2) 0.6 3) 0.36

1) 0.4 2) 0.098

triangle - page 115

1) equilateral triangle

2) right-angled triangle

3) scalene or right-angled triangle

4) isosceles

1) 6 2) 90°

triangular number - page 115

1) 15 2) 35

1) 465 2) 1260

triangular prism - page 115

1) 20

1) 374cm^3 2) 12cm^2

triangular pyramid - page 116

1) 4 2) 10

1) equilateral 2) 200cm^2

trinomial - page 116

1) yes

1) $a + 2a + b - c$

triple - page 116

1) 36

1) 1875

two-dimensional - page 116

1) octagon 2) B

1) 9 2) isosceles trapezium

U

unbiased - page 117

unfair - page 117

1) no 2) yes

1) 0.24

uniform - page 117

1) C

1) diagram 49

2) triangular prism

3) pentagonal prism

4) heptagonal prism

unit - page 117

1) A 2) 2

1) millilitres 2) 3

unlikely - page 117

1) yes 2) no

1) B 2) B

unlike terms - page 118

1) 3 2) 2

1) 5 2) 3

V

value - page 118

1) 72 2) £300 3) €525

1) £35 2) 400 3) 0.009

variable - page 118

1) x 2) x and y

1) 2 2) z = 38

vector - page 119

1) 3 units right and 8 units up

1) $\begin{pmatrix} 10 \\ -4 \end{pmatrix}$ 2) $\begin{pmatrix} -10 \\ 4 \end{pmatrix}$

3) $\begin{pmatrix} -11 \\ -5 \end{pmatrix}$ 4) $\begin{pmatrix} 1 \\ 8 \end{pmatrix}$

velocity - page 119

Venn diagram - page 119

1) 4 2) 5 3) 2 4) 3

1) 2, 6, 8, 10, 12, 14, 18, 20, 22, 24

2) 3, 5, 7, 11, 13, 15, 17, 19, 21, 23

3) 1, 9, 25

vertex - page 120

1) 7 2) 8

1) 4 2) 20 3) 0 4) 17

vertical - page 120

1) 90° 2) 2

1) diagram 50

vertically opposite angle - page 120

1) $a°$ = 23° 2) $b°$ = 157°

1) x = 138°

volume - page 121

1) 80cm^3 2) 343cm^3

3) 120mm^3

1) 12 2) 11 3) 56 $^1/_3$ m^3

vulgar fraction - page 121

1) C and D

1) $^1/_{21}$ 2) $^1/_{10}$

3) 19 $^1/_4$ 4) $^{13}/_6$

W

week - page 122

1) 35 days 2) 7 weeks

1) 52 weeks 2) 66.5 days

weight - page 122

1) a 2) 41kg

1) 9500g 2) 0.5832kg

3) 3.8kg 4) 1.9kg

west - page 122

1) yes 2) 180° 3) north

1) 270° 2) south-west 3) A

whole - page 123

1) $^3/_4$ 2) $^3/_5$

1) 600 2) 4

3) 600g 4) 972g

whole number - page 123

1) 98 2) 6

1) 8 2) 6

width - page 123

1) a and d 2) 6cm

1) 1cm 2) 8cm 3) 2400cm^3

X

x-axis - page 124

1) 90° 2) A

1) a and c 2) (1, -3)

x-intercept - page 124

1) 3 2) a

1) (0, 0) 2) (-3.5, 0)

Y

yard (yd) - page 125

1) 8yd 2) 36ft 3) 3ft

1) 13.5m 2) 192yd

3) 7209m^2

y-axis - page 125

1) c 2) 2

1) (5, 1) 2) diagram 51

3) (-5, 1) 4) 8 units^2

year - page 125

1) 23 years 2) 1095 days

1) 13 years 2) 52

3) 13 times

y-intercept - page 126

1) C 2) b

1) (0, 3) 2) (-2, 3)

3) (0, 9)

Z

Z-angle - page 126

zero - page 126

1) 0 2) 5

1) 0 2) 615

3) 34 4) impossible

zero angle - page 126

1) north

1) d 2) 0

zero index rule - page 127

1) 1 2) 8

1) 1 2) 2025

zigzag - page 127

1) diagram 52 2) diagram 53

1) A(0, 42), B(25, 26), C(35, 0)

2) $\begin{pmatrix} 35 \\ -42 \end{pmatrix}$ 3) diagram 54

Diagram Answers

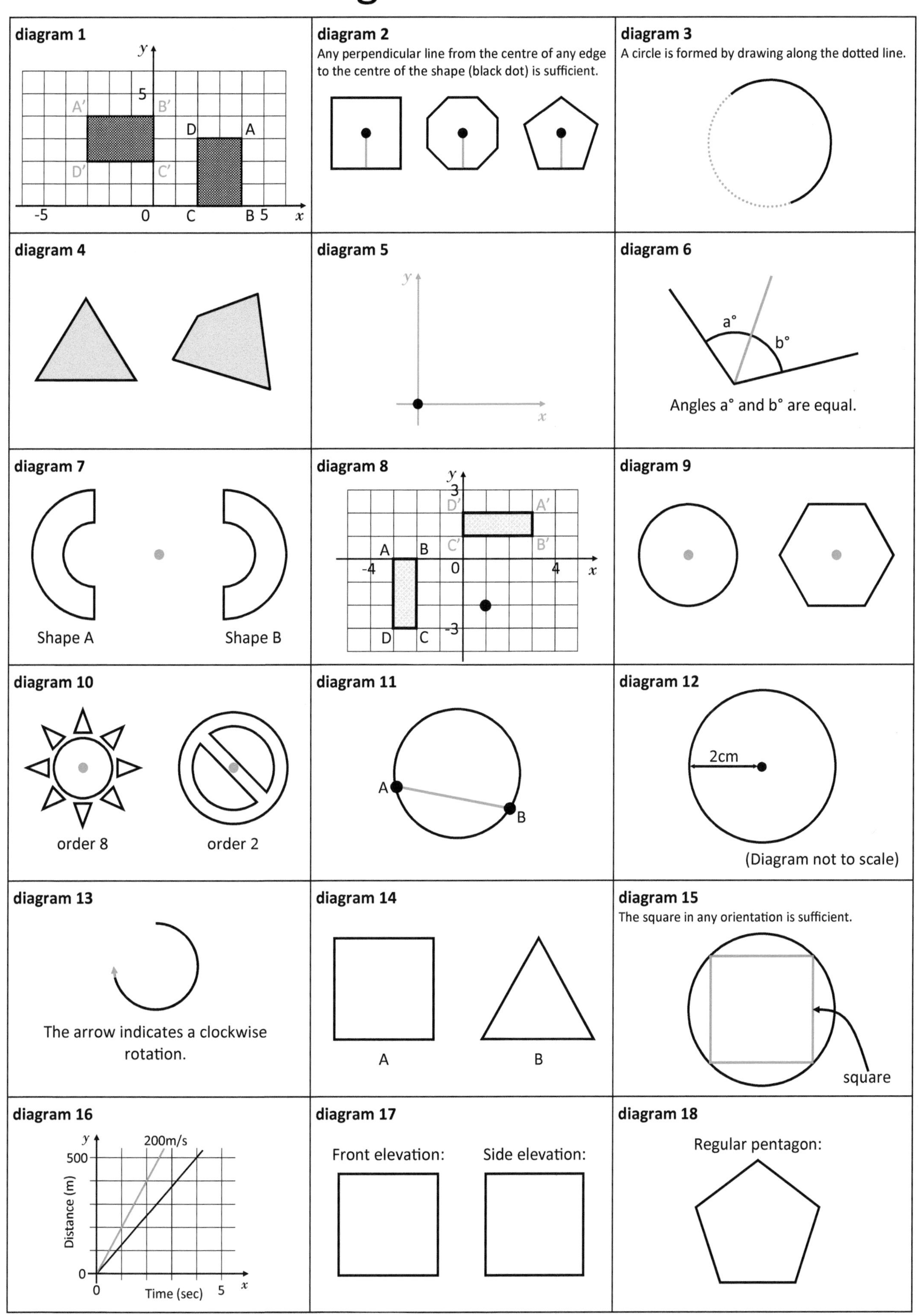

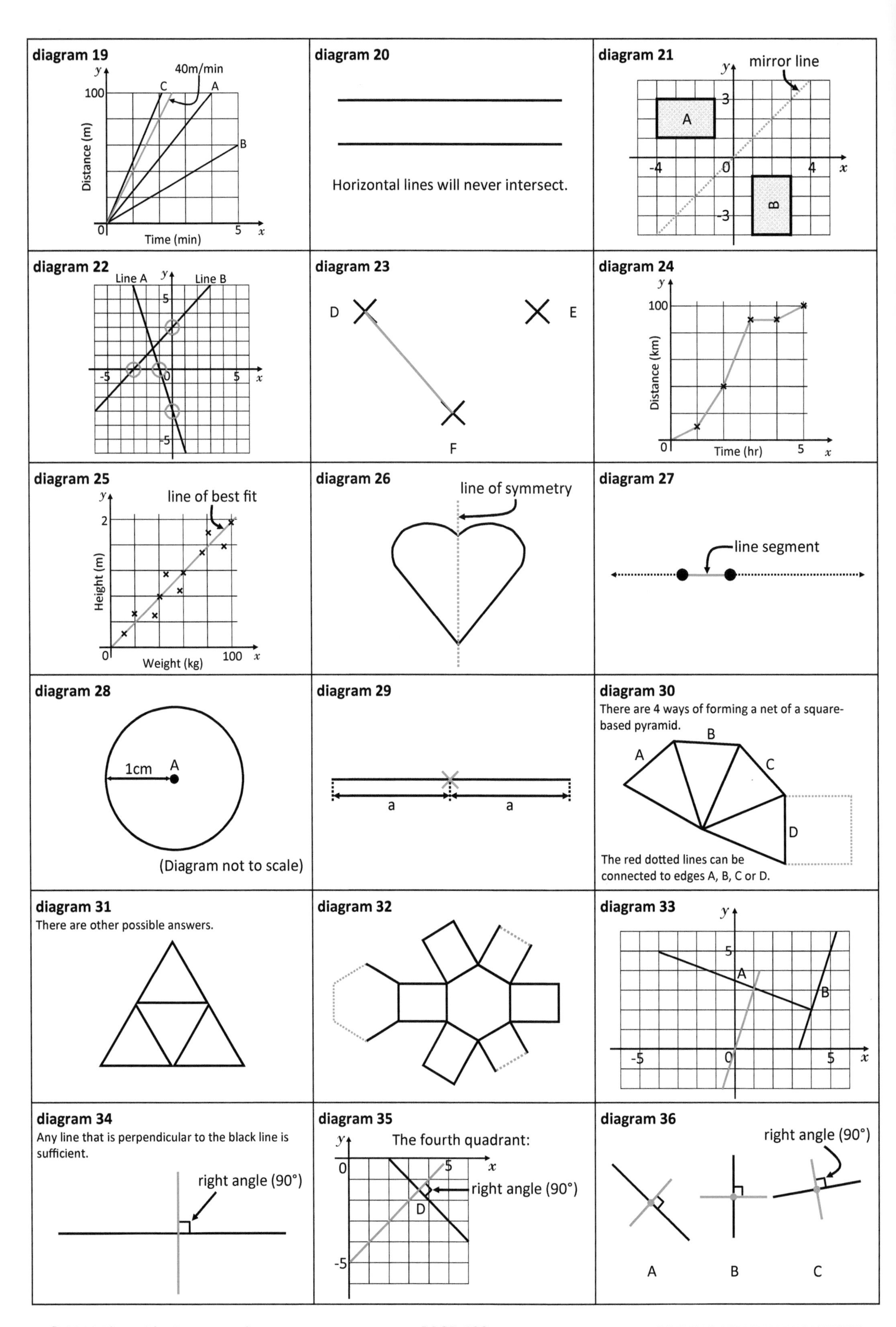
diagram 19
40m/min
100
C
A
B
Distance (m)
0
5
Time (min)
diagram 20
Horizontal lines will never intersect.
diagram 21
mirror line
3
A
-4
0
4
B
-3
diagram 22
Line A
Line B
5
-5
0
5
-5
diagram 23
D
E
F
diagram 24
100
Distance (km)
0
Time (hr)
5
diagram 25
line of best fit
2
Height (m)
0
Weight (kg)
100
diagram 26
line of symmetry
diagram 27
line segment
diagram 28
1cm
A
(Diagram not to scale)
diagram 29
a
a
diagram 30
There are 4 ways of forming a net of a square-based pyramid.
A
B
C
D
The red dotted lines can be connected to edges A, B, C or D.
diagram 31
There are other possible answers.
diagram 32
diagram 33
5
A
B
-5
0
5
diagram 34
Any line that is perpendicular to the black line is sufficient.
right angle (90°)
diagram 35
The fourth quadrant:
0
5
right angle (90°)
D
-5
diagram 36
right angle (90°)
A
B
C

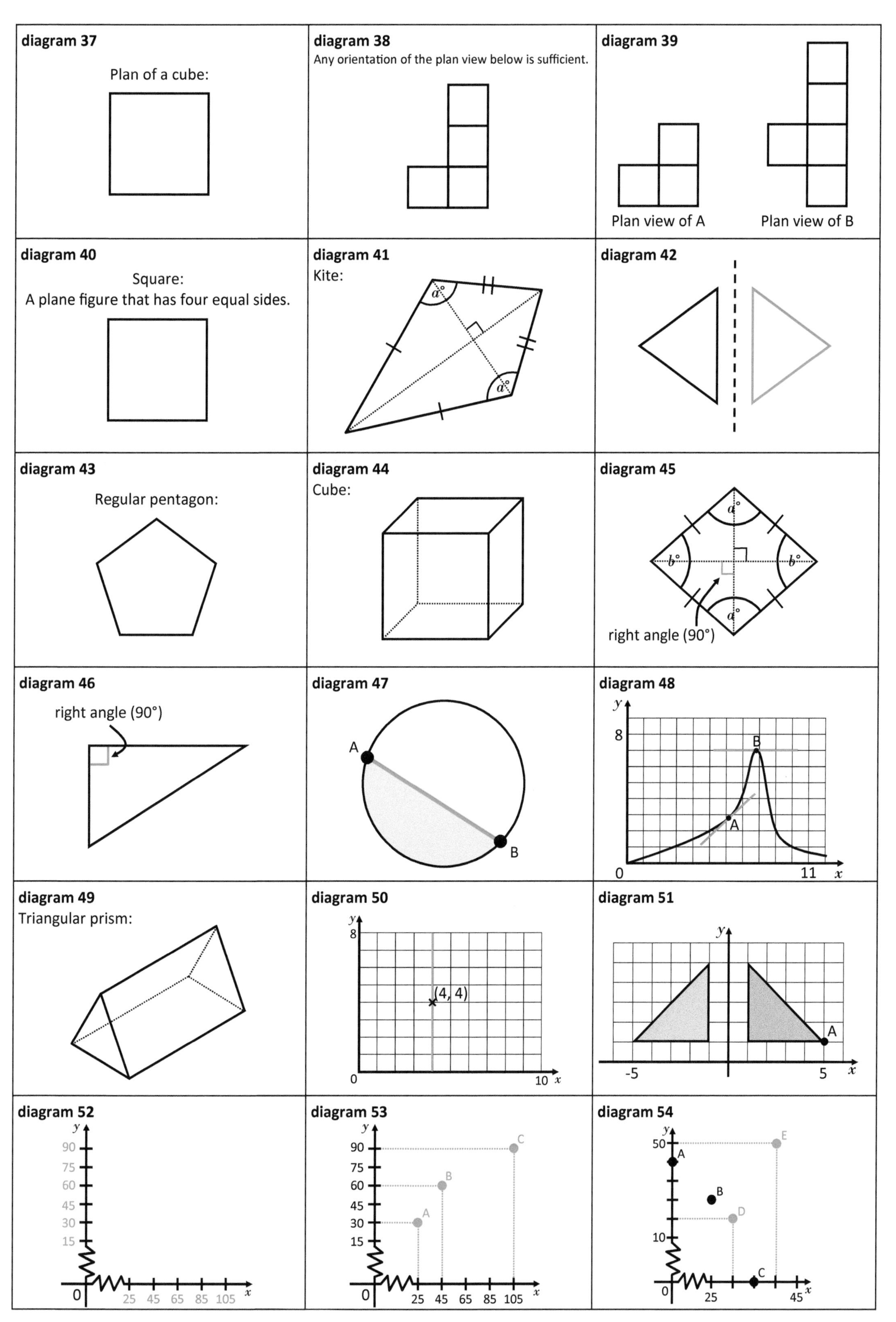
diagram 37
Plan of a cube:
diagram 38
Any orientation of the plan view below is sufficient.
diagram 39
Plan view of A
Plan view of B
diagram 40
Square:
A plane figure that has four equal sides.
diagram 41
Kite:
a°
a°
diagram 42
diagram 43
Regular pentagon:
diagram 44
Cube:
diagram 45
a°
b°
b°
a°
right angle (90°)
diagram 46
right angle (90°)
diagram 47
A
B
diagram 48
y
8
B
A
0
11
x
diagram 49
Triangular prism:
diagram 50
y
8
(4, 4)
0
10
x
diagram 51
y
A
-5
5
x
diagram 52
y
90
75
60
45
30
15
0
25
45
65
85
105
x
diagram 53
y
90
75
60
45
30
15
C
B
A
0
25
45
65
85
105
x
diagram 54
y
50
A
B
D
E
10
C
0
25
45
x

Your Handy Glossary

Learn the meanings of the terms listed below to expand your mathematical vocabulary.

Apothem - a line segment from the centre of a regular polygon to the midpoint of one of its sides.
Bearing - an angle given in three figures that is measured clockwise from the north direction, e.g. 025°.
BIDMAS - an acronym for Brackets, Indices, Division and Multiplication, and Addition and Subtraction. It is the agreed order of operations used to clarify which should be performed first in a given expression.
Bimodal - when a collection of data has two modes, e.g. if the dataset is: {1, 1, 1, 2, 4, 5, 5, 5}, the two modes are 1 and 5.
Bisect - to divide into two equal parts.
Coefficient - a constant that is placed before a variable in an algebraic expression, e.g. in the term $4x$, the coefficient is 4.
Complementary angles - two angles are complementary if they add up to 90°.
Cube number - a number produced when a digit is multiplied by itself twice, e.g. 1, 8, 27, 64.
Edge - a line segment that joins two vertices of a 2D shape, or a line segment at which two faces meet in a 3D shape.
Enlargement - a type of transformation in which the size of an object is changed whilst the ratio of the lengths of its sides stays the same.
Equidistant - the same distance from a common point.
Face - an individual surface of a 3D shape.
Fair - a fair item or event is free from bias.
Gallon - a unit of volume used for measuring liquids, equal to 8 pints or 4.55 litres.
Gradient - a gradient is a measure of the steepness of a straight line.
Highest common factor (HCF) - the largest number that is a factor of two or more given numbers, e.g. 5 is the highest common factor of 10 and 15.
Imperial units - the system of units first defined in the British Weights and Measures Act, e.g. 3 feet.
Inscribe - to draw a shape within another so that their boundaries touch but do not intersect.
Integer - a whole number, i.e. not a decimal or a fraction.
Isosceles trapezium - a trapezium which has one line of symmetry, two pairs of equal angles and one pair of parallel sides.
Leap year - a calendar year occurring every four years, totalling 366 days and including the 29th February, e.g. the year 2012 was a leap year.
Lowest common multiple (LCM) - the smallest number that is a multiple of two or more given numbers, e.g. 6 is the lowest common multiple of 2 and 3.
Metric units - The system of units based on multiples of 10, e.g. millimetre (mm), centimetre (cm) or metre (m).
Net - a 2D pattern that can be cut out and folded to make a 3D shape.
Parallel - lines that run side-by-side, always the same distance apart and never crossing, even if they are extended.
Perimeter - the total distance around the outside of a 2D shape.
Perpendicular - two lines are perpendicular if they intersect at an angle of 90° to each other.
Polygon - a 2D shape with three or more straight sides and no curved sides, e.g. triangle, pentagon, hexagon.
Polyhedron - a 3D shape with polygonal faces, e.g. triangular pyramid or octahedron.
Prime factor - one of a collection of prime numbers whose product is a particular number, i.e. a factor that is also a prime number.
Prime number - an integer greater than 1 that has no whole factors other than 1 and itself, e.g. 2, 3, 5.
Prism - a solid 3D shape with two identical, parallel end faces that are connected by flat sides.
Pyramid - a solid 3D shape whose base is a polygon and which has triangular faces that meet at the top at a single vertex, e.g. square pyramid.
Quadrilateral - a 2D shape with four straight sides. Quadrilaterals are polygons.
Reflective symmetry - a shape or an object has reflective symmetry if an imaginary line can be drawn that divides the shape into two, so that one half is a reflection of the other.
Regular - a regular polygon has sides of equal length.
Remainder - a number that is left over after division.
Rotational symmetry - a shape or an object has rotational symmetry if it can be rotated but still seems to have the same original position.
Scalene - a scalene triangle has sides of unequal lengths.
Sequence - a list of numbers or objects in a particular order defined by a specific pattern.
Square number - a number produced when a digit is multiplied by itself once, e.g. 1, 4, 9 or 16.
Supplementary angles - two angles are supplementary if they add up to 180°.
Triangle - a 2D shape with three straight sides. Triangles are polygons.
Triangular number - a figurate number that can be represented by a regular triangular arrangement of equally spaced points, e.g. 1, 3, 6:
Vertex - a point at which two or more straight lines meet.

Place Value

The numerical value of a digit in a number. For example, in the number 1234.567, the digit 3 has a place value of tens.

1	2	3	4	.	5	6	7
thousands	hundreds	tens	units	decimal point	tenths	hundredths	thousandths

Special Numbers

	1st	2nd	3rd	4th	5th	6th	7th	8th	9th	10th	11th	12th	13th	14th	15th	16th	17th	18th	19th	20th
Even	2	4	6	8	10	12	14	16	18	20	22	24	26	28	30	32	34	36	38	40
Odd	1	3	5	7	9	11	13	15	17	19	21	23	25	27	29	31	33	35	37	39
Square	1	4	9	16	25	36	49	64	81	100	121	144	169	196	225	256	289	324	361	400
Cube	1	8	27	64	125	216	343	512	729	1000	1331	1728	2197	2744	3375	4096	4913	5832	6859	8000
Triangular	1	3	6	10	15	21	28	36	45	55	66	78	91	105	120	136	153	171	190	210
Prime	2	3	5	7	11	13	17	19	23	29	31	37	41	43	47	53	59	61	67	71
Fibonacci	1	1	2	3	5	8	13	21	34	55	89	144	233	377	610	987	1597	2584	4181	6765

Equivalent Decimals, Fractions & Percentages

Percentage	5%	10%	15%	20%	25%	30%	35%	40%	45%	50%	55%	60%	65%	70%	75%	80%	85%	90%	95%	100%	150%
Fraction	$^{1}/_{20}$	$^{1}/_{10}$	$^{3}/_{20}$	$^{1}/_{5}$	$^{1}/_{4}$	$^{3}/_{10}$	$^{7}/_{20}$	$^{2}/_{5}$	$^{9}/_{20}$	$^{1}/_{2}$	$^{11}/_{20}$	$^{3}/_{5}$	$^{13}/_{20}$	$^{7}/_{10}$	$^{3}/_{4}$	$^{4}/_{5}$	$^{17}/_{20}$	$^{9}/_{10}$	$^{19}/_{20}$	$^{1}/_{1}$	$^{3}/_{2}$
Decimal	0.05	0.1	0.15	0.2	0.25	0.3	0.35	0.4	0.45	0.5	0.55	0.6	0.65	0.7	0.75	0.8	0.85	0.9	0.95	1	1.5

Mathematical Symbols

Symbol	Meaning
$+$	addition sign
$-$	subtraction sign
$\times$	multiplication sign
$\div$	division sign
$\pm$	positive or negative
$=$	equals sign
$<$	less than
$>$	greater than
$\approx$	approximately equal to
$\leq$	less than or equal to
$\geq$	greater than or equal to
$\neq$	not equal to
a^2	squared number
a^3	cubed number
$\%$	per cent
$\sqrt{a}$	square root
$\sqrt[3]{a}$	cubed root
$\dot{a}$	recurring number
$a : b$	ratio
a°	degrees
$\bar{a}$	mean
(x, y)	coordinates
∟	right angle
$\binom{x}{y}$	column vector (column matrix)
$^{a}/_{b}$	fraction
$\{a, b\}$	dataset
π	pi

Equivalent Periods of Time

1 minute	60 seconds
1 hour	60 minutes
1 day	24 hours
1 week	7 days
1 year	12 months (365 days)
1 leap year	366 days
1 decade	10 years
1 century	100 years
1 millennium	1,000 years

Roman Numerals

When a symbol appears after a numerically larger number, it is added, but if the symbol appears before a numerically larger number, it is subtracted.

1	**I**	40	XL
2	II	**50**	**L**
3	III	60	LX
4	IV	70	LXX
5	**V**	80	LXXX
6	VI	90	XC
7	VII	**100**	**C**
8	VIII	200	CC
9	IX	300	CCC
10	**X**	400	CD
20	XX	**500**	**D**
30	XXX	**1,000**	**M**

Time Conversion

24-hour clock	12-hour clock
00:00	12.00am
01:00	1.00am
02:00	2.00am
03:00	3.00am
04:00	4.00am
05:00	5.00am
06:00	6.00am
07:00	7.00am
08:00	8.00am
09:00	9.00am
10:00	10.00am
11:00	11.00am
12:00	12.00pm
13:00	1.00pm
14:00	2.00pm
15:00	3.00pm
16:00	4.00pm
17:00	5.00pm
18:00	6.00pm
19:00	7.00pm
20:00	8.00pm
21:00	9.00pm
22:00	10.00pm
23:00	11.00pm

Units of Measurement

	Metric system		Imperial system		
	Units	**Conversion**	**Units**	**Conversion**	**Metric approximation**
Mass	milligram (mg)	1mg = 0.1cg = 0.001g	ounce (oz)	1oz = $^{1}/_{16}$ lb	1oz ≈ 28g
	centigram (cg)	1cg = 10mg = 0.01g	pound (lb)	1lb = 16oz	1lb ≈ 0.45kg
	gram (g)	1g = 100cg = 0.001kg	stone (st)	1st = 14lb	1st ≈ 6kg
	kilogram (kg)	1kg = 1000g = 0.001t	ton	1 ton = 160st	1 ton ≈ 0.91 tonne
	tonne (t)	1t = 1,000,000g = 1000kg			
Length	millimetre (mm)	1mm = 0.1cm = 0.001m	inch (in or ")	1in = $^{1}/_{12}$ ft	1in ≈ 25mm
	centimetre (cm)	1cm = 10mm = 0.01m	foot (ft or ')	1ft = 12in	1ft ≈ 30cm
	metre (m)	1m = 100cm = 0.001km	yard (yd)	1yd = 3ft	1yd ≈ 91cm
	kilometre (km)	1km = 100,000cm = 1000m	mile	1 mile = 1760yd	1 mile ≈ 1.6km
Volume	millilitre (ml)	1ml = 0.1cl = 0.001l = 1cm^3	fluid ounce (fl. oz)	1fl. oz = $^{1}/_{20}$ pt	1fl. oz ≈ 28ml
	centilitre (cl)	1cl = 10ml = 100l = 10cm^3	pint (pt)	1pt = 20fl. Oz	1pt ≈ 0.57l
	litre (l)	1l = 0.01cl = 0.001kl = 1000cm^3	gallon (gal)	1gal = 8pt	1gal ≈ 4.5l
	kilolitre (kl)	1kl = 1000l = 1,000,000cm^3			

Types of Angles

Zero angle:
Equivalent to 0°.

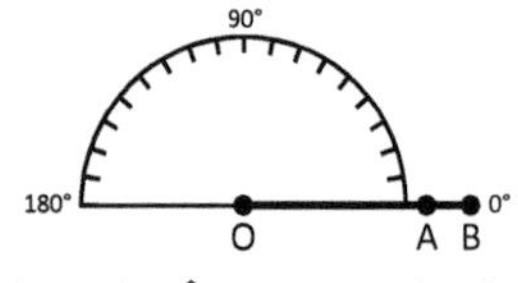

The angle AÔB is an example of a zero angle.

Acute angle:
An angle smaller than 90°, but greater than 0°.

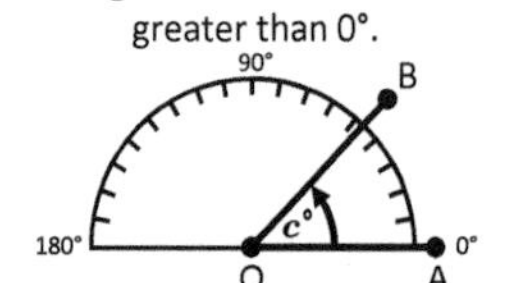

Angle c° (AÔB) is an example of an acute angle.

Right angle:
An angle of 90°.

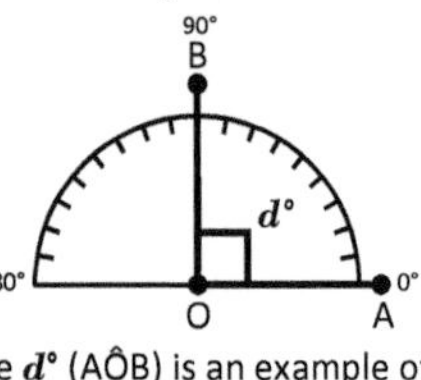

Angle d° (AÔB) is an example of a right angle.

Obtuse angle:
An angle between 90° and 180°.

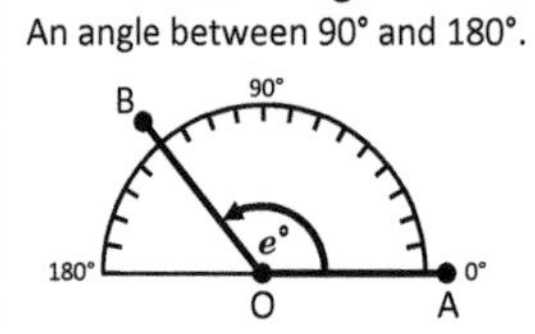

Angle e° (AÔB) is an example of an obtuse angle.

Flat angle:
The angle formed on a straight line, equal to 180°

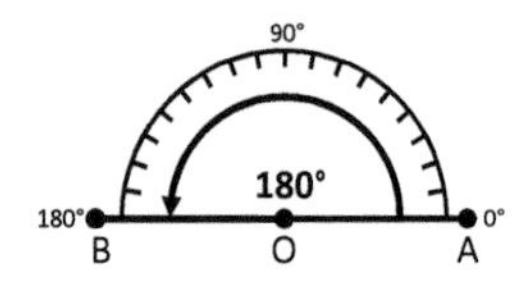

The angle AÔB is an example of a flat angle.

Reflex angle:
An angle above 180° but below 360°.

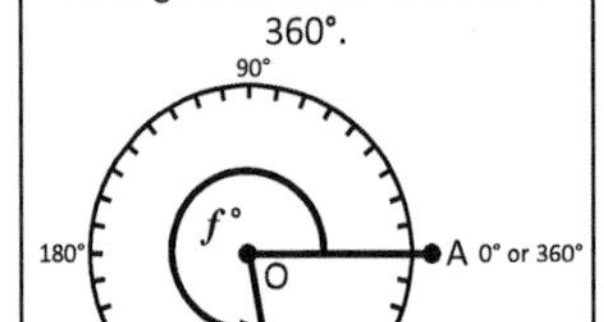

Angle f° (AÔB) is an example of a reflex angle.

Full rotation:
A full turn equal to 360°.

90°
360°
180°
0° or 360°
O
A B
270°

Pairs of Angles

Alternate angles:
The angles on opposite sides of a transversal between two parallel lines.

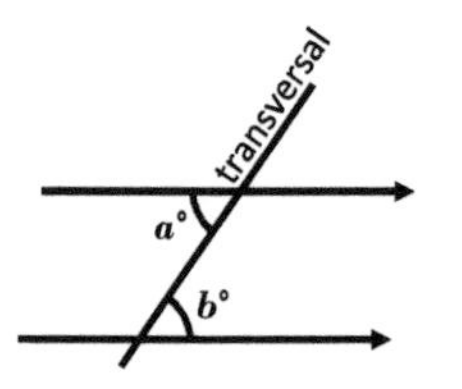

Alternate angles are always equal; i.e. $a° = b°$.

Complementary angles:
Two angles that add up to 90°.

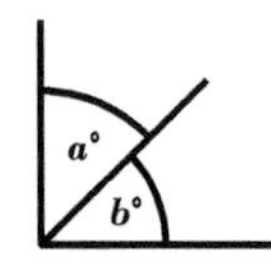

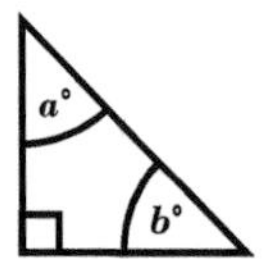

Since $a° + b° = 90°$, they are complementary.

Supplementary angles:
Any two angles that have a sum of 180°.

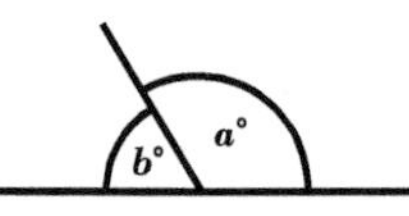

The two angles a° and b° are supplementary.

Vertically opposite angles:
Equal angles that are opposite each other when two lines are crossed.

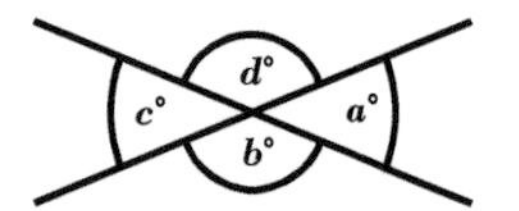

$a° = c°$ and $b° = d°$;
i.e. vertically opposite angles are always equal.

Corresponding angles:
The angles which are identical to each other between a transversal and parallel lines.

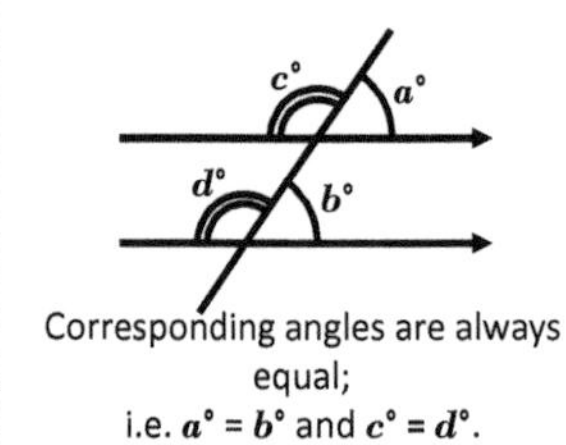

Corresponding angles are always equal;
i.e. $a° = b°$ and $c° = d°$.

Angles in a revolution:
The angles formed when lines intersect each other at a point.

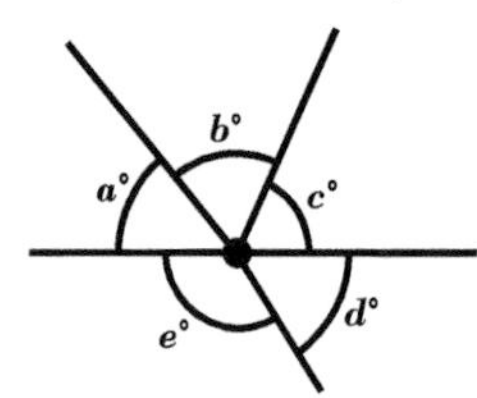

$a° + b° + c° + d° + e° = 360°$;
i.e. angles in a revolution always add up to 360°.

2D Shapes

Figures with two dimensions: length and width, but no depth.

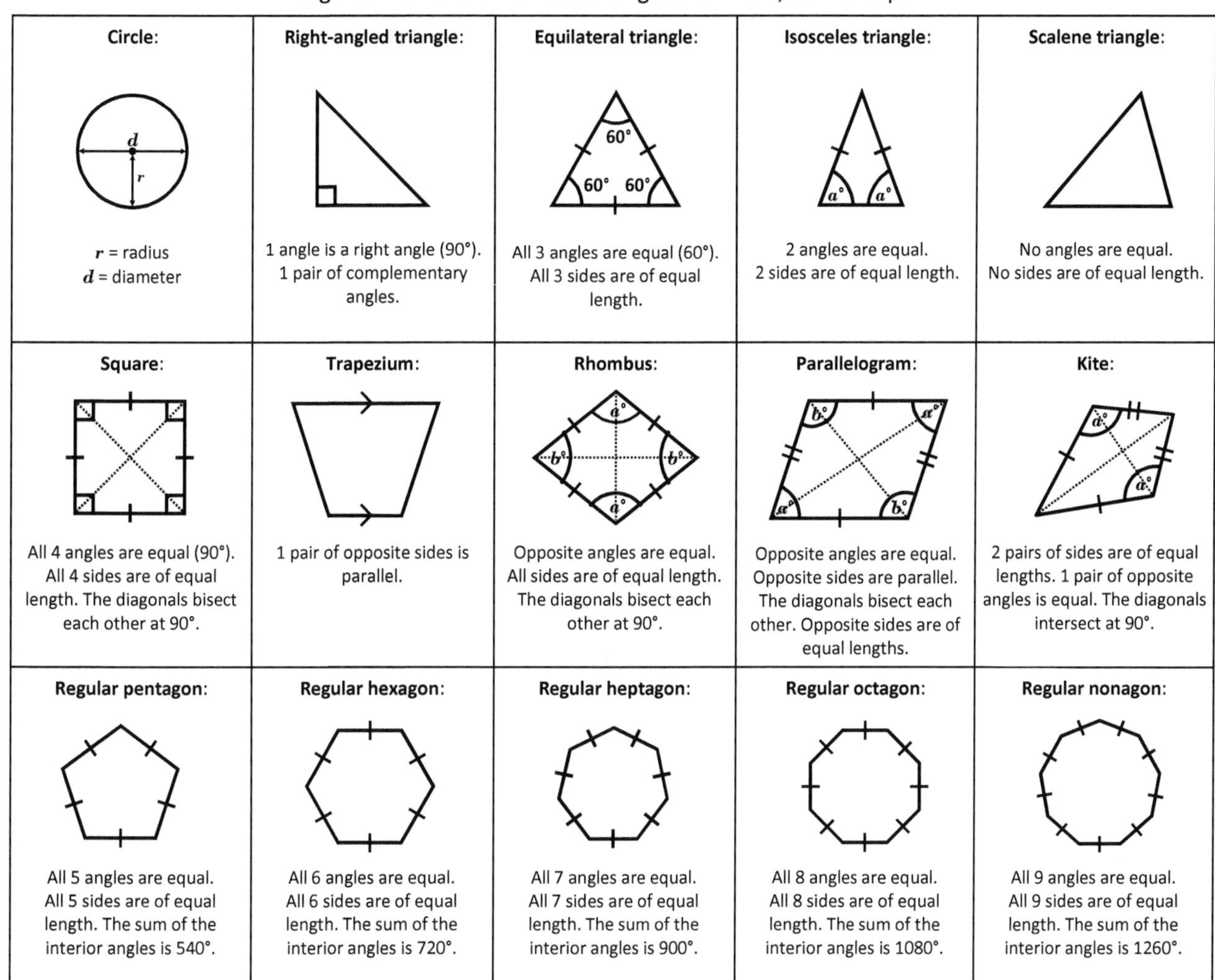

Circle:	Right-angled triangle:	Equilateral triangle:	Isosceles triangle:	Scalene triangle:
r = radius d = diameter	1 angle is a right angle (90°). 1 pair of complementary angles.	All 3 angles are equal (60°). All 3 sides are of equal length.	2 angles are equal. 2 sides are of equal length.	No angles are equal. No sides are of equal length.
Square:	**Trapezium:**	**Rhombus:**	**Parallelogram:**	**Kite:**
All 4 angles are equal (90°). All 4 sides are of equal length. The diagonals bisect each other at 90°.	1 pair of opposite sides is parallel.	Opposite angles are equal. All sides are of equal length. The diagonals bisect each other at 90°.	Opposite angles are equal. Opposite sides are parallel. The diagonals bisect each other. Opposite sides are of equal lengths.	2 pairs of sides are of equal lengths. 1 pair of opposite angles is equal. The diagonals intersect at 90°.
Regular pentagon:	**Regular hexagon:**	**Regular heptagon:**	**Regular octagon:**	**Regular nonagon:**
All 5 angles are equal. All 5 sides are of equal length. The sum of the interior angles is 540°.	All 6 angles are equal. All 6 sides are of equal length. The sum of the interior angles is 720°.	All 7 angles are equal. All 7 sides are of equal length. The sum of the interior angles is 900°.	All 8 angles are equal. All 8 sides are of equal length. The sum of the interior angles is 1080°.	All 9 angles are equal. All 9 sides are of equal length. The sum of the interior angles is 1260°.

3D Shapes

Figures with three dimensions: length, width and height.

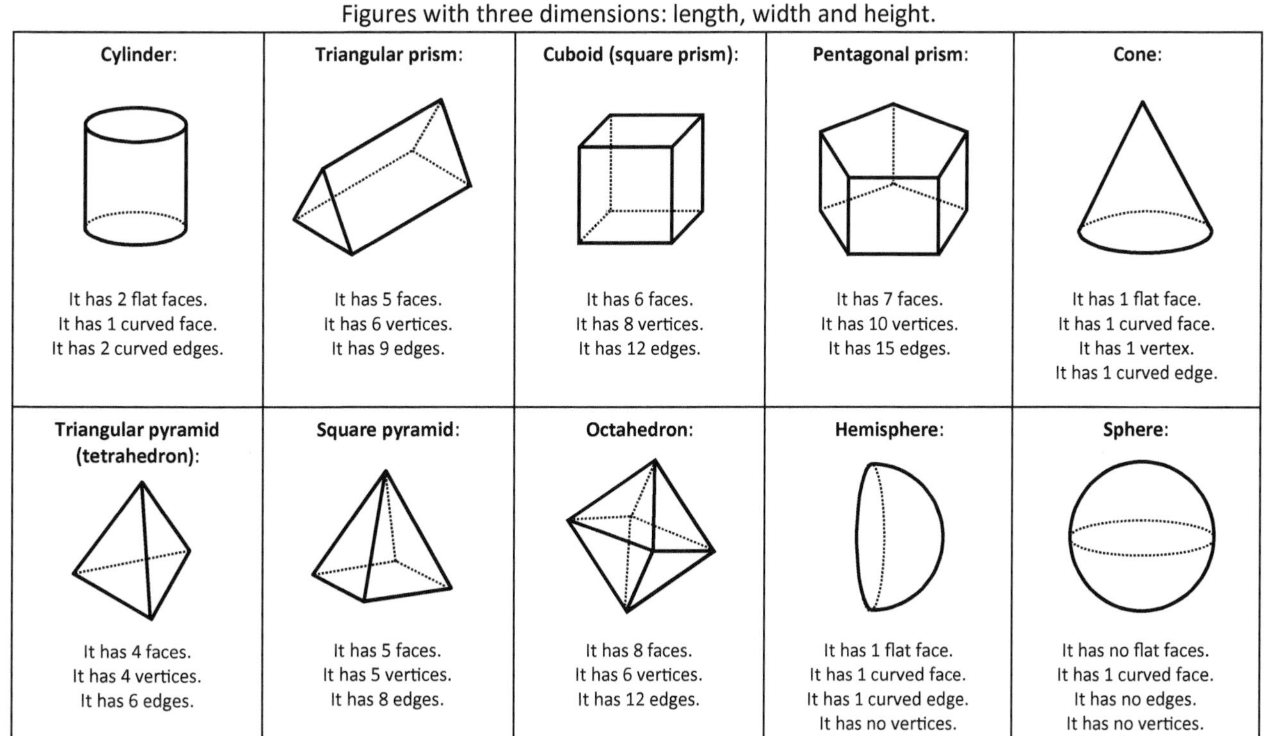

Cylinder:	Triangular prism:	Cuboid (square prism):	Pentagonal prism:	Cone:
It has 2 flat faces. It has 1 curved face. It has 2 curved edges.	It has 5 faces. It has 6 vertices. It has 9 edges.	It has 6 faces. It has 8 vertices. It has 12 edges.	It has 7 faces. It has 10 vertices. It has 15 edges.	It has 1 flat face. It has 1 curved face. It has 1 vertex. It has 1 curved edge.
Triangular pyramid (tetrahedron):	**Square pyramid:**	**Octahedron:**	**Hemisphere:**	**Sphere:**
It has 4 faces. It has 4 vertices. It has 6 edges.	It has 5 faces. It has 5 vertices. It has 8 edges.	It has 8 faces. It has 6 vertices. It has 12 edges.	It has 1 flat face. It has 1 curved face. It has 1 curved edge. It has no vertices.	It has no flat faces. It has 1 curved face. It has no edges. It has no vertices.

Area Formulae

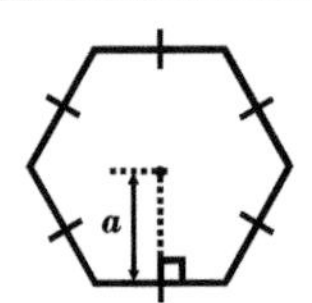

Area of a regular polygon = $^1/_2$ × apothem × perimeter
= $^1/_2 \times a \times p$

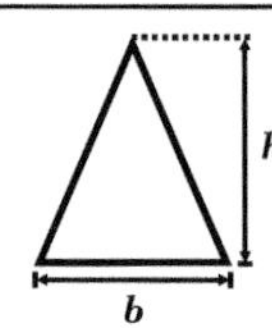

Area of a triangle = $^1/_2$ × base × perpendicular height
= $^1/_2 \times b \times h$

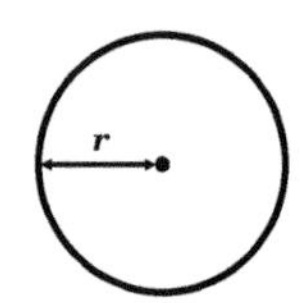

Area of a circle = pi × radius^2
= $\pi \times r^2$

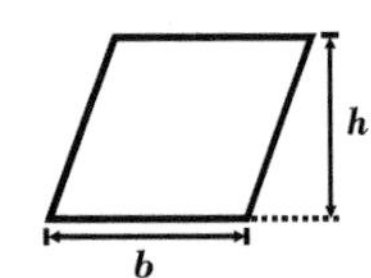

Area of a parallelogram = base × perpendicular height
= $b \times h$

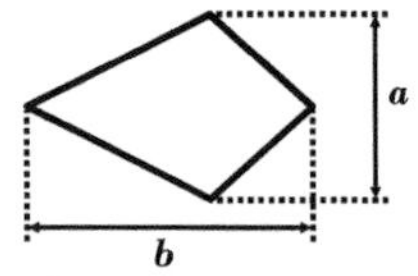

Area of a kite = $^1/_2$ × product of the two diagonals
= $^1/_2 \times a \times b$

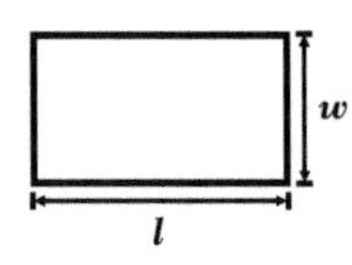

Area of a quadrilateral = length × width
= $l \times w$

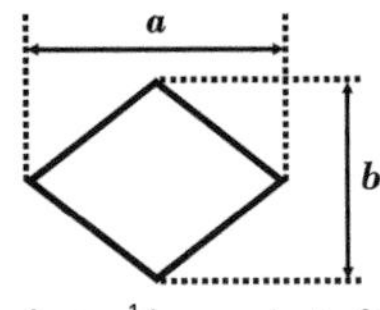

Area of a rhombus = $^1/_2$ × product of the two diagonals
= $^1/_2 \times a \times b$

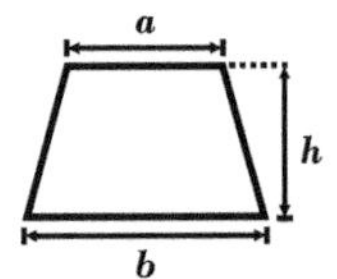

Area of a trapezium = $^1/_2$ × sum of the lengths of the parallel sides × perpendicular height
= $^1/_2 \times (a + b) \times h$

Volume Formulae

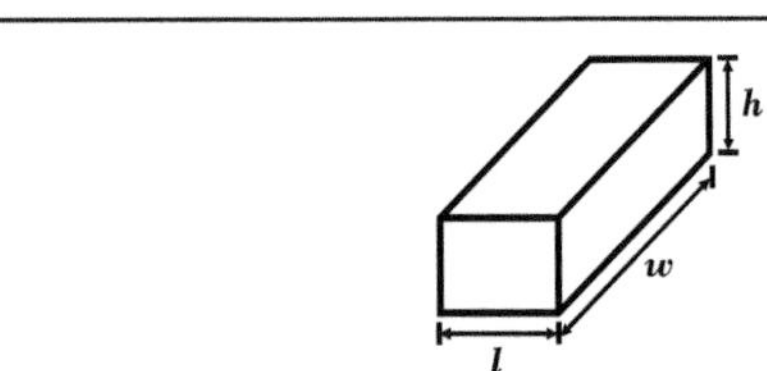

Volume of a cuboid = length × width × height
= $l \times w \times h$

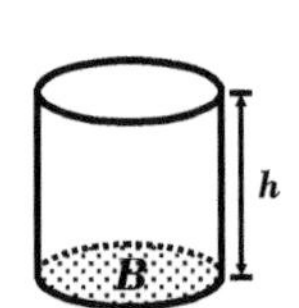

Volume of a prism = area of cross-section × height
= $B \times h$

Other Useful Formulae

Surface area of a 3D shape = sum of the areas of all the faces

Perimeter of a shape = sum of the lengths of all the sides

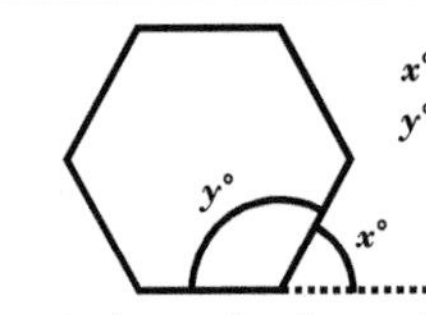

$x°$ is an exterior angle.
$y°$ is an interior angle.

An exterior angle of a regular polygon = $^{360°}/_{\text{number of sides}}$
= $^{360°}/_{n}$

An interior angle of a regular polygon = $^{180° \times (\text{number of sides} - 2)}/_{\text{number of sides}}$
= $^{180° \times (n - 2)}/_{n}$

Circumference of a circle = 2 × pi × radius
= $2 \times \pi \times r$

Probability

A measure of how likely it is for an event to occur.

The probability of event A happening is given by: P(A) = number of favourable outcomes ÷ total number of outcomes.

'And' rule:

The 'and' rule is used to find the probability of a combination of independent events.

The probability of events A and B happening is:

$P(A \text{ and } B) = P(A) \times P(B)$

The word 'and' is replaced by a multiplication sign.

'Or' rule:

The 'or' rule is used to find the probability of a combination of mutually exclusive events.

The probability of event A or B happening is:

$P(A \text{ or } B) = P(A) + P(B)$

The word 'or' is replaced by an addition sign.

Tree diagram:

One way of illustrating probability of events is by using branches, e.g. a tree diagram illustrating two tosses of an unbiased coin.

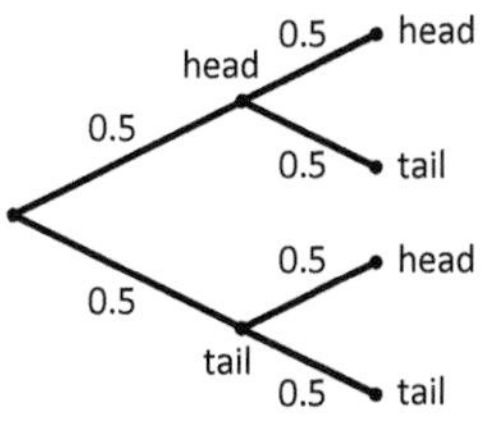

You can use the 'and' rule and 'or' rule with the tree diagram.
Simply multiply probabilities along the branches, and add probabilities down the columns.

Probability scale:

A scale, which goes from zero to one, measuring the likelihood of an outcome.

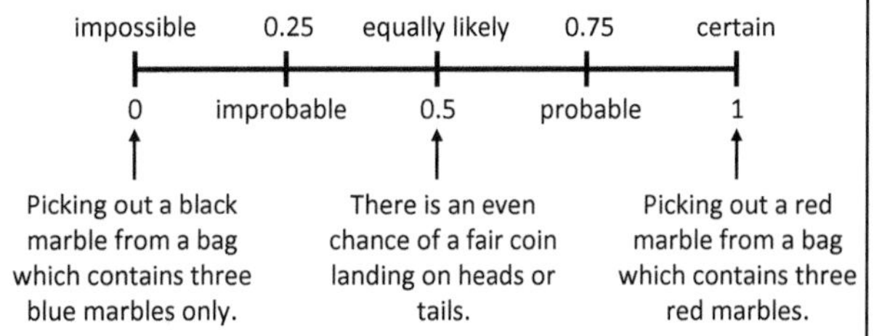

Remember that probabilities can be expressed using fractions, decimals or percentages.

Venn diagram:

A diagram showing all logical relations for a collection of sets using overlapping circles, non-overlapping circles and a rectangular boundary.

Venn diagram showing the first ten positive integers.

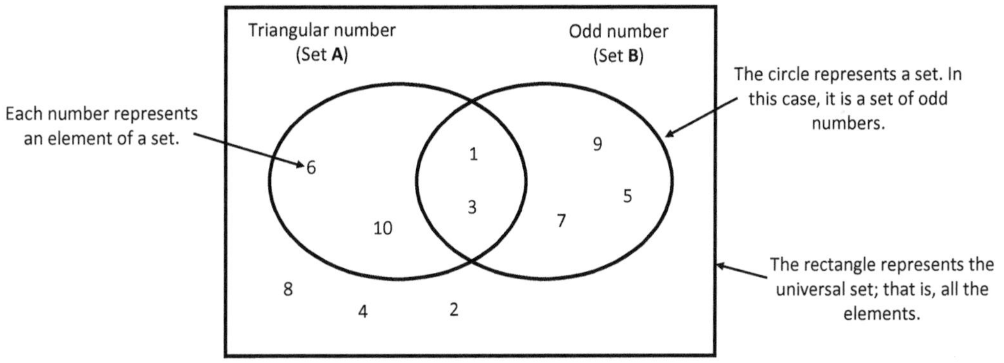

Some useful Venn diagram patterns.

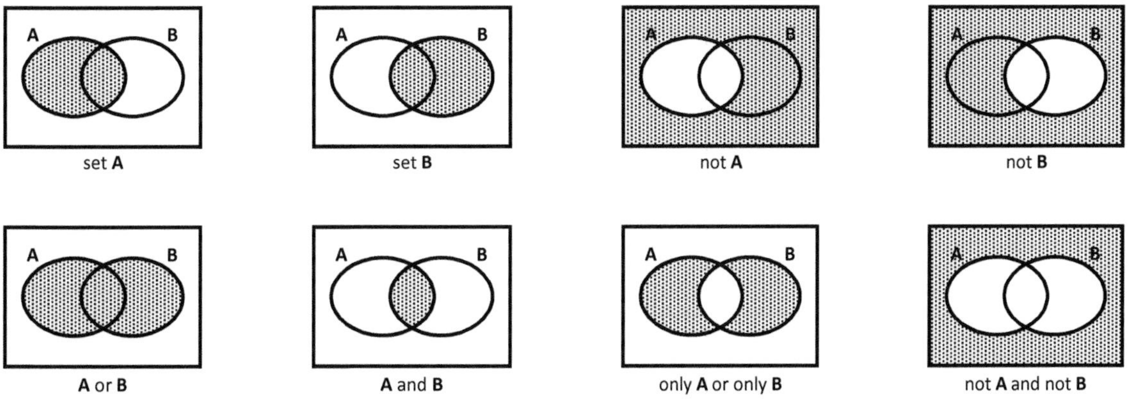

set **A**

set **B**

not **A**

not **B**

A or **B**

A and **B**

only **A** or only **B**

not **A** and not **B**

Other titles in the First Past The Post® Series

11 + Essentials CEM Style Practice Tests

Verbal Reasoning: Cloze Tests Book 1
9781908684288

Verbal Reasoning: Cloze Tests Book 2
9781908684356

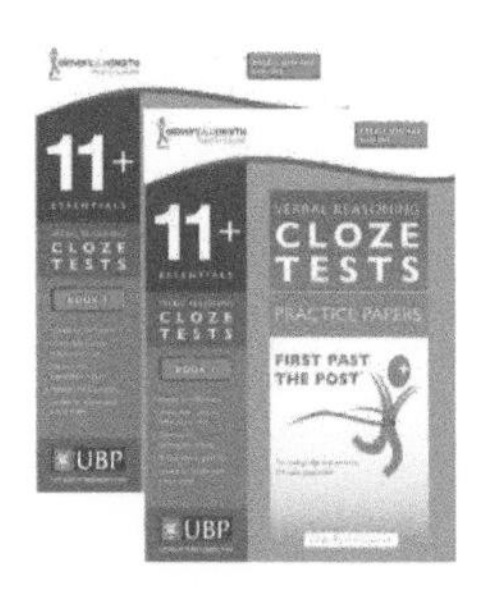

Verbal Reasoning: Grammar and Spelling Multiple Choice Books 1 & 2
9781908684646 | 9781908684790

Verbal Reasoning: Vocabulary Multiple Choice Books 1 & 2
9781908684639 | 9781908684783

Numerical Reasoning: Multi-part (Standard) Books 1 & 2
9781908684301 | 9781908684363

Numerical Reasoning: Multi-part (Multiple Choice) Books 1 & 2
9781908684769 | 9781908684776
NEW for 2016

Numerical Reasoning: Quick-fire (Standard) Books 1 & 2
9781908684431 | 9781908684448

Numerical Reasoning: Quick-fire (Multiple Choice) Books 1 & 2
9781908684653 | 9781908684752
NEW for 2016

English: Comprehensions Book 1
9781908684295

English: Comprehensions Book 2
9781908684486

3D Non-Verbal Reasoning Book 1
9781908684318

3D Non-Verbal Reasoning Book 2
9781908684479

Mental Arithmetic Book 1
9781908684462

Numerical Reasoning: Worded Problems Book 1
9781908684806
NEW for 2016

Maths Dictionary
9781908684493
NEW for 2016

11 + Practice Paper Packs

Non-Verbal Reasoning Practice Papers
9781908684134

English Practice Papers
9781908684103

Verbal Reasoning Practice Papers
9781908684127

Mathematics Practice Papers
9781908684110